5/-1-

INFRARED RADIATION

Infrared Radiation

HENRY L. HACKFORTH
Member of the Research Staff, Nortronics,
A Division of Northrop Corporation

McGRAW-HILL BOOK COMPANY, INC.

New York   Toronto   London   1960

INFRARED RADIATION

III

25397

Preface

In the last few years the field of infrared radiation and its applications has been expanding very rapidly. In the pure and applied sciences, in the engineering professions, in medical research and practice, in the space sciences, and in a large and rapidly growing number of industries and commercial enterprises the techniques and applications of infrared radiation are constantly growing. Increasing numbers of people in all walks of life are becoming interested and involved in this field of applied science.

Partly because of the impetus given to infrared research during the years of World War II and subsequently, when the accent was primarily on military applications, much of the information available on new developments was until recently of a classified nature. At the present time few textbooks are available on this subject, and these, with few exceptions, are of a specialized nature, dealing mainly with aspects of infrared spectroscopy. Persons desiring any information about infrared radiation are confronted by an ever-increasing mass of technical papers and articles, often of a highly specialized nature.

This book was started in early 1957 with the realization that there was a need for an introductory text on the subject of infrared radiation, its basic principles, and its applications in the modern world. This text has been written for use in junior college and university courses, and for those readers desiring background information in this important field. Available published material of an unclassified nature, together with contributions from the author, from manufacturers of scientific and commercial infrared equipment, and from outstanding research leaders in the field, is presented here in a logical sequence in an attempt to fulfill this purpose.

In Part I, Chaps. 1 through 8, the reader is introduced to the fundamental principles of infrared radiation, to the components, materials, limitations, and problems encountered, and to the scope and future possibilities of infrared systems. Chapter 1 describes the nature of infrared radiation and presents a brief history of its development. Chapter 2 defines the basic physical laws and develops a model of a generalized infrared system, used throughout this book, which traces the path of an infrared signal from its source to its final recording or display. Chapters 3 through 7 discuss in detail the "building blocks" used in this model—infrared sources, atmospheric transmission, optical components and systems, optical materials, infrared detectors, mechanical and electronic techniques. Chapter 8 discusses the fundamental principles of infrared system design.

Part II illustrates how these concepts are applied in practice, with Chaps. 8 through 12 devoted to infrared instruments and their uses, and to applications of infrared in the sciences, in industry, and in the rapidly growing field of space technology and its applied sciences.

In view of the introductory nature of this text, mathematics has been deliberately reduced to a minimum. Because of the conflicting demands imposed by the broad area covered and the necessary limitation on available space, the author realizes that shortcomings are inevitable and hopes that any omissions of significant work, and errors, will be called to his attention for the subsequent improvement of future editions.

The author gratefully acknowledges the helpful suggestions, constructive criticisms, and contributions to the text of the following individuals in particular: Professor Stanley S. Ballard of the University of Florida, Mr. W. Wolfe of the University of Michigan, Professor Alvin H. Nielsen of the University of Tennessee, Dr. Lewis Larmore of the Lockheed Aircraft Corporation, Dr. R. Clark Jones of the Polaroid Corp., Dr. G. P. Kuiper, Dr. Richard W. Kebler of the Linde Co., Mr. W. R. Runyan of Texas Instruments, Dr. Marcel J. E. Golay, Mr. Paul Mauer of the Eastman-Kodak Co., Mr. A. H. Canada of the General Electric Co., Dr. R. Laufer of the Office of Naval Research, Mr. C. S. C. Tarbet of Unicam Instruments Ltd., Mr. M. E. Lasser of the Philco Corp., and many others too numerous to mention.

The author also gratefully acknowledges the generous assistance of the following organizations in providing and granting permission to publish much interesting material on their modern scientific and industrial products: The Avionics Division of the Aerojet-General Corporation, Azusa, Calif.; Barnes Engineering Co., Stamford, Conn.; Bausch and Lomb Optical Co., Rochester, N.Y.; Beckman Instruments Inc., Fullerton, Calif.; Corning Glass Works, Corning, N.Y.; Eastman-Kodak Co., Rochester, N.Y.; The Eppley Laboratories, Newport,

R.I.; The General Electric Co., Ithaca, N.Y.; Infrared Industries Inc., Waltham, Mass.; ITT Laboratories, a Division of International Telephone and Telegraph Co., Ft. Wayne, Ind.; Linde Co., a Division of Union Carbide Corp., New York; Mine Safety Appliances Co., Pittsburgh, Pa.; North American Aviation Inc., Los Angeles, Calif.; The Norton Co., Worcester, Mass.; the Perkin-Elmer Corp., Norwalk, Conn.; Philco Corp., Philadelphia, Pa.; Raytheon Mfg. Co., Waltham, Mass.; Radio Corp. of America, Harrison, N.J.; Servo Corp. of America, Hicksville, N.Y.; Westinghouse Electric Corp., Bloomfield, N.J., and Unicam Instruments Ltd., Cambridge, England.

Every effort has been made to ensure due acknowledgment of extracts from the many references cited to the authors and publishers concerned. If, inadvertently in literature with which the author is unfamiliar, acknowledgment has been omitted, apologies are tendered to the authors concerned and due corrections will be made, upon notification, in future editions.

The author is greatly indebted to Dr. Stuart H. Fisher, who proofread the original manuscript and contributed invaluable comments and suggestions. Finally the author wishes to express his thanks to Miss M. J. Stampfel and to Mrs. M. R. Mesnard for their skillful and precise work in typing the manuscript.

Henry L. Hackforth

Contents

Contents   xi

PART II. APPLICATIONS OF INFRARED RADIATION

PART I

BASIC PRINCIPLES
OF INFRARED RADIATION

1

The Nature of Infrared Radiation

The nature of infrared radiation and some of its applications are described. A brief history of the development of infrared techniques is given.

1-1. WHAT IS INFRARED RADIATION?

Infrared radiation is an electromagnetic radiation. It is generated by vibration and rotation of the atoms and molecules within any material whose temperature is above absolute zero ($0°$K or $-273°$C).

Infrared radiation travels in straight lines outward from the source. It is propagated in a vacuum as well as in physical media such as air, gases, liquids, or solids. Unlike "heat waves," infrared radiation is not transferred by thermal convection or conduction in a physical medium. Yet infrared radiation is often loosely referred to as "heat waves." This term is a misnomer. It arose from the fact that infrared radiation generates heat in any absorbing object lying in its path since it causes vibrations or rotations within the atomic structure of the object; but so does any other form of electromagnetic radiation. Objects placed at the focal point of a lens in a high-intensity beam of visible light, or close to the source of a high-intensity radar beam, also become heated by a similar process. The hazards of excessive bodily exposure to intense X-ray or radar beams are well known.

The frequency band of infrared radiation ranges from approximately 1 million to 500 million megacycles. This lies between the higher-frequency region of visible light and the lower-frequency region of microwaves (Fig. 1-1). Consequently infrared radiation exhibits some of the characteristics of both visible light and of radar and radio waves. It can be optically focused and directed by lenses or mirrors, or dispersed by prisms. At the same time it can be transmitted like radio or radar waves through materials which are opaque to visible light. For

3

convenience, the term "infrared" will be abbreviated to IR for use throughout this book.

1-2. THE IR SPECTRUM

It is generally accepted that the IR spectrum lies between 0.72 and approximately 1,000 microns, that is, between the borders of visible light at the shorter-wavelength end and of microwaves at the longer-wavelength end of the IR spectrum.   The position of IR in the over-all electromagnetic spectrum is illustrated in Fig. 1-1.

In the IR region of the spectrum the unit of wavelength employed is the *micron* (μ), where

$$1 \text{ micron} = 1 \ \mu = 10^{-6} \text{ m} = 10^{-4} \text{ cm} \tag{1-1}$$

In the higher-frequency region of the spectrum (ultraviolet and beyond), the unit of wavelength employed is the *angstrom unit* (A) where $1 \ A = 10^{-10}$ meter.

In the visible-light region of the spectrum, both the angstrom and the micron are commonly employed as units of wavelength.

In the lower-frequency region (microwaves and radio waves), the units of wavelength commonly employed are the millimeter (mm), the centimeter (cm), and the meter (m).

It will be remembered that frequency ν and wavelength λ are related by

$$\lambda \nu = c \tag{1-2}$$

where c = velocity of light in a vacuum = 3×10^{10} cm/sec.

Equations (1-1) and (1-2) lead to the useful conversion formula

$$\text{Frequency in megacycles} = \frac{300 \times 10^6}{\text{wavelength in microns}} \tag{1-3}$$

In the electromagnetic spectrum, the various boundaries between the spectral regions associated with the different forms of radiation tend to overlap.   IR radiation, for example, somewhat overlaps the red end of the visible-light spectrum on the one hand and the radio-wave spectral region on the other.

As a result of developments in detectors and optical materials, three quite natural though purely arbitrary divisions of the IR spectrum are commonly used.   These are:

The "near-IR" region from approximately 0.7 to 1.5 μ

The "intermediate- or middle-IR" region from approximately 1.5 to 5.6 μ

The "far-IR" region from approximately 5.6 to 1,000 μ

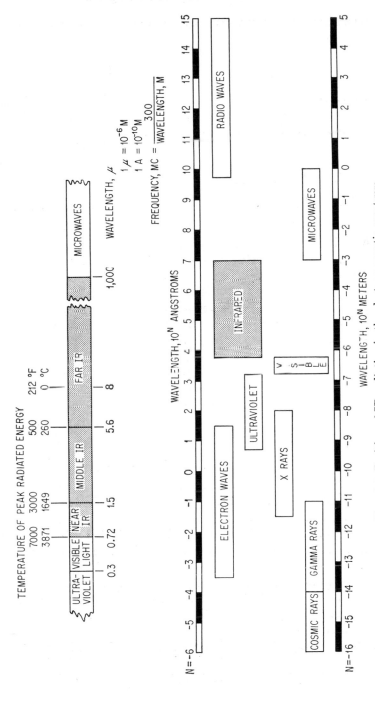

Fig. 1-1. Position of IR radiation in the electromagnetic spectrum.

5

1-3. ADVANTAGES AND DISADVANTAGES OF IR SYSTEMS

Radar and radio waves, occupying the section of the electromagnetic spectrum immediately to the right of the IR region (Fig. 1-1), are generated by means of tuned electrical circuits. Visible and ultraviolet light, lying in the electromagnetic spectrum immediately to the left of the IR region, are generated by electronic transitions within the atoms and molecules of the radiating source.

IR radiation, lying in between these two spectral regions, possesses characteristics common to both visible light and to radar and radio waves and in certain applications has outstanding advantages over both these forms of electromagnetic radiation.

The development of reliable, accurate, and sensitive IR detectors and optical materials has opened up an entirely new field of spectroscopy. Within the last two decades, IR radiation has emerged as a powerful analytical tool widely used today in practically all branches of pure and applied science. IR techniques are now used in chemical analysis, both quantitative and qualitative; for the investigation of the molecular structure of matter; in medical research and diagnosis; in astronomical research; in astronautics; and in many industries. Modern applications are described in more detail in Chaps. 10 and 11.

For detection purposes in both military and commercial applications, IR systems are generally smaller, lighter, less complex, and cheaper than comparable radar systems. The use of optical techniques results in greater simplicity of design and construction. Smaller and more rugged components can be used. The deleterious effects of side lobes, which occur in radar equipment, are not encountered. A primary advantage is that many IR systems are passive, that is, they do not require transmitting equipment in order to obtain a return signal from the target. Superior resolution and the difficulty of devising adequate countermeasures are direct results of the optical, passive nature of many IR detection systems.

Both IR and radar techniques received concentrated attention during World War II, chiefly for military applications. During the postwar years, extensive developments in both these sciences have been continued for military and commercial purposes. However, a much greater effort was concentrated on perfecting radar devices with the result that IR techniques and materials have a far greater developmental capability.

The fundamental particles which make up a molecule have natural frequencies of vibration and rotation which are determined by the molecular structure, the masses of the atoms, and the bonding forces within the molecules. When the frequency of incident IR radiation coincides with one or more of these natural frequencies of vibration or rotation, absorption by the molecule occurs at these frequencies or wavelengths. This phenomenon is known as *resonance absorption*.

Molecules of different substances, solid, liquid, or gaseous, having different structural groupings and geometrical configurations, exhibit characteristic absorption bands resulting from incident IR radiation. Figure 1-2 illustrates the various absorption regions of the IR spectrum. From 1.3 to 2.5 μ, in the *overtone region*, harmonics of the fundamental molecular vibrations cause absorption of IR radiation. From 2.5 to 25 μ approximately, the *fundamental vibration region*, absorption of IR radiation is caused by changes in the vibrational state of the molecule. From 25 to 1,000 μ approximately, the *rotation region*, absorption of incident IR radiation is caused by changes in the energy of rotation of the molecule.[1] *

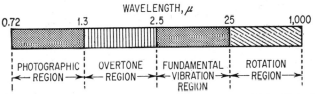

WAVELENGTH, μ

| 0.72 | 1.3 | 2.5 | 25 | 1,000 |

PHOTOGRAPHIC ← REGION → OVERTONE ← REGION → FUNDAMENTAL ← VIBRATION → REGION ROTATION ← REGION →

FIG. 1-2. Absorption-band periods of the IR spectrum. (*After Reference 1.*)

This phenomenon is used to advantage in IR spectroscopic analysis to identify or "fingerprint" both inorganic and complex organic substances by their characteristic absorption bands (see Chap. 11). In other applications of IR techniques, however, this can be a disadvantage. In IR search, tracking, and ranging systems, in IR photography and astronomical applications where maximum sensitivity to weak targets is required, considerable weakening of the received signal strength occurs because of absorption losses in the earth's atmosphere (see Chap. 4). In IR optical systems further transmission reduction occurs because of absorption losses in lenses, windows, and filters (see Chap. 5).

1-4. HISTORICAL BACKGROUND

Early Developments in IR Techniques. IR is not a new field. From early research work, following the discovery by Sir Isaac Newton (1666) that white light passed through a prism was split up into the

---

* Superior figures indicate numbered bibliographic references found at the end of chapters.

colors of the visible spectrum, the existence of radiation beyond the red end of the spectrum was known.   IR emission from a sodium flame was observed by Thomas Melville in 1752.   The astronomer Sir William Herschel (1800) investigated the distribution of radiant heat from the sun.   Thermometers placed in the solar spectrum showed that the most intense heating occurred at the red end of the visible spectrum and beyond.[2]

The foundations of modern IR spectroscopy had been laid.   By 1814 Fraunhofer had observed over 700 dark absorption lines in the IR spectrum.   In 1835 Talbot, with his statement "Light traversing a transparent medium is able to excite motion among its particles," had expressed, though incorrectly, the fundamental principle of resonance absorption.   In 1905 Coblentz published details of new spectroscopic techniques and prism spectra of a large number of solid, liquid, and gaseous materials.   Further research by Kirchhoff, Bunsen, Tyndall, Langley, Rubens, Nichols, R. W. Wood, Pfund, Randall, and others led to important advances in IR reflection, prism, and grating spectroscopy.[2]

The earliest applications of IR spectroscopic techniques to the chemical industry occurred in the 1920s.   By 1935 the value of IR spectroscopy as an analytical tool in the laboratories of the chemical and petroleum industries was fully realized.   However, prior to the outbreak of World War II, the few IR spectroscopes in existence were primarily hand-built models used in laboratories, and interest in IR techniques was chiefly academic.   A more detailed background of developments in this branch of IR technology is discussed in Chap. 11.

In Germany, the potential applications of IR were fully recognized, and a great deal of fundamental investigation in the basic fields of emission, atmospheric attenuation, and background radiation, as well as in the development of new IR detectors, optical materials, and scanning systems, was carried out in the 1930s.

World War II Developments in IR.   With the outbreak of war in 1939, the intensity of IR research in Germany was greatly accelerated. Accent was, of course, mainly on military applications, but such significant contributions were made that a brief discussion of German achievements in this field is considered essential to an understanding of the rapid growth of IR techniques.

The culmination of this research was the development of IR communication systems for land and sea uses, aircraft beacons, missile-homing devices, and several IR detecting and tracking systems for use against ground targets, ships, and aircraft.   Both passive and active IR systems were extensively developed.

Fundamental studies of atmospheric absorption effects were made. Laboratory studies of IR transmission through short paths of water vapor of various concentrations were carried out and verified in field tests. The dispersion and attenuation effects on IR in fog, rain, haze, and artificial smokes were investigated. The effects of background and camouflage were probed and special camouflage paints and coatings were developed.

Thorough investigations of detecting devices of all kinds resulted in the development of new and sensitive types of IR detectors. Lead sulfide photoconductive detector cells were developed and produced by the Electroacoustic Company (ELAC) in Kiel, where methods of depositing IR-sensitive surfaces by chemical precipitation were pioneered. Zeiss-Ikon at Dresden produced lead sulfide cells by the Gudden evaporation method. Techniques for improving the detectivity and wavelength response of these cells by the introduction of impurities and by cooling with solid carbon dioxide or liquid air were developed. Lead sulfide cells, with an NEFD of 10^{-11} watt/cm^2, were produced in quantity and used in practically all the IR devices employed during the war.[3]

By 1944 the first lead selenide photoconductive cells were ready for production by ELAC. New types of highly sensitive thermocouples and bolometers were developed. Fundamental research was also carried out on photoemissive and phosphor cells, with special attention being concentrated on image-conversion tubes designed to produce a visible image of an IR radiating target. In this field, an outstanding development was the *Bildwandler* image-conversion tube (see Chap. 5), which was used extensively during the war on passive detection devices operating in the near-IR region. Further details of these achievements are described in Chap. 7.

Great advances were made in the development of new optical materials and optical systems. Among the important new materials developed were KRS-5 and KRS-6 optics by Zeiss for IR transmission out to a wavelength of 40 μ or more. New optical glasses with excellent IR properties included aluminate glasses, Duran glass developed by the Schott Glass Works, and fused quartz produced by Heraeus.[3]

Both reflecting and refracting optical systems were used, and methods of reducing spherical aberration and coma by using correcting mirrors and Schmidt correcting plates were invented. Optical systems for IR use were achieved with f numbers as low as 0.6. The Germans used mirror optics wherever possible for maximum efficiency in the IR region. Protective and antireflection coatings for front-surface mirrors were evaporated, deposited, or coated on glass or aluminum. IR prisms of quartz, fused quartz, alkali halides, and various special glasses were developed by Zeiss, Steinheil, and I. G. Farbenindustrie.[3] A great deal of work was devoted to special filters designed for IR detecting systems, IR photography, and for IR spectroscopic applications. Methods of reducing interference caused by internal effects in detector cells, by background radiation, and by fluctuations in atmospheric IR radiation were pioneered. Further details of these important advances will be found in Chaps. 5 and 6.

Great importance was attached to IR photography, both for military applications and for applications in the fields of medicine, astronomy, spectroscopy, and camouflage. A variety of stable photographic emulsions highly sensitive to IR were developed. IR cameras were built to photograph both stationary and moving objects, gun-muzzle blasts, and projectile bursts. Special IR cameras with telephoto lenses were built to photograph convoys in the English Channel and coast installations at ranges up to 65 Km.[3] The evaporograph, developed by Czerny, extended the useful range of IR photography from 1.3 μ, the limit of conventional emulsions, out into the far-IR region (see Chap. 7).

The Germans realized early the importance of designing an IR system for a particular purpose. The wide range of specialized devices, such as the IR homing devices developed for various missiles like the antiaircraft rocket "Wasserfal" and for proximity fuses, testifies to this (see Chap. 11).

Similar development and research work was carried out by the Allied nations during the latter part of the war, and several examples will be found in succeeding chapters. However, German leadership in IR developments during the war period was generally recognized, as was British leadership in radar development, which at that time received much higher priority than IR research. The primary interest in the IR development work that was carried out, as in Germany, was centered on military applications. Various IR detecting, direction finding, and ranging devices were produced, of which the sniperscope and snooperscope, developed in the United States, are probably the most familiar. IR homing devices for missiles, equipment for night-driving vehicles without lights, IR beacons, and communication devices were built.

A great deal of attention was also focused upon commercial applications, particularly in the United States. A major wartime problem occurred in the synthetic rubber and petroleum industries concerning the accurate and rapid analysis of C_4 hydrocarbon fractions. Application of IR techniques to the solution of this problem resulted in the development of new and improved optical materials and IR detectors, and ultimately made possible the production of reliable, versatile, automatically recording IR spectrometers for the commercial market.

Postwar Developments in IR. Before 1939, very few IR spectrometers were available. Those that were, mostly hand built for laboratory research purposes, were time-consuming to operate and limited in their scope. The advent of commercially available, rapid, automatically recording IR spectrometers as a direct result of wartime advances in IR is probably the greatest single factor accounting for the numerous and rapidly increasing applications of IR techniques in modern industry. It has been estimated that between the years 1943 and 1953 in the United States alone, over 1,300 accurate and rapid recording IR spectrometers were manufactured.[4]

Today the desirable features of IR techniques, their rapidity, accuracy, ability to sample minute quantities and to return the sample intact, uniqueness of material identification, and uniformity of technique are factors which make IR indispensable in modern research and industry. IR spectroscopes and microscopes are used for the study of molecular forces and motions, for chemical and biochemical analysis. The ability of modern IR instruments to sample rapidly and uniquely has led to their extensive use in industry for automatic quality and process-control purposes (see Chaps. 10 and 11).

Another field of major activity continues to be in military applications. More versatile and sophisticated fire-control systems, employing IR search, detection, and tracking systems, and IR homing devices for aircraft and guided missiles are being developed. Military applications of IR techniques are generally of a classified nature. In this book only unclassified applications, some of which are described in Chap. 11, are discussed. This field alone is so extensive and versatile that a separate book would be required to cover it adequately.

In the commercial-aircraft field IR techniques are widely used. One of the most important and recent applications is the development of a lightweight IR device designed to give automatic warning of impending midair collisions.

Intensive development of new IR detectors and optical materials is heavily dependent upon advances in solid-state physics research which, in the last two decades, has grown into a major science. Recent discoveries have led to the development of new types of IR photoconductive detectors and image-conversion tubes (Chap. 7) and have extended the responsivity of such devices farther into the far-IR spectral region.

In Table 1-1 a list of the various types of IR devices itemizes some of their more important uses in science and industry. While this table

TABLE 1-1. SOME APPLICATIONS OF VARIOUS IR SYSTEMS

IR system	Applications
IR radiometers and IR pyrometers	IR thermography, IR photography; remote temperature measurement; determination of star temperatures; control of automatic assembly-line operations and industrial processes
IR cameras	Thermal image analysis; emissivity measurements; detection of hot spots in electrical circuits, reactors, etc.; quality control; detection of minute temperature differences; background radiation measurements; thermal gradients in chemical reactions; military thermal photography
IR monochromators	Single-wavelength and narrow-band investigations with IR spectrometers, microscopes, telescopes
IR spectrometers	Studies of molecular structure; investigation of chemical reactions; identification of complex compounds; quantitative and qualitative chemical analysis; rapid analysis for quality-control purposes; analysis of flames; solid-state studies
IR microscopes	Medical, biochemical, biological research; diagnostics; analysis of minute samples and rare substances—drugs, perfumes, tissues, cells, blood, muscle fiber
IR telescopes	Used in target detection and tracking devices; IR communications; investigation of solar spectrum; photography and study of celestial bodies; artificial satellite investigations; star trackers used in inertial navigation; IR photography; Auroral studies
IR continuous-process analyzers	Qualitative and quantitative analysis of gaseous and liquid streams; control of furnace temperatures and environments; industrial automatic-control applications
IR search and tracking systems	Fire-control applications; ships, vehicles, aircraft, rocket, satellite detection, anticollision warning for commercial aircraft; night-driving and reconnaissance applications

is by no means exhaustive in its scope, it will serve to give the reader an idea of the versatility and importance of this rapidly growing science.

Before proceeding to further discussion of these interesting and ever expanding fields of application, it is necessary first to understand the physical laws and basic principles governing the design and operation

of IR systems.   These are described in the following chapters of Part I
of this book.

REFERENCES

1. "Instruction Manual, IR-2 Spectrophotometer," Beckman Instruments, Inc., Fullerton, California.
2. Nielsen, A. H.: Recent Advances in Infrared Spectroscopy, *Office of Ordnance Research Tech. Memo.* 53-2, December, 1953.
3. Odarenko, T. M.: "German Wartime Developments in Infrared," Department of Commerce, *Office of Technical Services, Rept.* PB 95308, March, 1948.
4. Crawford, B.: *Sci. American*, October, 1953.

2

Basic Physical Laws and Principles

The fundamental physical laws governing radiation from black bodies, and their application to IR radiation are described. The difference between a passive and an active IR system is discussed. A generalized IR system used as a model throughout this book is developed, and the basic components of an IR system are outlined.

2-1. BLACK-BODY RADIATION

A *black body* is by definition any object which completely absorbs all radiation incident upon it. Conversely, the radiation emitted by a black body at any given temperature is the maximum possible. A black body is therefore an idealized or perfect absorber and radiator of radiation, at all temperatures and for all wavelengths. In IR work the black body is used as a standard. Its radiating and absorbing efficiency, called its *emissivity factor*, is said to be unity.

Any object, black body or otherwise, whose temperature is above absolute zero radiates energy throughout the IR spectrum. The amount and spectral characteristics of the IR energy radiated depend upon the absolute temperature of the object and also upon its nature and surface finish. A highly polished surface such as a silver- or aluminum-surfaced mirror is an extremely poor radiator and absorber of energy; its emissivity factor is close to zero. A black, rough surface such as lampblack is a highly efficient absorber and radiator of energy; its emissivity factor is close to unity. Objects with emissivity factors less than unity are termed *gray bodies,* and the great majority of objects encountered in practice fall into this category. A cavity blackened on the inside approaches the perfect black body. Such cavities are used as artificial black-body sources in the laboratory (Chap. 3). The tailpipe of a jet aircraft has under certain circumstances an emissivity approaching that of a black body.

14

The absolute temperature of the radiating object, the wavelength of the peak radiation emitted, the shape of the radiation intensity vs. wavelength curve, and the total radiated energy are related by the following fundamental laws of physics. These laws apply to black bodies. They can be amended to apply to gray bodies.

2-2. PLANCK'S LAW

The relationship between the radiation intensity, spectral distribution, and temperatures of a black body is given by Planck's law which states that

$$W_\lambda = \frac{c_1}{\lambda^5} (e^{c_2/\lambda T} - 1)^{-1} \qquad (2\text{-}1)$$

where W_λ = radiation emitted by the black body, per unit surface area per unit wavelength interval into a hemisphere, at a wavelength λ. It is measured in watts/cm² per unit wavelength. W_λ is called the *spectral radiant emittance* of the black body at wavelength λ and at temperature T.

T = absolute temperature of black body, °K

λ = wavelength of emitted radiation

e = base of natural logarithms = 2.718

c_1 and c_2 are constants. Their values depend upon the unit of wavelength λ used. If λ is in centimeters, then

$c_1 = 3.7402 \times 10^{-12}$ watt cm²

$c_2 = 1.43848$ cm deg

Figure 2-1 shows the spectral radiant emittance for black bodies at various absolute temperatures. The unit of wavelength for these curves is the micron. It will be noticed that as the temperature of the black body increases, the intensity of the radiant energy emitted increases rapidly.

2-3. WIEN'S DISPLACEMENT LAW

If in Eq. (2-1) we differentiate W_λ with respect to λ and set the derivative equal to zero, we obtain λ_m, the wavelength at which W_λ is a maximum

$$\lambda_m T = K \qquad (2\text{-}2)$$

where K is a constant

$K = 0.2897$ cm deg if λ_m is measured in centimeters

$\quad = 2897$ μ deg if λ_m is measured in microns

This is Wien's displacement law. It states that the wavelength of peak radiation λ_m multiplied by the absolute temperature of the black body is equal to a constant.   As the temperature of a black body increases, its radiation peak shifts to shorter wavelengths as shown in Fig. 2-1.

Substituting λ_m given by Eq. (2-2) into Eq. (2-1) we obtain

$$W_{\lambda_m} = 1.3T^5 \times 10^{-15} \qquad (2\text{-}3)$$

This shows that the intensity of radiant energy W_{λ_m}, measured in watts per square centimeter, emitted at the wavelength of peak radiation λ_m, measured in microns, increases approximately as the fifth power of

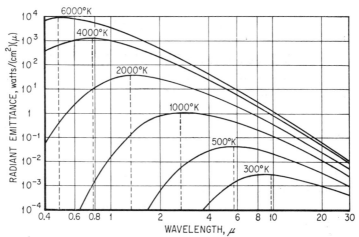

FIG. 2-1. Black-body radiant emittance vs. wavelength.

the absolute temperature of the black body.   In other words, doubling the absolute temperature of a black-body source approximately increases its peak IR-radiation energy thirty-twofold.

Wien's law enables the IR-system designer to rapidly calculate that position of the IR spectrum in which he is most interested for a specific application.   All he requires is the temperature of the source, if it is a black body, or the temperature and emissivity factor if it is a gray body.

For example, a jet tail pipe, considered as a black-body source at a temperature of 500°C, or 500 + 273 = 773°K, will emit its peak radiation at a wavelength given approximately by

$$\lambda_m = \frac{2{,}897}{773} = 3.75\,\mu$$

If the temperature of the source is lowered to 300°C (573°K) the wavelength of its peak radiation shifts to 5.05 μ.

2-4. STEFAN-BOLTZMANN LAW

The total radiant emittance into a hemisphere from a black body at an absolute temperature T is obtained by integrating W_λ, as given by Eq (2-1), with respect to λ, between the limits $\lambda = 0$ and $\lambda = $ infinity.

$$W = \int_{\lambda=0}^{\lambda=\infty} W_\lambda d\lambda = \sigma T^4 \qquad (2\text{-}4)$$

where W = total black-body radiant emittance, measured in watts/cm^2
    of the radiating surface
  σ = Stefan-Boltzmann constant
    = 5.673×10^{-5} erg/(cm^2) (sec) (deg^4)
    = 5.673×10^{-12} watt/(cm^2) (deg^4)
This is the Stefan-Boltzmann law. Note that since we have integrated over the whole wavelength region, W is not wavelength-dependent; W is dependent upon the fourth power of the absolute temperature of the black-body source.

2-5. EMISSIVITY

The above laws were all derived for a black body with an emissivity of 1.0. However, most bodies encountered in practice are not perfect black bodies. They are gray bodies which radiate or absorb less than a black body would at the same temperature. Their emissivity is always less than unity.

The emissivity factor of an object is a measure of its radiation (and absorbing) efficiency. It is defined as

Emissivity factor $\epsilon = $

$$\frac{\text{total radiant emittance of gray body}}{\text{total radiant emittance of a black body at the same abs temp}} \qquad (2\text{-}5)$$

Gray bodies do not therefore obey the laws governing a black body. These laws must be amended by multiplication by the emissivity factor. Thus, the Stefan-Boltzmann law applied to a gray body becomes

$$W = \epsilon \sigma T^4 \qquad (2\text{-}6)$$

where ϵ = emissivity factor of gray body
  T = absolute temperature, °K
  σ = Stefan-Boltzmann constant = 5.673×10^{-12} watt/(cm^2) (deg^4)
The emissivity factor is therefore an indication of the *grayness* of the radiating body. The lower the emissivity factor the *grayer* the body,

the higher the factor, that is, the nearer it approaches to unity, the *blacker* the body.

Not all sources behave like gray bodies. The emissivity of some surfaces varies with the wavelength. For some types of radiating source the energy spectrum may consist of a weak black-body type of

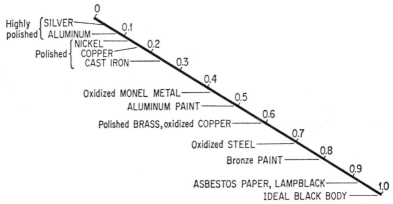

Fɪɢ. 2-2. Emissivity factors of various room-temperature surfaces. (*Based upon emissivity factors in "Handbook of Chemistry and Physics," 30th ed., p. 2244) Chemical Rubber Publishing Company, Cleveland, Ohio, 1957.*

continuous spectrum, upon which are superimposed stronger radiation peaks consisting of spectral lines or bands at certain wavelengths. Examples of this type of source are hot gases, flames, and certain types of electrical-discharge lamps. Radiation sources are discussed in greater detail in Chap. 3. However, for the majority of sources, the laws enumerated above, amended where necsesary for gray bodies, apply.

The wide range of emissivity factors for different types of low-temperature sources commonly encountered is illustrated in Fig. 2-2.

2-6. INVERSE-SQUARE LAW

Fɪɢ. 2-3. Inverse-square law.

Consider a black-body point source S and two detectors of equal sensitive area, say 1 cm^2, D_1 at a distance d cm from S, and D_2 at a distance $2d$ cm from S (Fig. 2-3). From the Stefan-Boltzmann law, Eq. (2-4), the total IR energy radiated by S into a hemisphere is W watts/cm^2 of the radiating surface.

Thus, W is the total IR energy radiated into a hemisphere of radius d on which D_1 is located, that is, into a surface area of πd^2 cm². But W is also the total IR energy radiated into a hemisphere of radius $2d$ on which D_2 is located, that is, into a surface area of $4\pi d^2$ cm². Therefore,

$$\text{IR energy received by } D_1 = \frac{W}{\pi d^2} = W'$$

$$\text{IR energy received by } D_2 = \frac{W}{4\pi d^2} = \frac{W'}{4}$$

We see that halving the distance of a detector from a point source quadruples the IR energy received by that detector. This is the *inverse-square law*, which states: "The intensity of radiation emitted from a point source varies as the inverse square of the distance between source and receiver."

2-7. LAMBERT'S LAW OF COSINES

Where the radiating surface is a plane black body and a perfect diffuser, then the radiant intensity emitted for all wavelength intervals varies as the cosine of the angle between the line of sight and the normal to the surface. This is Lambert's law of cosines. Referring to Fig. 2-4, a detector is situated at a distance d along a line of sight making an angle θ with the normal to a plane diffusing source of area A.

The total radiant emittance W of the source is given by Eq. (2-4) if the source is a black body or by Eq. (2-6) if it is a gray body. The radiant intensity received at the detector is then

$$J = \frac{WA}{2\pi d^2} \cos \theta \qquad (2-7)$$

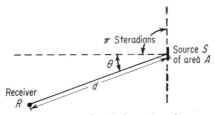

Fig. 2-4. Lambert's law of cosines.

where J is measured in watts per square centimeter of source area. By the inverse-square law J varies inversely as the square of the distance between source and receiver.

2-8. USE OF THE BASIC LAWS IN IR CALCULATIONS

The Stefan-Boltzmann law and Wien's law, which give the total radiant emittance and the wavelength of peak radiation for a black-body source at a given absolute temperature, are combined in Fig. 2-5 in a form useful for rapid calculations.

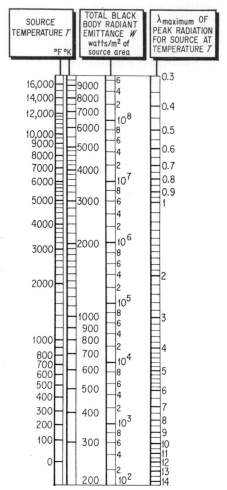

Fig. 2-5. Total black-body radiation W and $\lambda_{\max}$ for source at temperature T. (*Based upon nomograph by Joseph P. Chernock, Aviation Age, 1957, p. 116.*)

EXAMPLE 1

What is the total radiation emitted by a plane 500°C black-body source with an area of 2 m² (*a*) into a hemisphere? (*b*) per unit solid angle? (*c*) What is the wavelength of peak radiation from this source?

(*a*) 500°C = 500 + 273 = 773°K

Opposite this absolute temperature on scale 1 read off W on scale 2: $W = 2 \times 10^4$ watts/m². Therefore, for a 2-m² source, $W = 4 \times 10^4$ watts radiated into a hemisphere.

(b) Radiation emitted per steradian =

$$\frac{W}{2\pi} = \frac{2}{\pi} \times 10^4 \text{ watts/steradian.}$$

(c) Opposite 773°K on scale 1 read off on scale 3: $\lambda_m = 4.2\ \mu$.

EXAMPLE 2

A plane diffusing source at a temperature of 1320°F has an effective area of ½ m², and an emissivity of 0.2. (a) What is the radiation per unit solid angle subtended at the source in a direction of 30° off the normal? (b) In what wavelength region should an IR-detection system have its peak responsivity?

(a) From scale 1: 1320°F = 1000°K

From scale 2, for a black body ($\epsilon = 1.0$) at this temperature, $W = 6 \times 10^4$ watts/(m²) (2π steradians). For a source with an emissivity $\epsilon = 0.2$ and a ½-m² area,

$$\text{Radiation} = \frac{0.2W}{2} \text{ watts/}2\pi \text{ steradians}$$

$$= \frac{0.2W}{2 \times 2\pi} \text{ watts/steradian}$$

Applying Lambert's law of cosines for an angle of sight 30° off the normal, radiation = $0.2W/4\pi \cos 30 = 8.25 \times 10^2$ watts/steradian.

(b) Opposite 1000°K on scale 1 read on scale 3: $\lambda_m = 2.9\ \mu$. The peak responsivity of the IR detecting system should therefore lie in the 2.9-μ wavelength region.

The power radiated into a hemisphere by a black-body source at an absolute temperature T for all wavelengths below a given wavelength can be obtained by integrating Planck's equation (2-1) over the interval $\lambda = 0$ to the given wavelength, λ.

$$\text{Power radiated} = \int_0^\lambda W_\lambda \, d\lambda \text{ watts/(cm}^2)(2\pi \text{ steradians)} \quad (2\text{-}8)$$

The total power radiated into a hemisphere for all wavelengths is given by the Stefan-Boltzmann law

$$\text{Total power} = W = 5.673 \times 10^{-12}(T^4) \text{ watts/(cm}^2)(2\pi \text{ steradians)}$$
$$(2\text{-}9)$$

Hence, the percentage of total energy radiated in the wavelength region below wavelength λ is given by

$$\frac{100 \int_0^\lambda W_\lambda \, d\lambda}{W} \quad\quad (2\text{-}10)$$

The integration of Planck's equation can be carried out numerically or graphically from the black-body radiation curve appropriate to the source temperature (Fig. 2-1). A typical problem of this nature is illustrated by the following example.

EXAMPLE 3

A plane diffusing black-body source with an area of 0.75 m² has a temperature of 500°C. Find (a) the energy radiated in the 2- to 4-μ region. (b) At what wavelength does the maximum radiation occur?

(a) 550°C = 550 + 273 = 823°K

Opposite this temperature on scale 1 of Fig. 2-5 read off the total radiation on scale 2: $W = 2.5 \times 10^4$ watts/(m²)(2π steradians). From Eq. (2-10), the percentage of total radiation falling below 4-μ wavelength is 34 per cent and that falling below 2 μ is 2.5 per cent. The difference is 31.5 per cent. Therefore, 31.5 per cent of the total black-body radiation from this source lies in the 2- to 4-μ wavelength region. The energy radiated in this region is therefore

$$W \times 0.315 \times 0.75 = 5.9 \times 10^3 \text{ watts}/2\pi \text{ steradians}$$

(b) Opposite 823°K on scale 1 read off on scale 3: $\lambda_m = 4.4\ \mu$.

2-9. A GENERALIZED IR SYSTEM

Having discussed the fundamental laws governing the behavior of IR radiation, it is appropriate at this juncture to examine a typical IR system, its components, and their functions. Every IR system is tailored to do a specific job. Its components are chosen or designed to optimize the system performance for a specific wavelength region, for maximum detectivity, for high resolution, and so on, depending upon the type of source to be detected and the kind of information the system is required to furnish.

To aid in the understanding of the principles underlying the many IR systems of various types described in this book, a model of a generalized IR system is illustrated in Fig. 2-6. The model is composed of basic building blocks. Every IR system, active or passive, is composed of most if not all of these blocks. For example, all IR systems include a source or target, a background, an atmosphere or environment, optics, and a detector. Signal processing and display may be a highly sophisticated and specialized process involving mechanical, optical, and electronic techniques, as in an IR fire-control system, or a very simple process, as in an IR pyrometer. With the aid of this generalized model, which will be referred to constantly throughout this book, let us follow the path of IR radiation from its sources, step by step through the various modifications necessary for its final presentation in some form of display.

Radiation Sources. The primary source of IR radiation may be terrestrial, originating on the earth's surface or within its atmosphere, or celestial in nature. All sources may also be broadly classified into two categories: natural and artificial sources. Examples of natural sources are the sun, stars, planets, clouds, human beings, buildings, vehicles, ships, aircraft, and rockets. Examples of artificial or controlled sources are filaments, discharge and arc lamps, and calibrated

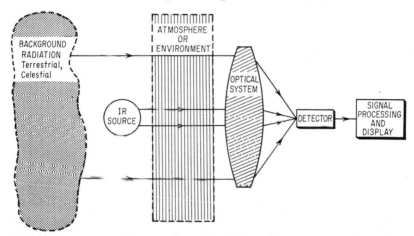

FIG. 2-6. Generalized IR system.

black-body sources used in laboratory work. IR energy is radiated from all these sources according to the physical laws examined in the first part of this chapter. Chapter 3 describes the various types of sources encountered in IR work in greater detail.

Background Sources. Superimposed on the IR radiation emitted from a primary source there may be additional background radiation of a terrestrial or celestial nature. For example, an IR system for detecting tanks and vehicles must do so against background radiation from trees, bushes, buildings, and the ground. An IR astronomical telescope must detect radiation from a distant source against background radiation from the sun, the sky, clouds, and celestial bodies. In many IR systems, special techniques must be employed for discriminating the source or target against its natural background. Background radiation causes noise in the IR system; this may overwhelm the target signal unless it is reduced. Background sources are discussed further in Chap. 3, and discriminating techniques are described in Chap. 5.

Atmosphere or Environment.   IR radiation emitted by the primary source and its background must pass through an environment or atmosphere before it enters the detecting system.   This environment may be a lengthy passage through the earth's atmosphere in the case of IR telescopes, cameras, search, and tracking systems.   It may be a shorter passage through a gaseous atmosphere in the case of radiometers or pyrometers monitoring, say, a production assembly or testing line. Or it may be a relatively short passage through a vacuum or an inert gas, in the case of IR monochromators or spectrometers.   Whatever the environment, with the sole exception of a vacuum, it modifies the original IR radiation by absorption or scattering.   This field is discussed in greater detail in Chap. 4.

Optics.   IR radiation from the primary source and its background, modified by passage through the intervening environment, arrives at the protecting window, or field lens, or mirror, or slit of the optical system of the IR instrument.

Optical systems employ aperture stops, slits, windows or irdomes, mirrors, lenses, prisms or gratings, or combinations of these optical elements, and serve two basic purposes.   The primary purpose of the optical system is to collimate and focus incoming IR energy on the detecting element of the instrument, with minimum transmission loss in the optical system.   The secondary purpose is twofold: (1) to optically filter out unwanted or background radiation, and (2) to limit the radiation incident on the detector to those wavelengths or wavelength bands desired.   Optical systems and the materials used in IR optical elements are described in detail in Chaps. 5 and 6.

Detector.   After passage through the optical system, IR radiation impinges on the sensitive surface of the detector.   The purpose of a detector is that of a transducer, it changes the incoming IR radiation into a voltage output.   The output signal from the detector is then available for electronic amplification and processing into a form suitable for display.

IR radiation reaches the sensitive surface of the detector within a wavelength band that is determined by the temperature and nature of the source and background, modified by the intervening atmosphere or environment and the optical system between the source and the detector.   The detector is chosen and the optical system is designed to ensure peak responsivity for this wavelength region.   Detectors are discussed in detail in Chap. 7.

Signal Processing and Display.   The detector output signal is extremely weak.   In order to extract information from it and to employ it for display purposes, amplification is required. This may take place in the detector itself, as in the case of the RCA type 7102 multiplier phototube. More often, the detector output signal is modulated so that established electronic techniques may be employed to achieve high amplification and at the same time reduce unwanted background noise. Modulation may take place either in the IR source itself, as in the case of IR communication systems which employ a pulsed source, or at the receiving end where mechanical, optical, or electronic techniques are used. Both frequency- and amplitude-modulation methods are employed.

The output signal may contain vital information that requires further processing for display purposes. The output signal from an IR search, detection, and tracking system, for example, contains information on the position of the target in the field of view. This information may have to be processed by specially designed electronic circuits consisting of preamplifiers, amplifiers, decoding, pulse-shaping, and gating networks. In spectroscopy, mechanical and optical devices are required to record the position and intensity of spectral lines or bands. Numerous examples of the techniques employed to extract information from the received IR signal are discussed in later chapters.

Various forms of display are employed. They may be visual, aural, electrical, photographic, or recorded. An aural signal in the form of a headphone noise, for example, may be used to indicate to the operator that an IR-detection system is on target. The received signal may, on the other hand, be displayed in visual-electrical form as an indicating light on a mosaic of lights. Many IR systems, such as sniperscopes, fire-control systems for tanks, or IR binoculars for night driving, employ image-converter tubes to display the target as a visual image on a phosphor screen. An IR camera uses a television-type scanning technique. IR astronomical telescopes and cameras display the image on photographic film. Most spectrometers and many IR instruments used for analysis and automatic process control in industry display the image graphically as a trace on a chart.

2-10. PASSIVE AND ACTIVE IR SYSTEMS

IR systems may be broadly divided into two categories, passive and active. A passive IR system detects only the IR radiation naturally emitted by the target or source. An active IR system employs an artificial source to illuminate the target, which then reradiates IR energy back to the detector system. Numerous examples of both types of systems are described in the text. Table 2-1 lists some of the more common active and passive IR systems.

TABLE 2-1. SOME TYPICAL EXAMPLES OF PASSIVE AND ACTIVE IR SYSTEMS

Passive systems	Active systems
IR radiometers, pyrometers	IR microscopes
IR camera	IR communication systems
IR search and track systems	IR searchlights
IR astronomical telescopes	IR snooperscope
IR viewers	IR spectrophotometers, spectrographs
IR sniperscope	IR continuous-process analyzers
	IR beacons

The Passive IR System.   The essential elements of a passive IR system are shown schematically in Fig. 2-7.   The great majority of IR systems in use today are of the passive type.

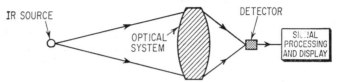

FIG. 2-7. Elements of passive IR system.

The radiation intensity of a source decreases with the distance from it according to the inverse-square law, so that a detecting system is ultimately limited by the range of the target.   The military advantages of a passive system are (1) its immunity from detection, since it radiates no IR energy, and (2) the difficulty of devising practicable countermeasures.

The Active IR System.   The essential elements of an active IR system are illustrated in Fig. 2-8.   IR radiation from a powerful artificial source, or IR searchlight, is filtered into a narrow-wavelength band, collimated, and directed in the form of a narrow beam onto the target.

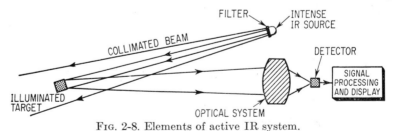

FIG. 2-8. Elements of active IR system.

IR energy reradiated by the illuminated target is collected and focused on a detector by the optical system of the receiver unit.

The active IR system has two major disadvantages.   The radiation intensity at the receiver varies inversely as the fourth power of the distance between a point-source target and the detector.   In the case of an extended target the square law applies. Unless a very highly collimated, narrow illuminating beam is used, range is severely limited by the inefficiency of the system due to excessive radiation losses. The system, being active, is more easily detected by an enemy.

Active IR systems were used quite extensively for military purposes during World War II, and, indeed, they reached a high degree of development. Examples such as the German *Lichtsprecher* IR communication system, based upon the modulation of IR radiation by voice-frequency signals, are discussed in Chap. 11. Simple IR blinker systems, used for signalling on land and for landing aircraft at night without lights, employed a beam spread of about twenty minutes of arc, and had ranges of approximately one mile.[3] Longer-range wide-beam, naval signalling systems employed mercury-lamp sources, lead sulfide detector cells, simple mirror optics, and exceeded ranges of 10 km.[3]

The advantages, disadvantages, and principles of operation of IR systems have been discussed. With this background, we now proceed to discuss in greater detail each building block of the model illustrated in Fig. 2-6. Commencing with source and background radiation, a more detailed examination of the factors and design principles involved in each basic building block is presented in Chaps. 3 through 7. Finally the application of these principles to the design of various IR instruments is described in Chaps. 8 and 9. In Part II the applications of IR instruments and techniques used in modern science and industry are discussed.

REFERENCE

3. Odarenko, T. M.: "German Wartime Developments in Infrared," Department of Commerce, *Office of Technical Services, Rept.* PB 95308, March, 1948.

ADDITIONAL BIBLIOGRAPHY

De Vos, J. C.: Evaluation of the Quality of a Black Body, *Physica,* vol. 20, p. 669, 1954.

Forsythe, W. E.: "Smithsonian Physical Tables," Smithsonian Institute, Washington, 1954.

Jenkins, F. A., and H. E. White: "Fundamentals of Optics," 3d ed., McGraw-Hill Book Company, Inc., New York, 1957.

Richtmyer, F. K., E. H. Kennard, and T. Lauritsen: "Introduction to Modern Physics," 5th ed., McGraw-Hill Book Company, Inc., New York, 1955.

Wilkes, G. B.: "Measurement of the Total Normal Emissivity of Materials," Massachusetts Institute of Technology, Cambridge, Mass., April, 1951.

3

Infrared Radiation Sources

The various types of radiation sources are classified and their uses are described. Artificial and controlled sources and the construction, operation, and uses of laboratory-standard black-body reference sources are described. Natural sources and the effects of background sources are discussed.

3-1. TYPES OF IR-RADIATION SOURCE

The phenomenal increase, during the last two decades, in the use of IR techniques for industrial and military applications has accelerated the development of artificial and controlled IR sources of various types. It has also accented the development of methods for discriminating between these IR sources and their natural background radiation.

The radiation from black bodies was discussed in Chap. 2, and it was shown that the wavelength of the maximum or peak emitted radiation is entirely dependent upon the source temperature. Radiation is in the form of a continuous spectrum the characteristics of which are governed by the Planck and Stefan-Boltzmann laws.

Few of the several types of radiation sources encountered in practice behave like perfect black bodies. Some sources behave like gray bodies, others emit a band spectrum or a line spectrum superimposed upon a black-body-type continuous spectrum. Instead of attempting to classify IR-radiation sources by the type of radiation emitted, it is more logical to regard the various types of sources as falling into the following three main categories: (1) artificial and controlled, (2) natural, and (3) interfering or background. Figure 3-1 summarizes the various types of IR sources.

28

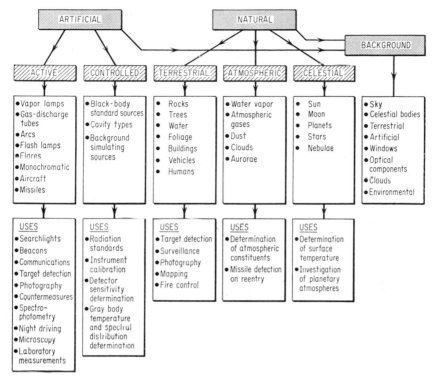

Fig. 3-1 Types of IR source.

3-2. ARTIFICIAL SOURCES

This type of IR source includes vapor lamps, gas-discharge tubes, arcs, flash lamps, flares, and artificial black-body sources. Although a measure of control is implied in the operation of all these sources—gas-discharge tubes, for example, are operated at a certain pressure—they are generally referred to as *active* sources. Exceptions are the artificial black-body sources, used for laboratory standards, which are termed *controlled* sources. The majority of these sources generate a wide-frequency spectrum and require the use of filters or monochromators to limit their radiation to the desired IR-wavelength band.

3-3. ACTIVE SOURCES

A wide variety of active types of IR sources were developed during World War II, mainly for military applications. Among the low-pressure gas-discharge tubes developed were the *sodium-discharge tube* and the *helium-discharge tube*. The latter operated at a pressure of 10 mm of mercury at 50 to 60 volts, and radiated approximately 80 per cent of its energy in the IR spectral region.[3] It was found, however, that the total energy radiated by these low-pressure discharge tubes was too low for military use.

The *Osram high-pressure mercury-arc lamp*[3] reached an advanced state of development and was widely employed. With water-cooled tungsten electrodes it operated at pressures up to 200 atm. Its most intense radiation occurred in the visible region so that filters were used to limit the radiation to the near-IR spectral band. The *carbon arc*, operating at 4200°K,[3] and the Beck arc operating at 5500°K also developed their most intense radiation in the visible spectrum and required filters to adapt them for IR use. These arc lamps were extensively used as illumination sources in signalling and communication systems, for beacons, and in active IR systems for target detection in the near-IR spectral region. Arc sources are rather bulky and have a short operating life.

Aircraft (particularly jet aircraft) and rockets are powerful active sources of IR radiation. The primary sources of IR radiation on aircraft are the hot metal of a jet tail pipe or an engine exhaust manifold and the jet plume, which has a higher temperature but lower emissivity. At supersonic speeds the aircraft's skin becomes an IR source because of aerodynamic heating. The ram-stagnation temperature depends upon the aircraft's speed and altitude. Aerodynamic heating contributes to forward-aspect radiation. IR radiation from aircraft and rocket exhausts usually consists of continuous, black-body-type, background radiation on which are superimposed emission bands due to water vapor, carbon dioxide occurring in the jet plume, and other chemical constituents of the jet or rocket plume. Large aircraft emit several kilowatts of IR energy. The human body, by comparison, emits approximately 2 watts of IR energy. The wavelength of peak IR emission depends upon the source temperature according to Wien's law (Fig. 2-1).

Flash lamps such as the *Edgerton arc* are used for IR photography. High-intensity *IR flares* are specially designed as an attempt to confuse military IR-detection systems. Several active sources, which have been extensively used as IR searchlights, beacons, in IR communication systems, and in the laboratory, are described in the following paragraphs.

3-4. THE NERNST GLOWER

This IR-radiation source is extensively used in spectrophotometry and in the laboratory. Peak IR-radiation output occurs at about 2μ. Advantages of the Nernst glower are a wide radiation spectrum and long life.

The glower itself consists of a cylindrical rod or tube of refractory oxides with platinum leads at each end.   When heated to dull-red heat the glower will conduct alternating current and then becomes a powerful source of IR radiation.   Starting temperature is achieved by means of an auxiliary heater coil, of platinum wire wound on a ceramic form, which is placed in close proximity to the glower and backed by a reflector (Fig. 3-2).   The amount of current passing through the glower via the platinum leads is indicated on a meter, and in normal operation is about 0.6 amp.

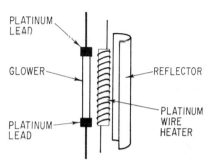

FIG. 3-2. Elements of Nernst glower. (*After Reference 1.*)

Once the glower is operating satisfactorily, the auxiliary heater is turned off.[1]

3-5. TUNGSTEN-FILAMENT LAMPS

Tungsten-filament lamps are widely used in spectrographic work and in IR communication systems.   These small tungsten-filament lamps, operated at 20 to 30 amp, produce a peak output of IR radiation in the lead sulfide detector responsive region, from about 0.7 to 3μ.   They are generally used with quartz windows and with cooled or uncooled lead sulfide detector-amplifier systems.

During World War II the German Army and Navy made extensive use of these radiation sources in their *Lichtsprecher* voice-modulated IR-beam communication systems.   For telegraphic communication, portable blinker-type equipment, in which the IR transmitter was operated by a telegraph key, was used.   These systems were successfully used on land, at sea, and for ship-to-shore communication purposes.   The radiation-source output was collimated into a narrow beam and confined to the near-IR spectrum by means of suitable filters. Since the resultant beam was invisible to the human eye, these IR systems were particularly invaluable for signalling and communication by night.

3-6. MERCURY AND XENON HIGH-INTENSITY SHORT-ARC LAMPS

Mercury and xenon high-intensity short-arc lamps are more powerful sources, used for longer-range communication systems, IR searchlights, and IR beacons. Developed originally in Germany during World War II, these sources are now made commercially in the United States and in Europe. They employ sturdy tungsten electrodes mounted in thick-walled quartz bulbs filled with mercury vapor and xenon gas at a pressure of about 2 atm.[5] The addition of xenon gas shortens the warm-up time required. Considerable heat is generated in these lamps, which operate at up to about 50 amp and 1,000 watts, causing the bulbs to become red hot. Radiation is emitted in the near-IR, through the visible, and in the near-ultraviolet spectral regions.

3-7. CESIUM-VAPOR ARC LAMPS

Cesium-vapor arc lamps, developed in the United States during the latter part of World War II, emit strong radiation in the near-IR spectral region with resonance spectral lines at 0.852 and 0.894 μ. These sources can be produced in various sizes, ranging from 500 watts up, for long-range communications, to low-power sealed-beam-type headlights.[5] They have the advantages of long life and, because vapor is employed, suitability for modulation at voice frequencies. Cesium-vapor lamps are also used in IR searchlights and beacons, and, with suitable filter combinations, form excellent monochromatic sources for applications in spectroscopy.

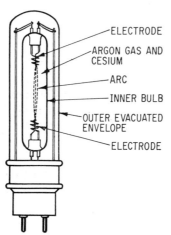

ELECTRODE

ARGON GAS AND CESIUM

ARC

INNER BULB

OUTER EVACUATED ENVELOPE

ELECTRODE

FIG. 3-3. Diagram of 100-watt type CL-2 cesium-vapor arc lamp. (*Courtesy Westinghouse Electric Corporation, Bloomfield, N.J.*)

Illustrated in Fig. 3-3 is the 100-watt type CL-2 cesium-vapor lamp manufactured by the Westinghouse Electric Corporation.[5] The inner bulb, containing argon gas at about 20 cm of mercury pressure and several tenths of a gram of cesium metal, has two electrodes to anchor the arc to its center. Since the inner bulb operates at a temperature of about 325°C, it must be enclosed in an outer, evacuated envelope to conserve heat. These lamps, operating at 5.5 amp, have a useful life of over 500 hr.   Approximately 21 per cent of the power supplied is radiated as IR energy.[5]

3-8. SPECIAL SOURCES

Certain IR sources, because of their unique characteristics, are useful for special applications.   Examples of this type of source are monochromatic sources and a source widely used in IR microscopy.

Zirconium Oxide–Arc Sources.   These are very bright spot sources generated by a concentrated arc.   They are made in various sizes and are extensively used in IR microscopy.   For this application they have the advantage over larger and more conventional sources, which, because of their size, limit the depth of focus attainable in a microscope and require the preparation of extremely thin samples for study.

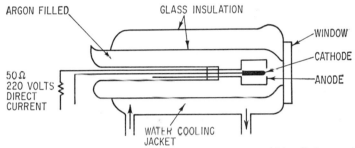

FIG. 3-4. Zirconium oxide concentrated-arc source.   (*After Reference 6.*)

The zirconium oxide concentrated-arc lamp[6] produces less scattered light.   This requires less magnification, resulting in greater depth of focus and reduced spectral distortion of the image.   Thicker sample specimens, which are much easier to prepare, can be used.   The source is illustrated schematically in Fig. 3-4.   It is sealed in an argon atmosphere, surrounded by a water-cooled jacket to dissipate the heat produced when operating, and is generally used with a rock-salt or KRS-5 window.

Monochromatic Sources.   Monochromatic sources emit IR radiation at a particular wavelength or frequency, or at least within a very narrow wavelength-band.   This is in contrast with the usual type of IR source which, as we have seen, emits IR radiation over a broad wavelength-region.

Few simple monochromatic sources are available in the IR spectral region.   The cesium-vapor lamp emits two bright radiation bands: at 0.85 and 0.89 μ, respectively.   Although these wavelengths can be

isolated from the remainder of the IR spectrum by the use of appropriate combinations of filters, this lamp is not a true monochromatic
source.

A monochromatic source useful for laboratory measurements is the
helium Geissler tube,[7] illustrated in Fig. 3-5.   This source emits IR
radiation in the region of 1 to 3 μ with two strong lines at 1.08 and
2.06 μ respectively.   These lines are far enough apart to be isolated
independently by means of filter combinations.   The 2.06-μ line may
be completely isolated by a combination of Corning glass filters No.
2540 and No. 4784; the 1.08-μ line can be isolated by using 1 cm of

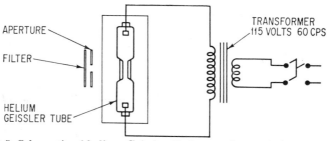

FIG. 3-5. Schematic of helium Geissler discharge tube.   (*After Reference 7.*)

water in a glass absorption-cell plus a Corning No. 2540 glass filter.[7]
The radiant output of this discharge tube is very stable and it has been
used to measure the detectivity of detector cells at the wavelengths of
these two lines.   It also has other applications.

IR measurements at other wavelengths can be made by employing
an artificial black-body source, with appropriate filter combinations to
screen out unwanted radiation, or by means of an IR monochromator.
This instrument, however, is both expensive and too cumbersome for
many applications.   It is described in Chap. 9.

3-9. CONTROLLED SOURCES

The tremendous increase in industrial applications of IR techniques
since the war has led to the development of commercially available
black-body standard sources, controllable over a wide range of source
temperatures.   These sources are used as primary radiation standards
for the calibration of IR instruments such as pyrometers and radiometers, and as standards of comparison for other IR sources.

There is no material with an emissivity of 1.0, which behaves like a
perfect black body.   Perfect black-body conditions giving an emitted-
radiation spectrum with an exact Planckian distribution can only be

achieved when a radiating area is in thermal equilibrium and of infinite thickness.

Cavity-type radiation sources very closely approach ideal black-body conditions if they are properly designed. It can be shown[8] that, for a uniformly heated cavity at a given temperature, the radiation emitted is the same in all directions and is independent of the material used for construction of the cavity. The choice of material used depends upon its emissivity, cost, and the ease with which it can be machined. It has been shown by Gouffe[9] that a material of emissivity factor 0.75, in the form of a conical 15° cavity, will have a total hemispherical emissivity factor of 0.99. Calculations show that as the surface emissivity of the material decreases, the apex angle of the cavity must increase. The construction of a cavity source requires precise and uniform temperature distribution along the cavity walls. Emissivity is not affected by slight variations in the walls of the cavity.

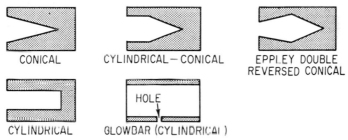

CONICAL   CYLINDRICAL – CONICAL   EPPLEY DOUBLE
                                            REVERSED CONICAL

CYLINDRICAL   GLOWBAR (CYLINDRICAL)

Fig. 3-6. Types of cavity black-body source.

Several commercial types of standard-reference sources employing these principles of construction are available. Some approach the radiation output of an ideal black body to within 1 per cent. The temperature of the source is precisely maintained at a selected level by means of an electronic servo control system. The sources are available in a variety of controllable temperature ranges from ambient to about 1000°C. Cavity materials used are generally steel, aluminum, or copper, blackened by oxidation or by zapon black. Cavity shapes employed are conical, cylindrical, spherical, or double-reversed conical (Fig. 3-6). Cavity temperatures are measured by a thermistor or thermocouple. These cavity-radiation sources emit a continuous spectrum which very closely approximates a Planckian distribution and which is dependent exclusively upon the absolute temperature of the radiator. They are supplied with a set of limiting apertures of different sizes. If it is desired to maintain the aperture temperature close to the ambient temperature, a series of baffle plates is mounted between the cavity and the aperture as in Fig. 3-7.   These baffle plates are water-cooled or provided with a suitable heat sink.

Typical Black-body Standard Source.   Modern standard-reference sources employ these principles in their construction.   An excellent example of a commercial instrument of this type is a standard source, made by the Servo Corporation of America,[8] illustrated in Fig. 3-7.

It consists of a 15° conical cavity, machined in a cylindrical copper core which is threaded on its outside surface for a heating coil.   The inner surface of the cavity is oxidized by heating; its emissivity is approximately 0.7.   The cavity temperature is measured by a bead thermistor inserted in the core.   Heat losses are reduced by (1) end plates made of Transite and (2) a cylindrical reflector surrounding the core axis and insulated by floss from the finned housing.   Variable

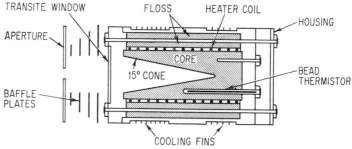

FIG. 3-7. Servotherm® black-body standard source.   (*Courtesy Reference 8, and Servo Corporation of America, Hicksville, N.Y.*)

apertures and baffle plates of Transite and aluminum sheet are provided.   The temperature is controlled to a fraction of a degree by a high-gain closed-loop servo system which continuously balances a sensitive thermally controlled resistance bridge.

Applications of Standard Sources.   One of the important applications of a standard-reference source is the determination of the black-body sensitivity of thermal detectors such as bolometers, thermocouples, and thermopiles.   The thermal detector is illuminated by a known quantity of black-body radiation from the standard source, and its response is recorded.

Since the standard source is temperature stabilized, it is used as a reference standard in the analysis of the IR absorption and transmission characteristics of various substances.   It is used to measure the transmission of an IR monochromator[8] by measuring the energy entering and leaving the monochromator under identical conditions.

Another important application of the standard source is its use as a standard to determine the temperature and spectral distribution of gray bodies. It is used as a comparator in this application as well as for the establishment of secondary standards. It is also used as a standard for the calibration of such IR instruments as pyrometers and radiometers. These instruments, like the black-body source, obey the black-body laws. That is, the theoretical relation between the temperature and the intensity of radiant energy is known. By setting the standard source at a number of different temperatures, a pyrometer may be calibrated. It can then be used to determine the temperature of any other type of black- or gray-body source.

For example,[8] suppose the object whose temperature is to be measured is a gray body with an emissivity factor ϵ. Its radiant energy is represented by the Stefan-Boltzmann equation

$$W = \epsilon \sigma T^4$$

where T = true temperature, °K
For a black body, $\epsilon = 1$ and

$$W = \sigma T_R^4 \qquad (3\text{-}1)$$

where T_R = radiation temperature, °K
Thus

$$\frac{T_R}{T} = \epsilon^{\frac{1}{4}} \qquad (3\text{-}2)$$

If ϵ is known, the temperature T of the body can be calculated. If T is known, the emissivity ϵ of the gray body can be calculated. An emissivity-measuring instrument is described in Chap. 9.

3-10. NATURAL SOURCES

The various types of IR sources discussed so far have all been artificially generated or man-made sources. Numerous IR sources occur in nature. They cannot be controlled by man. These natural sources may be broadly classified into three categories.

Terrestrial Sources. These are natural sources occurring on the surface of the earth. Every object with a temperature above absolute zero (0°K or −273°C) radiates IR energy. Trees, bushes, rocks, earth, sand, water, and so on are all natural sources. Spectral characteristics of the radiation emitted depend upon both the source temperature and such surface characteristics as emissivity and reflectivity. Surfaces such as rock, sand, and metal both emit IR energy and reflect IR energy from the sun.

An object at a different absolute temperature than its surroundings

FIG. 3-8. Photographs of power station at night—upper photograph made by Barnes infrared camera.   (*Courtesy Barnes Engineering Company, Stamford, Conn.*)

can be detected.   This principle is used in IR search, tracking, and ranging devices.   The IR radiation from the background may seriously diminish the ability of an IR device to detect the required target. Means must be provided in this case for discriminating it from the background radiation by the use of (1) space-filtering techniques employing a chopper, reticle, or scanning system to distinguish between the sizes of the target and background images; (2) spectral filtering techniques using optical IR filters to limit the received radiation to the desired spectral region; and (3) electronic filtering techniques.

In applications to IR photography, the response of the IR camera depends upon the variation of surface temperature over the area photographed. This is clearly illustrated in Figs. 3-8 and 3-9. Hot smoke-

FIG. 3-9. Visual photograph (*upper*) and thermal photograph (*lower*) made by Barnes infrared camera of Ford automobile. (*Courtesy Barnes Engineering Company, Stamford, Conn.*)

stacks and hot areas in the factory building appear white or light-colored; cold areas appear dark. A temperature-gradation scale in photographs like this enables an estimate of the actual temperatures of various areas of the building to be made.

Atmospheric Sources. Dust particles, water droplets, and molecules of the various gases occurring in the earth's atmosphere behave like secondary sources of IR radiation. They scatter reflect, and absorb and reemit primary radiation illuminating them from both celestial and terrestrial sources.

Familiar examples of this in the visible region are sunlight reflected and scattered by clouds and the glow over a city at night. These effects extend into the IR spectral region. They are most pronounced in the near-IR spectral region. Here the principal secondary sources of radiation are scattered and reflected sunlight by day, moonlight by night. This background radiation affects the performance of such IR devices as fire-control and detection instruments, astronomical telescopes, and cameras. It must be eliminated as much as possible by suitable filtering devices.

Celestial Sources. The third natural radiation source comprises the heavenly bodies—the sun, planets, stars, nebulae, etc. Here the principal sources of IR radiation are, of course, the sun by day and the moon by night.

The total radiant power received from the sun is of the order of 136.5 watts/ft^2 normal to the earth's surface. Of this solar radiation, approximately 182 mw/ft^2 is received at the earth's surface from the sun at wavelengths longer than 3 μ. By comparison, the total power received from the same solid angle of the sky in the same spectral region is approximately 0.079 mw/ft^2 (of surface area). It is seen, therefore, that the sun is an extremely intense source of radiation. In fact, certain detector cells such as lead sulfide suffer damage to their sensitive surfaces when pointed toward the sun for appreciable periods of time. They may have to be protected against this exposure by means of an eyelid or automatic shutter arrangement that shields the detector cell when it is pointing in the direction of the sun.

The sun closely resembles a black-body source at a temperature of 6500°K, which is approximately the average temperature of its outer surface. If it could be viewed from a point in space completely outside the earth's atmosphere, the solar radiation spectrum would be expected to resemble a Planckian distribution curve, peaking, according to Wien's law, at a wavelength of about 0.45 μ (Fig. 3-10). Emission bands from hot gases, sunspots, solar flares, and other fluctuations on the outer surface of the sun, which superimpose slight perturbations on this curve, are not shown in the figure.

Viewed from the earth's surface, however, the solar radiation spectrum is radically changed by absorption, scattering, and, to a much smaller extent, reradiation into the intervening atmosphere. Although the energy received from the sun peaks in the visible region, considerable radiation extends well out into the far-IR spectral region, as shown in Fig. 3-10.[10] As altitude above the earth's surface is increased the radiation spectrum of the received solar energy approaches that of a black-body curve. The intensity of received radiation increases, scattering in the near IR is reduced, and the strength and width of the absorption bands are reduced.   This has been confirmed by the IR spectrographic records obtained by Gates et al. in June, 1955, from a skyhook plastic balloon flight to an altitude of over 100,000 ft,[11] and discussed more fully in Chap. 4.

From the point of view of an observer on or relatively close to the earth's surface, the next most important celestial source of IR radiation is the moon.   The bulk of the energy received from the moon is solar radiation, modified (1) by reflection from the lunar surface, (2) by possibly very slight absorption by the lunar atmosphere which may contain small amounts of inert and heavy gases, and (3) by absorption and scattering in those portions of the earth's atmosphere that it may

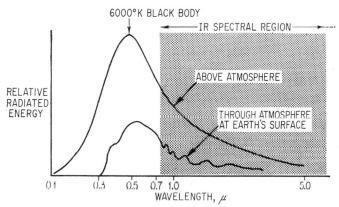

Fig. 3-10. Spectral distribution of solar radiation.   (*Based upon Reference 10.*)

traverse before reaching the observer.   Since the temperature of the lunar surface exceeds absolute zero, particularly during the 15-day period of sunlight, the moon also radiates as a true source.   It has been estimated[12] that the surface-dust layer reaches a temperature as high as 373°K during the lunar day and falls to about 120°K during the lunar night, while the surface temperature below the dust layer is a constant 230°K, which corresponds to peak radiation at a wavelength of about 12.6 μ.

As seen from the earth, the next brightest celestial sources of IR radiation are the planet Venus, followed by the star Mira.   The planets and stars are very weak point sources of IR radiation, compared to the sun and moon, and can be disregarded except in certain astronomical applications which will be discussed later.

Summarizing, the radiation characteristics of celestial sources depend primarily upon the source temperature.   At high altitudes the spectral distribution of radiation closely follows Planck's law.   At low altitudes it is modified by the earth's atmosphere and varies considerably with the zenith angle of the celestial body, as well as with the altitude of the viewer above the earth's surface, as described in the following section.

3-11. BACKGROUND RADIATION SOURCES

Regardless of the nature of the source, a certain amount of background or interfering radiation will be present.   This appears in the detection system as unwanted noise and must be reduced or eliminated if possible.

In the case of artificial sources employed in signalling and communications devices, beacons, and active IR systems generally, background effects are controlled by narrow-band cutoff filters at both the source and the detector end of the system.   Background radiation in controlled black-body standard sources is reduced by using heat sinks or water-cooling devices on the baffles placed between the source and aperture.   Spectral and space-filtering devices and electronic filtering techniques are used to reduce background effects in detection systems employed for terrestrial or air-borne applications.   These three background-discrimination methods are also employed in IR astronomical telescopes of the type described in Chap. 9.

Background Radiation in the Day and Night Skies.   IR radiation from the sky by day or by night depends upon a number of factors. IR radiation contributing to the over-all background is emitted from atmospheric constituents at their ambient temperatures; from the sun by scattering in the atmosphere and by reflection from clouds; and, to a much lesser extent, from the moon and other celestial bodies which contribute a low-level background radiation at night.   IR radiation-intensity and spectral distribution vary with (1) the water vapor and carbon dioxide contents of the atmosphere, more noticeably than with other atmospheric constituents; (2) the angle of elevation which determines the length of the path traversed through the atmosphere; (3) the temperature of the atmosphere, particularly in its lower levels; and (4) the altitude above the earth's surface.   They are also affected by clouds and haze.

This section is confined to the case of an observer situated on the earth's surface or within the earth's atmosphere and looking away from the earth.   The opposite case, that of an observer situated in space and looking down toward the earth and its atmosphere, is discussed in Chap. 12.

The spectral distribution of energy radiated from clear day and night skies is shown, not to scale, in Fig. 3-11, which illustrates the primary differences between the day and night sky background radiation normal to the earth's surface.

At night, the short-wavelength background radiation, caused by the scattering of sunlight by air molecules, dust, and other particles, disappears. Long-wavelength background radiation is present because of the black-body radiation of the atmosphere; this is modified by absorption and emission bands from atmospheric constituents, such as water vapor, carbon dioxide, carbon monoxide, and ozone, at their ambient temperatures.

The principal absorption bands are indicated in Fig. 3-11. Since the ambient temperature is lower at night, atmospheric radiation peaks at a longer wavelength at night than in daytime. Radiation from the clear night sky approximates that of a black body at 273°K, with the

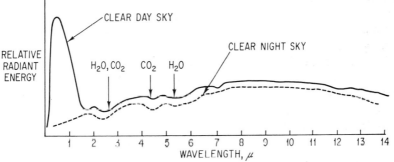

FIG. 3-11. Spectral energy distribution of background radiation from clear day and night skies.

peak intensity occurring at a wavelength of about 10.5 μ. Over-all, the energy level is slightly lower than that of a clear daytime sky. Total IR radiation from the night sky is of a low order near the zenith. As the elevation angle of look above the horizon is reduced, radiation intensity increases. The sharpest increases occur at low elevation angles where the length of path traversed through the atmosphere is greater and the temperature and concentration of atmospheric gases and water vapor are higher. Toward the horizon, radiation is emitted from a deep layer of air and water vapor, of which the effective emissivity is very close to unity. The horizon, therefore, behaves like a true black body at its ambient temperature.

At night the average temperature of the earth is close to that of the lower atmosphere. The earth behaves like a gray body with a relatively high emissivity factor. At night, therefore, the characteristics of the background radiation of both earth and sky are very similar.

By day, looking up from the surface of the earth or at low altitudes, the background radiation from the sky is considerable in the directions of both the sun and the horizon, and in any direction is more intense than at night. Radiation intensity in a clear sky, caused by scattering of the sun's radiation, peaks at approximately 0.45 μ in the visible region.

Considerable radiation extends into the near-IR spectral region, with intensity falling off rapidly in the middle-IR region (Fig. 3-11). Radiation caused by scattering and reflection of sunlight from the clouds has similar spectral characteristics.

Rayleigh's scattering theory predicts a rapid decrease in the intensity of scattered radiation with increasing wavelength. This is confirmed by measurements of sky brightness in the visible and near-IR spectral regions respectively.[13] Zenith brightness varies with both atmospheric pressure and zenith angle, increasing near the horizon in a manner similar to that of the night sky. Bright cloud edges and horizon effects cause sharp gradients and fluctuations in radiation from the daytime sky.

Although radiation from most targets occurs in the wavelength region beyond 3 μ, the problem of discriminating it from daylight background radiation and its fluctuations is a serious one for IR search and tracking devices. The background radiation can be greatly reduced by optically filtering out all received radiation below 3 μ.

This procedure, however, seriously limits the performance of those devices intended for daytime search and tracking applications which employ lead sulfide detector cells, whose spectral response falls off rapidly—beyond 3.5 μ if cooled to dry ice temperatures; beyond about 4 μ if cooled to liquid nitrogen temperatures. The newer types of cell, such as lead telluride, lead selenide, indium antimonide, and certain doped germanium cells, have good spectral response out to 6 μ or beyond, but their detectivities are less than that of a good lead sulfide detector cell.

A less serious type of daylight-sky background radiation is that extending beyond 3-μ wavelength. This is caused by the normal reradiation of the atmospheric constituents, water vapor, carbon dioxide, ozone, and the hydroxyl radicals (Chap. 4), at their ambient atmospheric temperatures. This type of sky radiation is of low intensity; it has a more uniform intensity gradient, with the major fluctuations in gradient occurring near the horizon.

This type of sky radiation occurs in the middle- and far-IR spectral regions. The temperature and emissivity of these gaseous constituents depend upon meteorological conditions. They may exhibit widely varying characteristics, as shown by observations of sky radiance.[14]

Since the temperature and concentration of atmospheric constituents decrease with altitude, this type of background radiation may be expected to decrease with increasing altitude.

Clouds produce considerable variation in sky background, both by day and by night. Their greatest effect, occurring at wavelengths below about 3 μ, is caused by reflection of solar radiation from the cloud surfaces. Low, bright clouds produce a larger increase in background radiation intensity at this wavelength than do darker or high clouds. This essentially meteorological variation in sky background changes continually with time and location. At wavelengths longer than 3 μ, the background radiation intensity caused by clouds is higher than, but similar to, that of the clear sky.

One of the most serious cloud effects on IR-detection systems is that due to a bright cloud edge—which, in effect, is equivalent to a relatively small local source of IR radiation—which may be comparable in area to that of the target. Marked energy discontinuities are caused by bright cloud edges. Discrimination from this background effect requires the use of space-filtering techniques, to distinguish the smaller target area from the somewhat larger area of the cloud edge, in addition to spectral filtering techniques.

Terrain produces a higher over-all background-energy distribution than that of the clear, blue sky. This is caused by reflected sunlight in the short-wavelength region and by thermal emission at the longer wavelengths. This latter effect varies considerably with the nature of the terrain. The absence of sharp thermal discontinuity between an object and its surroundings caused by a high level of background radiation greatly complicates the problem of the detection of terrestrial targets, both from the ground and from the air.

3-12. SOURCE RADIATION INTENSITY

IR radiation from black-body standard-reference sources very closely approximates true black-body radiation and obeys the laws enumerated in Chap. 2.

Other sources may deviate widely from black-body characteristics. Generally speaking, for optimum detection of a source the following information is required: (1) the spatial and spectral characteristics of the source radiation, (2) the nature of the background radiation from which it is to be discriminated. Spatially, energy is radiated from the source with an angular distribution given by Lambert's law of cosines. Since the source radiation is usually complex, it should be described as a source-radiant intensity, $W_\lambda(\theta)$, measured in watts per steradian per micron, at a given emission angle θ.

3-13. ATTENUATION OF SOURCE RADIATION

Whatever the type of source, radiation from it will be reduced in intensity and altered in characteristics by the atmosphere encountered between the source and the receiver. The degree and nature of attenuation vary with the nature of the atmosphere and the length of path through it. In most cases the atmosphere encountered is that of the earth; this varies with altitude and weather conditions. In other cases, for example with certain types of laboratory instruments such as spectrometers, IR analyzers, or IR microscopes, the atmosphere encountered is a rare gas, a vacuum, or a sample of the gas to be analyzed. The effects of atmospheric attenuation are discussed in Chap. 4.

Further attenuation of the source radiation is caused by filtering effects and transmission losses encountered in the optical system. These are produced by absorption, refraction, and reflection in irdomes, windows, filters, prisms, mirrors, and lenses. These effects are discussed in Chaps. 5 and 6.

REFERENCES

1. "Instruction Manual, IR-2 Spectrophotometer," Beckman Instruments, Inc., Fullerton, California.
3. Odarenko, T. M.: "German Wartime Developments in Infrared," Department of Commerce, *Office of Technical Services, Rept.* PB 95308, March, 1948.
5. Beese, Norman C.: Light Sources for Optical Communication, Office of Naval Research, *Proc. Infrared Inform. Symposia*, vol. 3, no. 3, p. 164, December, 1958.
6. Hall, M. B., and Nestor, R. G.: *J. Opt. Soc. Am.*, vol. 42, p. 257, 1952.
7. McFee, Raymond H.: *J. Opt. Soc. Am.*, vol. 42, p. 67, 1952.
8. Marcus, Norman: A Blackbody Standard, *Instr. and Automation*, vol. 28, no. 3, March, 1955.
9. Gouffe, Andre: *Rev. opt.*, vol. 24, nos. 1–3, 1945.
10. Fusca, James A.: Satellite Reconnaissance Optics, pt. I, *Aviation Week*, Jan. 19, 1959, p. 91.
11. Gates, D. M., Murcray, D. G., Shaw, C. C., and Herbold, R. J.: Near Infrared Solar Radiation Measurements by Balloon to an Altitude of 100,000 Feet, *J. Opt. Soc. Am.*, vol. 48, no. 12, p. 1010, December, 1958.
12. Stone, Irving: *Aviation Week*, June 16, 1958, p. 165.
13. Pierce, K.: Investigation of the Spectral Energy Distribution from Clouds and Blue Sky in the Near Infrared, *Univ. Mich., Eng. Research Inst. Tech. Rept.* TR 41, February, 1953.
14. Sloan, R., Shaw, J. H., and Williams, D.: Infrared Emission Spectrum of the Atmosphere, *J. Opt. Soc. Am.*, vol. 45, p. 455, 1955.

4

Atmospheric Transmission
of IR Radiation

The factors affecting IR transmission through the earth's atmosphere are discussed. Physical laws approximating the absorption, scattering, and general attenuation of IR radiation by gaseous constituents and particles occurring in the atmosphere are described. IR-transmission studies made in the lower and upper atmosphere are discussed.

Transmission of IR radiation through the earth's atmosphere is dependent upon the concentration and distribution of gaseous and molecular particles composing the atmosphere. This, in turn, is dependent upon meteorological conditions, particularly in the lower atmosphere where the water-vapor, gaseous, and dust contents may vary continuously. The atmospheric transmission of IR radiation, therefore, varies continuously with the weather conditions and also changes with altitude above sea level.

Theoretical studies can give only an approximate indication of this dependence. These studies are backed up by a growing body of evidence resulting from transmission measurements at various altitudes and wavelengths and under different meteorological conditions. From this data, empirical formulas and mathematical models can be constructed to give a good approximation of atmospheric transmission in various air masses. Studies of this nature are of primary importance in the design and application of both terrestrial and air-borne IR-detection devices.

The earth's atmospheric gases consist of polyatomic molecules such as methane (CH_4), triatomic molecules such as water vapor (H_2O), nitrous oxide (N_2O), carbon dioxide (CO_2), or ozone (O_3), and diatomic molecules such as carbon monoxide (CO). In the earth's atmosphere at the lower altitudes, the temperature is not high enough, nor the pressure low enough, to cause the dissociation of these molecules into their individual atoms, as is the case in the sun's atmosphere. Some dissociation occurs at very high altitudes, but the atmosphere there is extremely rare and the effect is negligible in comparison with conditions in the entire atmospheric belt. Consequently the earth's atmosphere exhibits the characteristics of *band spectra* rather than true line spectra, which are produced only by monatomic gases.

Attenuation of radiation throughout the IR region results from the resonance-absorption bands of the atmospheric constituents. It is high for triatomic molecules such as water vapor, carbon dioxide, and ozone. As we have seen, the periodic motions of the electrons in the atoms of a source, vibrating and rotating at certain frequencies, result in the radiation of electromagnetic waves at those frequencies. The atmospheric constituents contain bound charges or electrons with natural frequencies of vibration and rotation which depend upon the construction of the molecule. When these characteristic frequencies are matched by that of the incident radiation, resonance absorption occurs. When the electric-field vector of an incident electromagnetic wave varies with a frequency which exactly matches the natural vibration frequency of a charged particle in the atmosphere, a large amplitude of vibration results and the energy absorbed is reradiated as resonance radiation of the same frequency. This is uniformly distributed in all directions. In effect, in a particular direction, the incident radiation is attenuated or absorbed.

A different form of attenuation is caused by scattering of the incident radiation by dust nuclei and water droplets. This form of attenuation increases rapidly as the visible region of the spectrum is approached. It is negligible in the middle-IR region at wavelengths longer than about 4 μ.

4-1. ABSORPTION

The absorption spectrum of IR radiation passing through the earth's atmosphere consists of the absorption spectra of the resonant vibration-rotation bands of the various atmospheric constituents. These include the primary constituents, water vapor, carbon dioxide, and ozone, and the principal minor constituents carbon monoxide, nitrous oxide, methane, and hydrogen deuterium oxide ("heavy water"). Very minute quantities of other gases are present, including the rare gases; however, their comparative effect on atmospheric transmission is negligible.

Of the primary constituents, water vapor is the principal attenuator of IR radiation.   It causes the greatest transmission loss over the IR spectrum.   In any particular volume of the earth's atmosphere, up to an altitude of about 30,000 ft, the concentration and distribution of water vapor are continually changing.   Consequently the prediction of IR-transmission losses due to atmospheric water vapor depends upon the accuracy of meteorological forecasts.

Next in importance as an attenuator of IR radiation is carbon dioxide.   The distribution of carbon dioxide in the atmosphere is practically constant.   Its attenuation of IR radiation is more easily calculated and is virtually independent of weather conditions.

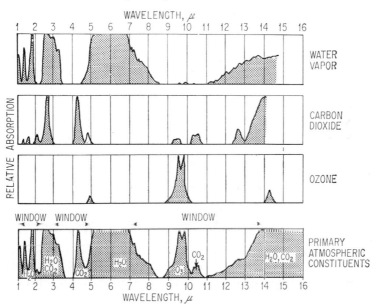

FIG. 4-1. IR-absorption bands of primary atmospheric constituents (for average conditions at sea level).

Practically all atmospheric ozone is limited to a layer at an altitude of approximately 80,000 ft.   For most purposes the effect of ozone on IR transmission below this altitude can be neglected.

Figure 4-1 shows the IR-absorption bands (shaded) at sea level, and the IR-transmission windows (clear areas), of these primary constituents of the atmosphere out to a wavelength of 15 μ.   The wavelength regions between absorption bands are called *windows*.   These are regions of maximum IR transmission.   Absorption bands of one atmospheric constituent may partly fill a window of another constituent.   An over-all picture of the principal windows in the atmosphere at sea level is shown, at the bottom of Fig. 4-1, out to a wavelength of 15 μ.

It is a composite picture, for an average atmosphere, of the effects of all the atmospheric constituents depicted in Fig. 4-1.

If a single absorption band were examined in a high-resolution spectrograph it would be found to consist of many hundreds of thousands of individual absorption lines (Fig. 4-2). Increases in atmospheric pressure and temperature cause individual broadening of these lines. Increase in atmospheric pressure causes a marked broadening of the absorption lines and corresponds to a considerable increase in absorption. Increases in temperature cause a very slight increase in atmospheric absorption. These effects cause a reduction in atmospheric absorption with increase in altitude above the earth's surface.

In the case of carbon dioxide the spectral lines of an absorption band are fairly equally spaced. Those for a water-vapor absorption band, however, have random spacing. The intensities of individual lines vary within wide limits. Consideration of this, together with the

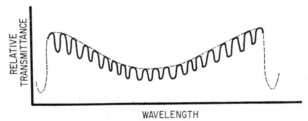

FIG. 4-2. High-resolution appearance of a typical absorption band.

broadening effects on spectral lines of pressure, temperature, and altitude, makes the construction of a mathematical model describing the absorption of an atmospheric constituent between given wavelength limits an extremely complicated process. Fractional absorption must be expressed over a narrow wavelength band and integrated or summed within the wavelength limits desired. Assumptions must be made regarding the intensity and distribution of spectral lines.

In spite of the difficulties encountered, three mathematical models of atmospheric transmittance have been devised and give results which are good approximations of the actual conditions:

1. The first is the Elsasser model, which assumes equal spacing and intensity of the individual spectral lines and shows that the fractional absorption follows an error-function law. This model is described in the succeeding sections.

2. The second model for atmospheric spectral-band absorption postulates random spacing of the individual spectral lines and includes the effects of Lorentz, or altitude broadening of the lines.

3. The third model is a combination of the first two. The second

and third models describe the effects of spectral-band absorption at higher altitudes more accurately than does Elsasser's model. However, at the lower altitudes Elsasser's model is widely used.

4-2. ABSORPTION BY WATER VAPOR

For monochromatic (single-wavelength) radiation, absorption by water vapor is dependent upon the wavelength, according to the exponential law

$$A_\lambda = 1 - I_\lambda/I_{0\lambda} = 1 - e^{\alpha\lambda w} \tag{4-1}$$

where A_λ = fractional absorption

$I_\lambda/I_{0\lambda}$ = fractional transmission

$I_{0\lambda}$ = intensity of radiation at wavelength λ

I_λ = intensity of radiation after passing through w cm of precipitable water

α_λ = exponential absorption coefficient for wavelength λ

w = water-vapor content expressed in terms of the precipitable water encountered in the total path length of the radiation

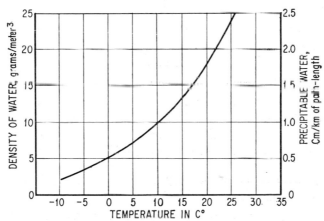

FIG. 4-3. Density of saturated water vapor.   (*After Reference 15*.)

The value of w is obtained from the absolute humidity (the quantity of water vapor in air, in grams per cubic meter), which can be computed from observations of the relative humidity and the temperature of the atmosphere. The relationship between these quantities is shown[15] in Fig. 4-3.

For example, for a temperature of 20°C and a relative humidity of 50 per cent, from Fig. 4-3

$$w = 1.75 \times 0.5 = 0.875 \text{ cm/km path length}$$

A 2,000-yd atmospheric path length at 80°F and 100 per cent relative humidity contains approximately 4.8 cm of precipitable water.

Equation (4-1) applies only to monochromatic radiation, so that the exponential-function law of absorption is at best only an approximate expression of the true conditions. A closer approximation results if the fractional absorption is expressed over a wavelength interval $\Delta\lambda$, and the nature of an absorption band is considered. This has been done by Elsasser,[16] who made the assumptions that the absorption lines are equally spaced and of equal intensity. For a wavelength interval $\Delta\lambda = \lambda_2 - \lambda_1$, which is large compared to the individual line spacing, he showed that the fractional absorption A followed an error-function law:

$$A = 1 - \frac{I}{I_0} = \frac{1}{\lambda_2 - \lambda_1} \int_{\lambda=\lambda_1}^{\lambda=\lambda_2} A_\lambda \, d\lambda$$
$$= erf \frac{\sqrt{\lambda \, d\alpha \, w}}{\delta} \tag{4-2}$$

where λ_1 and λ_2 correspond to the centers of two absorption lines separated by the wavelength interval $\Delta\lambda = \lambda_2 - \lambda_1$, μ

I_0 = total IR intensity in the interval $\Delta\lambda$

I = total IR intensity in the interval $\Delta\lambda$ after passage through w cm of precipitable water vapor

δ = the constant separation assumed for the individual absorption lines, μ

d = half-width of an absorption line

α = mean exponential-absorption coefficient, defined by

$$\frac{1}{\lambda_2 - \lambda_1} = \int_{\lambda=\lambda_1}^{\lambda=\lambda_2} \alpha_\lambda \, d\lambda \tag{4-3}$$

writing

$$2\sqrt{d\alpha}/\delta = \beta \tag{4-4}$$

Eq. (4-2) becomes

$$A = erf(\beta/2 \sqrt{\pi w}) \tag{4-5}$$

where β = error-function absorption coefficient

In practice, since this model is an approximation in view of the assumptions upon which it is based, observed values of IR absorption by atmospheric water vapor deviate somewhat from the values given by the error-function law. Actually they lie between the values predicted by this law and those predicted by the exponential law, Eq. (4-1). Since these deviations are smaller than the errors encountered in meteorological data, the error-function law of absorption is widely used.

Table 4-1 lists the values of the error-function absorption coefficient β for water vapor, given as a function of the wavelength λ for sea-level conditions.[15]   The transmittance values for various values of w, computed from the values of β given in Table 4-1, are listed as a function of λ in Table 4-2 and plotted in Fig. 4-4 out to a wavelength of 7 μ.

TABLE 4-1. H_2O ERROR-FUNCTION ABSORPTION COEFFICIENTS β FOR SEA-LEVEL CONDITIONS (WAVELENGTH, μ)*

λ	β	λ	β	λ	β
0.3	0.20	2.6	7.30	4.9	0.75
0.4	0.20	2.7	7.30	5.0	0.85
0.5	0.14	2.8	6.00	5.1	1.15
0.6	0.10	2.9	3.20	5.2	1.55
0.7	0.09	3.0	1.50	5.3	2.10
0.8	0.11	3.1	1.30	5.4	2.80
0.9	0.35	3.2	1.30	5.5	4.00
1.0	0.10	3.3	1.35	5.6	5.50
1.1	0.30	3.4	1.30	5.7	7.30
1.2	0.20	3.5	1.15	5.8	11.40
1.3	0.80	3.6	0.95	5.9	11.40
1.4	1.00	3.7	0.70	6.0	10.70
1.5	1.30	3.8	0.55	6.1	9.00
1.6	1.15	3.9	0.50	6.2	3.60
1.7	1.12	4.0	0.45	6.3	4.75
1.8	3.00	4.1	0.40	6.4	8.00
1.9	0.95	4.2	0.40	6.5	11.10
2.0	0.40	4.3	0.40	6.6	11.50
2.1	0.20	4.4	0.45	6.7	7.90
2.2	0.13	4.5	0.50	6.8	7.30
2.3	0.14	4.6	0.55	6.9	6.50
2.4	0.27	4.7	0.60	7.0	5.00
2.5	2.80	4.8	0.70		

* SOURCE: L. Larmore.[15]

The absorption of IR radiation by water vapor varies with atmospheric temperature and pressure, since an increase in either will cause a broadening of the absorption lines and, therefore, a net increase in absorption.   The temperature effect is so slight that it can usually be ignored.   The effect of pressure changes is considerable.   The correction factor H, to be applied to the sea-level absorption computed by the error-function law, is, to a very close degree of approximation, given by[18]

$$H = \sqrt{P/P_0} \qquad (4\text{-}6)$$

where P = atmospheric pressure at the altitude considered
    P_0 = atmospheric pressure at sea level
H is given in Table 4-3 for various altitudes, h, in feet above sea level.[15]

TABLE 4-2. ATMOSPHERIC TRANSMITTANCE OF WATER VAPOR AT SEA LEVEL
w = precipitable water, cm
(*After L. Larmore.*[15])

μ \ w, cm	0.01	0.02	0.05	0.1	0.2	0.5	1	2	5	10	20	50	100
0.3	0.980	0.972	0.955	0.937	0.911	0.860	0.802	0.723	0.574	0.428	0.263	0.076	0.012
0.4	0.980	0.972	0.955	0.937	0.911	0.860	0.802	0.723	0.574	0.428	0.263	0.076	0.012
0.5	0.986	0.980	0.968	0.956	0.937	0.901	0.861	0.804	0.695	0.579	0.433	0.215	0.079
0.6	0.990	0.986	0.977	0.968	0.955	0.929	0.900	0.860	0.779	0.692	0.575	0.375	0.210
0.7	0.991	0.987	0.980	0.972	0.960	0.937	0.910	0.873	0.800	0.722	0.615	0.425	0.260
0.8	0.989	0.984	0.975	0.965	0.950	0.922	0.891	0.845	0.758	0.663	0.539	0.330	0.168
0.9	0.965	0.951	0.922	0.890	0.844	0.757	0.661	0.535	0.326	0.165	0.050	0.002	0
1.0	0.990	0.986	0.977	0.968	0.955	0.929	0.900	0.860	0.779	0.692	0.575	0.375	0.210
1.1	0.970	0.958	0.932	0.905	0.866	0.790	0.707	0.595	0.406	0.235	0.093	0.008	0
1.2	0.980	0.972	0.955	0.937	0.911	0.860	0.802	0.723	0.574	0.428	0.263	0.076	0.012
1.3	0.726	0.611	0.432	0.268	0.116	0.013	0	0	0	0	0	0	0
1.4	0.930	0.902	0.844	0.782	0.695	0.536	0.381	0.216	0.064	0.005	0	0	0
1.5	0.997	0.994	0.991	0.988	0.982	0.972	0.960	0.944	0.911	0.874	0.823	0.724	0.616
1.6	0.998	0.997	0.996	0.994	0.991	0.986	0.980	0.972	0.956	0.937	0.911	0.860	0.802
1.7	0.998	0.997	0.996	0.994	0.991	0.986	0.980	0.972	0.956	0.937	0.911	0.860	0.802
1.8	0.792	0.707	0.555	0.406	0.239	0.062	0.008	0	0	0	0	0	0
1.9	0.960	0.943	0.911	0.874	0.822	0.723	0.617	0.479	0.262	0.113	0.024	0	0
2.0	0.985	0.979	0.966	0.953	0.933	0.894	0.851	0.790	0.674	0.552	0.401	0.184	0.006
2.1	0.997	0.997	0.991	0.988	0.982	0.972	0.960	0.944	0.911	0.874	0.823	0.724	0.616
2.2	0.998	0.997	0.996	0.994	0.991	0.986	0.980	0.972	0.956	0.937	0.911	0.860	0.802
2.3	0.997	0.994	0.991	0.988	0.982	0.972	0.960	0.944	0.911	0.874	0.823	0.724	0.616
2.4	0.980	0.972	0.955	0.937	0.911	0.860	0.802	0.723	0.574	0.428	0.263	0.076	0.012
2.5	0.930	0.902	0.844	0.782	0.695	0.536	0.381	0.216	0.064	0.005	0	0	0
2.6	0.617	0.479	0.261	0.110	0.002	0	0	0	0	0	0	0	0
2.7	0.361	0.196	0.040	0.004	0	0	0	0	0	0	0	0	0
2.8	0.453	0.289	0.092	0.017	0.001	0	0	0	0	0	0	0	0
2.9	0.689	0.571	0.369	0.205	0.073	0.005	0	0	0	0	0	0	0
3.0	0.851	0.790	0.673	0.552	0.401	0.184	0.060	0.008	0	0	0	0	0
3.1	0.900	0.860	0.779	0.692	0.574	0.375	0.210	0.076	0.005	0	0	0	0
3.2	0.925	0.894	0.833	0.766	0.674	0.506	0.347	0.184	0.035	0.003	0	0	0
3.3	0.950	0.930	0.888	0.843	0.779	0.658	0.531	0.377	0.161	0.048	0.005	0	0
3.4	0.973	0.962	0.939	0.914	0.880	0.811	0.735	0.633	0.448	0.285	0.130	0.017	0.001
3.5	0.988	0.983	0.973	0.962	0.946	0.915	0.881	0.832	0.736	0.635	0.502	0.287	0.133
3.6	0.994	0.992	0.987	0.982	0.973	0.958	0.947	0.916	0.866	0.812	0 738	0.596	0.452
3.7	0.997	0.994	0.991	0.988	0.982	0.972	0.960	0.944	0.911	0.874	0.823	0.724	0.616
3.8	0.998	0.997	0.995	0.994	0.991	0.986	0.980	0.972	0.956	0.937	0.911	0.860	0.802
3.9	0.998	0.997	0.995	0.994	0.991	0.986	0.980	0.972	0.956	0.937	0.911	0.860	0.802
4.0	0.997	0.995	0.993	0.990	0.987	0.977	0.970	0.960	0.930	0.900	0.870	0.790	0.700
4.1	0.997	0.994	0.991	0.988	0.982	0.972	0.960	0.944	0.911	0.874	0.823	0.724	0.616
4.2	0.994	0.992	0.987	0.982	0.973	0.958	0.947	0.916	0.866	0.812	0.738	0.596	0.452
4.3	0.991	0.984	0.975	0.972	0.950	0.937	0.910	0.873	0.800	0.722	0.615	0.425	0.260
4.4	0.980	0.972	0.955	0.937	0.911	0.860	0.802	0.723	0.574	0.428	0.263	0.076	0.012
4.5	0.970	0.958	0.932	0.905	0.866	0.790	0.707	0.595	0.400	0.235	0.093	0.008	0
4.6	0.966	0.943	0.911	0.874	0.822	0.723	0.617	0.478	0.262	0.113	0.024	0	0
4.7	0.950	0.930	0.888	0.743	0.779	0.658	0.531	0.377	0.161	0.048	0.005	0	0
4.8	0.940	0.915	0.866	0.812	0.736	0.595	0.452	0.289	0.117	0.018	0.001	0	0
4.9	0.930	0.902	0.844	0.782	0.695	0.536	0.381	0.216	0.064	0.005	0	0	0
5.0	0.915	0.880	0.811	0.736	0.634	0.451	0.286	0.132	0.017	0	0	0	0
5.1	0.885	0.839	0.747	0.649	0.519	0.308	0.149	0.041	0.001	0	0	0	0
5.2	0.846	0.784	0.664	0.539	0.385	0.168	0.052	0.006	0	0	0	0	0
5.3	0.792	0.707	0.555	0.406	0.239	0.062	0.008	0	0	0	0	0	0
5.4	0.726	0.611	0.432	0.268	0.116	0.013	0	0	0	0	0	0	0
5.5	0.617	0.479	0.261	0.110	0.035	0	0	0	0	0	0	0	0
5.6	0.491	0.331	0.121	0.029	0.002	0	0	0	0	0	0	0	0
5.7	0.361	0.196	0.040	0.004	0	0	0	0	0	0	0	0	0
5.8	0.141	0.004	0.001	0	0	0	0	0	0	0	0	0	0
5.9	0.141	0.044	0.001	0	0	0	0	0	0	0	0	0	0
6.0	0.180	0.058	0.003	0	0	0	0	0	0	0	0	0	0
6.1	0.260	0.112	0.012	0	0	0	0	0	0	0	0	0	0
6.2	0.652	0.524	0.313	0.153	0.043	0.001	0	0	0	0	0	0	0
6.3	0.552	0.401	0.182	0.060	0.008	0	0	0	0	0	0	0	0
6.4	0.317	0.157	0.025	0.002	0	0	0	0	0	0	0	0	0
6.5	0.164	0.049	0.002	0	0	0	0	0	0	0	0	0	0
6.6	0.138	0.042	0.001	0	0	0	0	0	0	0	0	0	0
6.7	0.322	0.162	0.037	0.002	0	0	0	0	0	0	0	0	0
6.8	0.361	0.196	0.040	0.004	0	0	0	0	0	0	0	0	0
6.9	0.416	0.250	0.068	0.010	0	0	0	0	0	0	0	0	0
7.0	0.532	0.377	0.161	0.048	0.005	0	0	0	0	0	0	0	0

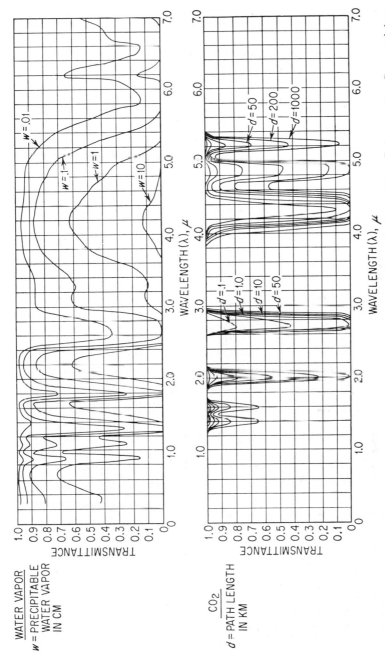

FIG. 4-4. Atmospheric transmittance at sea level of water vapor and carbon dioxide. (*After Reference 15. Computed from Elsasser's error function.*)

55

TABLE 4-3. ALTITUDE CORRECTIONS FOR H_2O AND CO_2 SEA-LEVEL ABSORPTION
(*After L. Larmore.*[15])

Altitude, ft	$\left(\dfrac{P}{P_0}\right)^{\frac{1}{2}}$ Correction for H_2O vapor	$\left(\dfrac{P}{P_0}\right)^{1.5}$ Correction for CO_2
1,000	0.981	0.940
2,000	0.961	0.833
3,000	0.942	0.840
4,000	0.923	0.774
5,000	0.904	0.743
6,000	0.886	0.699
7,000	0.869	0.660
8,000	0.852	0.620
9,000	0.835	0.580
10,000	0.819	0.548
15,000	0.739	0.404
20,000	0.670	0.299
30,000	0.552	0.168
40,000	0.441	0.085
50,000	0.348	0.042
60,000	0.272	0.020
70,000	0.214	0.010
80,000	0.167	0.005
90,000	0.134	0.002
100,000	0.105	0.001

The error-function absorption A_h at an altitude h is then given by

$$A_h = HA \qquad (4\text{-}7)$$

where H = altitude-correction factor given by Eq. (4-6)

A = error-function fractional absorption at sea level

The water-vapor content in the atmosphere varies considerably with time at any location because of changing weather conditions. Average conditions can be approximated by calculations based upon a statistical evaluation of meteorological data compiled for different types of air mass. Figure 4-5 shows the observed variation of water-vapor concentration with altitude in a clear air mass in the Eastern United States.[15] Concentration of water vapor at altitudes above about 30,000 ft is extremely small in clear air conditions. In the stratosphere, recent measurements made from high-altitude aircraft, although indicating the presence of more water vapor than was expected, showed a relative humidity of less than 1 per cent.[17]

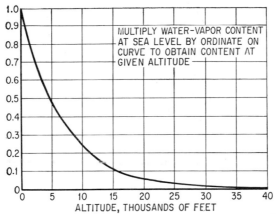

FIG. 4-5. Variation of atmospheric water-vapor content with altitude. (*After Reference 15.*)

4-3. ABSORPTION BY CARBON DIOXIDE

Next to water vapor, carbon dioxide causes the largest atmospheric absorption of IR radiation.   The concentration of carbon dioxide in the atmosphere is only 0.029 per cent by volume,[18] and it has been found that this concentration is constant up to a very high altitude. Because of this and the fact that atmospheric distribution of carbon dioxide varies only slightly with time, the attenuation of IR radiation due to absorption by carbon dioxide is practically independent of weather conditions.

Principal absorption bands occur at 2.7, 4.3, and 15 μ, as illustrated in Figs. 4-1 and 4-4.   It is found that for wavelengths out to 7 μ the error-function absorption law is a good approximation.[15]

$$A = erf(K \sqrt{d}) \tag{4-8}$$

where A = error-function fractional absorption

K = error-function absorption coefficient

d = path length

The values of K versus wavelength λ (in microns) at a sea-level pressure of 1 atm are given in Table 4-4.   Table 4-5 lists the atmospheric transmittance of carbon dioxide for wavelengths up to 7 μ, and for various path lengths d, measured in kilometers.[15]

Increase in atmospheric pressure causes a broadening of the absorption lines of carbon dioxide as it does for those of water vapor.   Since the concentration of carbon dioxide in the atmosphere is very nearly constant, however, the reduced atmospheric pressure at high altitudes

TABLE 4-4. CO_2 ERROR-FUNCTION ABSORPTION COEFFICIENT FOR SEA-LEVEL
CONDITIONS (WAVELENGTH, μ)
(*After L. Larmore.*[15])

λ	K	λ	K	λ	K
0.3	0	2.6	0	4.9	14
0.4	0	2.7	112	5.0	0.8
0.5	0	2.8	77	5.1	0.3
0.6	0	2.9	1.8	5.2	7.9
0.7	0	3.0	0	5.3	1.9
0.8	0	3.1	0	5.4	0
0.9	0	3.2	0	5.5	0
1.0	0	3.3	0	5.6	0
1.1	0	3.4	0	5.7	0
1.2	0	3.5	0	5.8	0
1.3	0.1	3.6	0	5.9	0
1.4	2	3.7	0	6.0	0
1.5	0.4	3.8	0	6.1	0
1.6	2	3.9	0	6.2	0
1.7	0.1	4.0	1.1	6.3	0
1.8	0	4.1	9.7	6.4	0
1.9	0.1	4.2	185	6.5	0
2.0	12	4.3	750	6.6	0
2.1	1	4.4	309	6.7	0
2.2	0	4.5	24	6.8	0
2.3	0	4.6	2.7	6.9	0
2.4	0	4.7	2.7	7.0	0
2.5	0	4.8	13.5		

results in a smaller carbon dioxide content for a given path length. The altitude-correction factor to apply to the sea-level absorption values for carbon dioxide in Table 4-5 is proportional to the 1.5 power of the relative pressure at the given altitude, compared with sea level. These correction factors are listed in Table 4-3 for altitudes from sea level to 100,000 ft.[15]

EXAMPLE

Find the fractional transmittance and absorption in carbon dioxide of radiation of 2-μ wavelength for a 50-km path length at 15,000 ft altitude.

From Table 4-3, the correction factor at 15,000 ft = 0.404. Thus, a 50-km path length at this altitude is equivalent to a sea-level path length of

$$50 \times 0.404 = 20.2 \text{ km}$$

From Table 4-5, at 2.0 μ, for a path length of 20.2 km transmittance = 0.69; absorption = $1 - 0.69 = 0.31$.

TABLE 4-5. ATMOSPHERIC TRANSMITTANCE, CO_2, SEA LEVEL

d = path length, km

(*After L. Larmore.*[15])

λ, μ		0.3	0.4	0.5	0.6	0.7	0.8	0.9	1.0	1.1	1.2	1.3	1.4	1.5	1.6	1.7	1.8	1.9	2.0
d =	0.1	1.000	1.000	1.000	1.000	1.000	1.000	1.000	1.000	1.000	1.000	1.000	0.996	0.999	0.996	1.000	1.000	1.000	0.978
d =	0.2	1.000	1.000	1.000	1.000	1.000	1.000	1.000	1.000	1.000	1.000	1.000	0.995	0.999	0.995	1.000	1.000	1.000	0.969
d =	0.5	1.000	1.000	1.000	1.000	1.000	1.000	1.000	1.000	1.000	1.000	1.000	0.992	0.998	0.992	1.000	1.000	1.000	0.951
d =	1	1.000	1.000	1.000	1.000	1.000	1.000	1.000	1.000	1.000	1.000	1.000	0.999	0.988	0.998	0.988	0.999	1.000	0.999	0.931
d =	2	1.000	1.000	1.000	1.000	1.000	1.000	1.000	1.000	1.000	1.000	0.999	0.984	0.997	0.984	0.999	1.000	0.999	0.903
d =	5	1.000	1.000	1.000	1.000	1.000	1.000	1.000	1.000	1.000	1.000	0.999	0.975	0.995	0.975	0.999	1.000	0.999	0.847
d =	10	1.000	1.000	1.000	1.000	1.000	1.000	1.000	1.000	1.000	1.000	0.998	0.964	0.993	0.964	0.998	1.000	0.998	0.785
d =	20	1.000	1.000	1.000	1.000	1.000	1.000	1.000	1.000	1.000	1.000	0.997	0.949	0.990	0.949	0.997	1.000	0.997	0.699
d =	50	1.000	1.000	1.000	1.000	1.000	1.000	1.000	1.000	1.000	1.000	0.996	0.919	0.984	0.919	0.996	1.000	0.996	0.541
d =	100	1.000	1.000	1.000	1.000	1.000	1.000	1.000	1.000	1.000	1.000	0.994	0.885	0.976	0.885	0.994	1.000	0.994	0.387
d =	200	1.000	1.000	1.000	1.000	1.000	1.000	1.000	1.000	1.000	1.000	0.992	0.838	0.967	0.838	0.992	1.000	0.992	0.221
d =	500	1.000	1.000	1.000	1.000	1.000	1.000	1.000	1.000	1.000	1.000	0.987	0.747	0.949	0.747	0.987	1.000	0.987	0.053
d =	1,000	1.000	1.000	1.000	1.000	1.000	1.000	1.000	1.000	1.000	1.000	0.982	0.649	0.927	0.649	0.982	1.000	0.982	0.006

λ, μ		2.1	2.2	2.3	2.4	2.5	2.6	2.7	2.8	2.9	3.0	3.1	3.2	3.3	3.4	3.5	3.6	3.7
d =	0.1	0.998	1.000	1.000	1.000	1.000	1.000	0.799	0.871	0.997	1.000	1.000	1.000	1.000	1.000	1.000	1.000	1.000
d =	0.2	0.997	1.000	1.000	1.000	1.000	1.000	0.718	0.804	0.995	1.000	1.000	1.000	1.000	1.000	1.000	1.000	1.000
d =	0.5	0.996	1.000	1.000	1.000	1.000	1.000	0.569	0.695	0.993	1.000	1.000	1.000	1.000	1.000	1.000	1.000	1.000
d =	1	0.994	1.000	1.000	1.000	1.000	1.000	0.419	0.578	0.990	1.000	1.000	1.000	1.000	1.000	1.000	1.000	1.000
d =	2	0.992	1.000	1.000	1.000	1.000	1.000	0.253	0.432	0.985	1.000	1.000	1.000	1.000	1.000	1.000	1.000	1.000
d =	5	0.987	1.000	1.000	1.000	1.000	1.000	0.071	0.215	0.977	1.000	1.000	1.000	1.000	1.000	1.000	1.000	1.000
d =	10	0.982	1.000	1.000	1.000	1.000	1.000	0.011	0.079	0.968	1.000	1.000	1.000	1.000	1.000	1.000	1.000	1.000
d =	20	0.974	1.000	1.000	1.000	1.000	1.000	0	0.013	0.954	1.000	1.000	1.000	1.000	1.000	1.000	1.000	1.000
d =	50	0.959	1.000	1.000	1.000	1.000	1.000	0	0	0.927	1.000	1.000	1.000	1.000	1.000	1.000	1.000	1.000
d =	100	0.942	1.000	1.000	1.000	1.000	1.000	0	0	0.898	1.000	1.000	1.000	1.000	1.000	1.000	1.000	1.000
d =	200	0.919	1.000	1.000	1.000	1.000	1.000	0	0	0.855	1.000	1.000	1.000	1.000	1.000	1.000	1.000	1.000
d =	500	0.872	1.000	1.000	1.000	1.000	1.000	0	0	0.772	1.000	1.000	1.000	1.000	1.000	1.000	1.000	1.000
d =	1,000	0.820	1.000	1.000	1.000	1.000	1.000	0	0.683	1.000	1.000	1.000	1.000	1.000	1.000	1.000	1.000	1.000

λ, μ		3.8	3.9	4.0	4.1	4.2	4.3	4.4	4.5	4.6	4.7	4.8	4.9	5.0	5.1	5.2	5.3	5.4
d =	0.1	1.000	1.000	0.998	0.983	0.673	0.098	0.481	0.057	0.995	0.995	0.976	0.975	0.999	1.000	0.986	0.997	1.000
d =	0.2	1.000	1.000	0.997	0.975	0.551	0.016	0.319	0.949	0.993	0.993	0.966	0.064	0.998	0.999	0.080	0.995	1.000
d =	0.5	1.000	1.000	0.996	0.961	0.445	0	0.115	0.903	0.989	0.989	0.945	0.943	0.997	0.999	0.968	0.993	1.000
d =	1	1.000	1.000	0.994	0.944	0.182	0	0.026	0.863	0.985	0.985	0.922	0.920	0.995	0.998	0.955	0.989	1.000
d =	2	1.000	1.000	0.991	0.921	0.059	0	0.002	0.807	0.978	0.978	0.891	0.886	0.994	0.998	0.936	0.984	1.000
d =	5	1.000	1.000	0.986	0.876	0.003	0	0	0.699	0.966	0.966	0.828	0.822	0.990	0.996	0.899	0.976	1.000
d =	10	1.000	1.000	0.980	0.825	0	0	0	0.585	0.951	0.951	0.759	0.750	0.986	0.994	0.857	0.966	1.000
d =	20	1.000	1.000	0.971	0.755	0	0	0	0.439	0.931	0.931	0.664	0.652	0.979	0.992	0.799	0.951	1.000
d =	50	1.000	1.000	0.955	0.622	0	0	0	0.222	0.891	0.891	0.492	0.468	0.968	0.988	0.687	0.923	1.000
d =	100	1.000	1.000	0.937	0.485	0	0	0	0.084	0.845	0.845	0.331	0.313	0.954	0.984	0.569	0.891	1.000
d =	200	1.000	1.000	0.911	0.322	0	0	0	0.014	0.783	0.783	0.169	0.153	0.935	0.976	0.420	0.846	1.000
d =	500	1.000	1.000	0.859	0.118	0	0	0	0	0.663	0.663	0.030	0.021	0.897	0.961	0.203	0.760	1.000
d =	1,000	1.000	1.000	0.802	0.027	0	0	0	0	0.539	0.539	0.002	0.001	0.855	0.946	0.072	0.066	1.000

λ, μ		5.5	5.6	5.7	5.8	5.9	6.0	6.1	6.2	6.3	6.4	6.5	6.6	6.7	6.8	6.9	7.0
d =	0.1	1.000	1.000	1.000	1.000	1.000	1.000	1.000	1.000	1.000	1.000	1.000	1.000	1.000	1.000	1.000	1.000
d =	0.2	1.000	1.000	1.000	1.000	1.000	1.000	1.000	1.000	1.000	1.000	1.000	1.000	1.000	1.000	1.000	1.000
d =	0.5	1.000	1.000	1.000	1.000	1.000	1.000	1.000	1.000	1.000	1.000	1.000	1.000	1.000	1.000	1.000	1.000
d =	1	1.000	1.000	1.000	1.000	1.000	1.000	1.000	1.000	1.000	1.000	1.000	1.000	1.000	1.000	1.000	1.000
d =	2	1.000	1.000	1.000	1.000	1.000	1.000	1.000	1.000	1.000	1.000	1.000	1.000	1.000	1.000	1.000	1.000
d =	5	1.000	1.000	1.000	1.000	1.000	1.000	1.000	1.000	1.000	1.000	1.000	1.000	1.000	1.000	1.000	1.000
d =	10	1.000	1.000	1.000	1.000	1.000	1.000	1.000	1.000	1.000	1.000	1.000	1.000	1.000	1.000	1.000	1.000
d =	20	1.000	1.000	1.000	1.000	1.000	1.000	1.000	1.000	1.000	1.000	1.000	1.000	1.000	1.000	1.000	1.000
d =	50	1.000	1.000	1.000	1.000	1.000	1.000	1.000	1.000	1.000	1.000	1.000	1.000	1.000	1.000	1.000	1.000
d =	100	1.000	1.000	1.000	1.000	1.000	1.000	1.000	1.000	1.000	1.000	1.000	1.000	1.000	1.000	1.000	1.000
d =	200	1.000	1.000	1.000	1.000	1.000	1.000	1.000	1.000	1.000	1.000	1.000	1.000	1.000	1.000	1.000	1.000
d =	500	1.000	1.000	1.000	1.000	1.000	1.000	1.000	1.000	1.000	1.000	1.000	1.000	1.000	1.000	1.000	1.000
d =	1,000	1.000	1.000	1.000	1.000	1.000	1.000	1.000	1.000	1.000	1.000	1.000	1.000	1.000	1.000	1.000	1.000

An important feature of carbon dioxide, apart from its occurrence in the atmosphere as one of the principal absorbers of IR radiation, is its presence as a hot radiating gas in the exhausts of jet aircraft and rockets. At 500°C, carbon dioxide has a strong emission and absorption band in the neighborhood of 4.4 μ. Hot carbon dioxide emission is largely reabsorbed from 4.2 to 4.35 μ by the carbon dioxide occurring in the intervening cold atmosphere, but is strongly transmitted from 4.35 to about 4.75 μ.

4-4. ABSORPTION BY OZONE

The bulk of atmospheric ozone is concentrated in a layer at an altitude between 10 and 40 km, with maximum concentration occurring between 20 and 30 km. This layer of ozone effectively shields the earth's surface from a high proportion of the sun's ultraviolet light between 0.2 and 0.3 μ, and absorbs IR radiation at 4.7 and 9.6 μ, principally at 9.6 μ, with two weaker absorption bands at about 4.7 and 14.2 μ.[19] Below the 20-km altitude the absorption effect of ozone on IR radiation is very small.

Table 4-6 gives values of the transmittance and absorption coeffi-

TABLE 4-6. TRANSMITTANCE AND ERROR-FUNCTION ABSORPTION COEFFICIENTS OF ATMOSPHERIC OZONE (AT ZERO ZENITH ANGLE)
(*After L. Larmore.*[15])

Wavelength, μ	Transmittance	Absorption coeff.
4.5	1.00	0
4.6	0.90	0.006
4.7	0.74	0.152
4.8	0.83	0.098
4.9	0.89	0.011
5.0	1.00	0

cients for ozone in the neighborhood of the 4.7-μ band[15] for paths perpendicular to the ozone layer.

For inclined paths, the fractional absorption A through the ozone layer is given by [15]

$$A = erf(K' \sqrt{\sec \theta}) \qquad (4\text{-}9)$$

where A = fractional absorption

K' = error-function absorption coefficient

θ = zenith angle of inclined path, i.e., angle between the path and the normal to the ozone layer

Absorption by ozone is therefore considered only in IR astronomical applications when measuring the radiation from celestial bodies, or when tracking artificial satellites or high-speed, high-altitude aircraft or missiles.

4-5. ABSORPTION BY MINOR CONSTITUENTS

At the higher altitudes, since the atmospheric content of water vapor becomes very small, the IR-absorption bands of carbon dioxide, ozone, and of the minor constituents of the atmosphere assume greater importance.

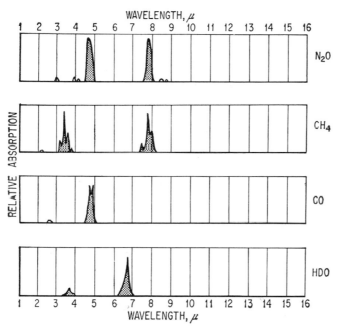

FIG. 4-6. IR-Absorption bands of minor atmospheric constituents.

The minor constituents of interest, and their relative-absorption bands over a wavelength region of 1 to 9 μ, are shown in Fig. 4-6. Nitrous oxide exhibits a weak absorption band near 4 μ, and fairly strong absorption bands at 4.5 and 7.8 μ. Carbon monoxide exhibits an absorption band at 4.7 μ. Methane shows absorption lines at about 3.1 and 3.5 μ and a narrow band at 7.7 μ. "Heavy water," occurring in the upper atmosphere, exhibits absorption lines between 3.5 and 3.85 μ, and an absorption band at 6.7 μ.

These minor constituents, as previously mentioned, also emit IR resonance radiation and contribute to the sky radiance beyond a wavelength of 4 μ. Their distribution throughout the earth's atmosphere is uniform.

4-6. ATMOSPHERIC SCATTERING

An entirely different form of attenuation of IR radiation, which is not dependent upon the natural frequencies of vibration of molecular particles as in the case of attenuation by absorption, is the mechanism of scattering.

Rayleigh Scattering. For particles smaller in diameter than the wavelength of the incident radiation, Rayleigh's law indicates that spectral radiance due to scattering rapidly decreases with increase in wavelength. Under these conditions, Rayleigh's law states that

$$I_s/I_0 = kv^2\lambda^{-4} \qquad (4\text{-}10)$$

where I_s = intensity of scattered radiation
  I_0 = intensity of incident radiation
  v = volume of the scattering particles
  λ = wavelength of incident radiation
  k = a constant

This shows that visible light is scattered more than the longer-wavelength IR radiation. This also accounts for the blue color of the sky, since scattering by the earth's atmosphere is greatest at the blue end of the visible spectrum. The red and yellow coloring of sunsets and sunrises is due to increased scattering of the longer wavelengths in the visible spectrum caused by particles of dust and smoke and the longer path lengths near the horizon. In the IR spectrum, scattering is greatest in the near-IR region adjoining the visible spectrum, and decreases rapidly for longer wavelengths. The Rayleigh scattering theory is limited, however, to scattering by atmospheric particles whose diameters are considerably smaller than the wavelengths of the incident radiation. Rayleigh's theory applies, therefore to molecular particles.

Mie Scattering. For larger particles such as those occurring in haze, smog, and fog, where particle diameters may range from about 0.1 to over 100 μ, the Mie scattering theory applies. Application of this far more complicated theory to atmospheric scattering involves the classification of particle size and index of refraction by statistical methods. The Mie scattering functions, which are converging infinite series, have been calculated, on electronic computing machines, for a wide range of particle sizes and refractive indexes and are available in tabular form.

This form of scattering, unlike Rayleigh scattering, which is strongly wavelength-dependent, is nonselective or independent of wavelength. It also assumes negligible absorption, and is applicable therefore to the atmospheric windows discussed earlier.

Data on the observed distribution and diameters of scattering nuclei in the atmosphere are required in order to estimate their attenuating effects on IR radiation. Sea-level investigations by Gebbie et al.[20] used the Mie scattering theory to derive scattering coefficients of this type. From their observed data, the IR transmittance over given path lengths was estimated as a function of the visibility and the wavelength.

4-7. ATMOSPHERIC ATTENUATION OF IR RADIATION

In the atmosphere, transmission of IR radiation is reduced or attenuated by both absorption and scattering, which occur together. Absorption may be much greater than scattering, or vice versa, depending upon the nature of the atmosphere, the particle size, and the wavelength considered, but both phenomena are present. Furthermore, the combined sum of the per cents of absorption, scattering, and transmission always totals 100. The combined total of the absorption and scattering coefficients is often referred to as the *extinction coefficient*. Thus for a given wavelength

$$I = I_0 e^{-(k_a+k_s)d} = I_0 e^{-k_e d} \qquad (4\text{-}11)$$

where I = intensity of emergent IR radiation
  I_0 = intensity of incident IR radiation
  k_a = absorption coefficient
  k_s = scattering coefficient
  $k_e = k_a + k_s$ = extinction coefficient
  d = path length in the atmosphere

We have seen that attenuation of IR radiation by absorption in the earth's atmosphere is wavelength-dependent, resulting in absorption bands within definite wavelength intervals, separated by intervals of negligible absorption known as *windows*. Attenuation by scattering on the other hand, while strongly wavelength-dependent for very small particle sizes as in Rayleigh scattering, becomes independent of wavelength when the particle sizes are large, and Mie scattering occurs. In the visible region of the spectrum this is very evident. The sky is blue, but fog is white.

4-8. ATTENUATION IN HAZE AND SMOG

Haze may occur within an altitude range from sea level to about 20,000 ft. Particle diameters are approximately within the range from 0.1 μ to a few microns. Haze particles include wind-blown dust and small water droplets forming around dust particles. Smog, prevalent in large industrial areas, occurs at lower altitudes, from sea level up to the temperature-inversion level, which may range from a few hundred to a few thousand feet above the surface of the earth. Smog particles, which include many organic chemical compounds, also occur in approximately the same diameter range. Both haze and smog absorb and scatter IR radiation, with the latter effect predominating.

IR transmission decreases exponentially with the path length through haze or smog, and is wavelength-dependent. Measurements by Gebbie et al.[20] in natural haze in the IR spectral region out to 12 μ indicate the extinction coefficient for scattering, referred to its value at 0.61 μ, varies, to a good approximation, as the wavelength raised to the minus 0.7 power. In Los Angeles smog, apparently, the particle size is smaller than in most smogs. Measurements indicate that in the 8- to 14-μ window it is quite transparent to IR radiation.[21] IR techniques are proving of increasing value in smog analysis.

4-9. ATTENUATION IN FOG

Fog is composed of water droplets with diameters ranging from approximately a few tens of microns to over 100 μ. As the particle size increases, measurements confirm the Mie scattering theory by indicating that scattering increases and becomes nonselective or independent of wavelength. Attenuation of IR radiation is also caused by water-vapor absorption, resulting in relatively narrow wavelength bands where attenuation is high.

In light fogs, the near-IR spectral region is superior to visible light for the detection of objects. As the water droplets increase in size and visibility decreases to about 1,000 yd, near-IR detection devices become virtually useless, but middle- and far-IR devices have from two to four times the detection range of visible light.

4-10. ATTENUATION IN CLOUDS AND RAIN

As in the case of fog, clouds and rain contain water droplets, primarily of larger sizes, with diameters often exceeding 100 μ. Attenuation of IR radiation in a cloud is primarily due to scattering by the water droplets with selective absorption by liquid water as a secondary cause, this latter following the exponential law. At a wavelength of 2 μ, absorption coefficients as high as 25 per centimeter have been observed.

With the exception of high cirrus and lenticular types of cloud consisting of small ice particles with a small attenuation coefficient, the majority of clouds occur at altitudes below 30,000 ft. In rain and in most clouds, IR radiation has no appreciable advantage over visible light due to the excessive attenuation undergone. Only microwaves and radio waves, with wavelengths 1 cm or longer, are unaffected by scattering. IR techniques are practicable for short-range applications only under these conditions.

4-11. ATMOSPHERIC-TRANSMISSION STUDIES

Apart from spectroscopic studies, the majority of work in the IR field to date has been concentrated in the spectral region of 0.7 to about 7 μ. This is largely because of the lack of small, highly sensitive detectors suitable for rapid scanning techniques and with fast time constants. To a somewhat smaller degree work in this field has also been limited until recently by the lack of good IR lens and filter materials in the longer-wavelength regions. As these tools become available as the result of optical-material and solid-state-physics research currently in progress, the useful field of IR will be extended to longer and longer wavelength regions.

Even in the near- and middle-IR spectral regions a great deal of information on atmospheric transmission is lacking, especially at the higher altitudes and over long distances. The brief discussion of recent studies in the 0.7- to 15-μ region which follows will indicate the type of research required and future areas of development.

Elder and Strong[22] in 1953 reviewed available data in this region, which they divided into eight *windows*. To a good approximation, it was found that

$$T' = -K \log w + T_0 \qquad (4\text{-}12)$$

where T' = average transmission of window

w = water-vapor concentration in the path length considered

K, T_0 = empirical constants which differ for each *window*

Studies of the spectrum of solar radiation transmitted through the atmosphere have been made by Goldberg et al. and, more recently, by Mohler at Michigan University,[23,24] by Shaw et al. at Ohio State University,[25] and others. These resulted in the publication of high-resolution solar-spectrum atlases covering the spectral region from 0.7 to 13 μ. Quantitative solar spectral measurements were made in 1956 by

Templin et al.[26] at Mt. Chacaltaya, Bolivia, at an altitude of 17,100 ft, in the wavelength region from 1.0 to 5.5 μ, with a double-pass lithium fluoride prism spectrometer. Useful data on the absorption coefficient of the atmosphere as a function of wavelength in different air masses were obtained.

The total absorption of water-vapor and carbon dioxide bands was investigated by Howard et al. at Ohio State University,[27,28] using a multiple traversal cell, under controlled laboratory conditions. Altitude was simulated by evacuating the absorption cell and adding predetermined amounts of water vapor, carbon dioxide, and purified dry nitrogen. Nitrogen is present in the atmosphere but in its pure form does not absorb IR radiation. Its molecules cause a broadening of the absorption lines of water vapor and carbon dioxide through collisions with their molecules. The quantity of nitrogen, path lengths, partial pressures of the gases, and the total pressure were varied in these studies.

Long-path open-air transmission studies over land and sea have been made by several groups of investigators. Among these, Gebbie et al.[20] investigated atmospheric transmission for path lengths up to 20,000 yd under various weather conditions, and for source temperatures ranging between 373 and 6000°K. Arnulf[29] in France studied IR transmission under fog conditions over land. Similar studies have been made by Rockwood in the United States. Taylor and Yates[30] conducted near-IR atmospheric-transmission studies, for path lengths up to 10 miles, over Chesapeake Bay.

Very little information exists on the atmospheric transmission of IR along vertical and slant paths at high altitudes. The Royal Radar Establishment, Great Malvern, England, and the Royal Aeronautical Establishment, Farnborough, England, used high-flying aircraft equipped with rapid-scanning spectrographs and automatic-recording hygrometers for this type of study and to obtain solar data.[31,32] Altitudes studied varied from 30,000 to above 50,000 ft. It was found that at 30,000 ft absorption due to water vapor was extremely small. However, water vapor in minute quantities does exist at high altitudes, often in layers. Observations of the solar spectrum have indicated the existence of water-vapor absorption between an altitude of 50,000 ft and the sun, indicating the presence of some water vapor in the stratosphere.

Measurements made from very-high-flying aircraft, from balloons, and from rockets have made it possible to study the solar spectrum at radiation wavelengths which do not penetrate the earth's atmosphere. Measuring devices carried aloft in these investigations include photon counters, photographic and photoelectric spectrographs, and thermoluminescent phosphors. Additionally a great deal of work is being carried out at the various large observatories throughout the world. The near-IR solar spectrum was recorded by Gates and associates,[11] on a Littrow-type IR spectrograph, employing a quartz prism and a lead sulfide detector cell, at an altitude of 103,000 ft in an unmanned, skyhook plastic, balloon. Experiments of this type can provide more valuable information than that obtained from relatively short rocket flights. Valuable information, on (1) total absorption in various bands as a function of altitude correlated with the amount of absorbing constituent above these altitudes, (2) the effect of pressure on the absorption of various constituents; and (3) the absorption effects of the minor constituents of the earth's atmosphere, can be obtained.

Many additional areas require further research, and the accumulation of more experimental data. These include IR-transmission measurements over horizontal, vertical, and slant paths of different lengths through the earth's atmosphere; high-resolution measurements to study the pressure dependence of absorption bands and the effects of the minor constituents on transmission; and measurements at longer wavelengths in the far-IR spectral region.

REFERENCES

11. As in Chapter 3.
15. Larmore, Lewis: Transmission of Infrared Radiation through the Atmosphere, Office of Naval Research, *Proc. Infrared Inform. Symposia*, vol. 1, no. 1, June, 1956.
16. Elsasser, W. M.: Heat Transfer by Infrared Radiation in the Atmosphere, *Harvard Meteorological Series* 6, Harvard University Press, Cambridge, Mass., 1942.
17. Murgatroyd, J., et al.: Some Recent Measurements of Humidity from Aircraft up to Heights of 50,000 Feet over Southern England, *Quart. J. Roy. Meteorol. Soc.*, vol. 81, pp. 533–537, October, 1955.
18. Goody, R. M.: "The Physics of the Stratosphere," *Cambridge University Press*, New York, 1954.
19. Gutowsky, H. S., and Peterson, E. M.: The Infrared Spectrum and Structure of Ozone, *J. Chem. Phys.*, vol. 18, p. 481, 1950.
20. Gebbie, H. A., et al.: Atmospheric Transmission in the 1 to 14 Micron Region, *Proc. Roy. Soc. (London)*, A206, p. 87, 1951.
21. Fusca, James A.: Satellite Reconnaissance Optics, part II, *Aviation Week*, Jan. 26, 1959.
22. Elder, T., and Strong, J.: *J. Franklin Inst.*, vol. 225, p. 159, 1953.
23. Goldberg, L., et al.: "Atlas of the Solar Spectrum from 0.84 to 2.55 Microns," University of Michigan Press, Ann Arbor, 1950.
24. Mohler, O. C.: "Table of Solar Spectrum Wavelengths 1.20 to 2.55 Microns," University of Michigan Press, Ann Arbor, 1955.
25. Shaw, J. H., et al.: *Astrophys. Jour.*, vol. 113, p. 268, 1951; *ibid.*, vol. 116, p. 554, 1952.

26. Templin, H. A., Talbert, W. W., and Morrison, R. E.: Quantitative Solar Spectral Measurements at Mt. Chacaltaya, Office of Naval Research, *Proc. Infrared Inform. Symposia*, vol. 3, no. 4, p. 98, December, 1958.
27. Howard, J. N., and Chapman, R. M.: *J. Opt. Soc. Am.*, vol. 42, pp. 423, 856, 1952.
28. Howard, J. N., Burch, D. E., and Williams, D.: *J. Opt. Soc. Am.*, vol. 46, pp. 186, 237, 242, 334, 452, 1956.
29. Arnulf, A.: Transmission by Haze and Fog, 0.35 to 10 Microns, paper at Fourth Congress of International Commission on Optics, Massachusetts Institute of Technology, Cambridge, Mass., April 2, 1956.
30. Taylor, J. H., and Yates, H. W.: *J. Opt. Soc. Am.*, vol. 47, p. 223, 1957.
31. Brown, A. H., and Roberts, V.: *J. Sci. Instr.*, vol. 30, p. 5, 1953.
32. Jones, F. E., and Roberts, V.: *Proc. Roy. Soc. (London)*, A 236, p. 171, 1956.

ADDITIONAL BIBLIOGRAPHY

B. E. Cohn: "Daylight Luminescence and Infrared Absorption," Denver University, Colorado, 1950.
Elder, Tait, and Strong, John: The Infrared Transmission of Atmospheric Windows, *J. Franklin Inst.*, vol. 225, p. 189, 1953.
Elsasser, W. M.: "Progress of Theoretical Work on Atmospheric Radiation," Utah University, Salt Lake City, Utah, 1951.
Gibbons, Matthew G.: Wavelength Dependence of the Scattering Coefficient for Infrared Radiation in Natural Haze, *J. Opt. Soc. Am.*, vol. 48, no. 1, p. 172, March, 1958.
Hilsum, C.: "Atmospheric Attenuation of Infrared and Visible Radiation," Admiralty Research Laboratory, Teddington, England, 1948.
Kaplan, L. D.: "Absorption of Infrared Radiation by CO_2, with Meteorological Applications," University of Chicago Press, Chicago, 1947.
Meltzer, R. J.: "High Altitude Infrared Transmission of the Atmosphere," Johns Hopkins Press, Baltimore, 1949.
Migeotte, M., Neven, L., and Swensson, J.: "An Atlas of Nitrous Oxide, Methane, and Ozone Infrared Absorption Bands," Part I: "Photometric Records;" Part II: "Measures and Identification," Technical Final Report, Contract AF 61(514)-432, Air Force Cambridge Research Center, Cambridge, Mass.
Plass, G. N.: "Physics of the Atmosphere," Johns Hopkins Press, Baltimore, 1950.
Plass, G. N.: Parallel Beam and Diffuse Radiation in the Atmosphere, *J. Meteorol.*, vol. 9, pp. 429–436, December, 1952.
Podolsky, B.: "Scattering of Infrared Radiation by Haze, and Haze Measuring Instruments," University of Cincinnati Research Foundation, Cincinnati, Ohio, 1949.
Robinson, G. D.: "Notes on Measurement and Estimation of Atmospheric Radiation," Kew Observatory, England, April, 1944.
Strong, J.: "The Infrared Atmospheric Transmission Problem," Johns Hopkins Press, Baltimore, 1948.

5

IR Optical Components and Systems

Optical components used in IR systems are described. Their advantages, disadvantages, and limitations are discussed. The principal causes of image distortion and their correction are described. Combinations of optical components to form IR optical systems of various types are illustrated.

5-1. PURPOSE AND DESIRABLE FEATURES OF IR OPTICAL SYSTEMS

The primary purposes of the optical system are to collect IR radiation from the source and to focus it on the surface of the detector. The secondary purpose of an optical system is to improve the ratio of signal to noise by optically filtering out as much external background noise as possible, while admitting the received IR signal with minimum transmission loss.

The field of view required of the optical system varies considerably with its application. The instantaneous field of view is determined by both the effective width of the entrance aperture and the focal length of the optical system. We shall see that while a large field of view is desirable in order to concentrate as much radiation as possible on the detector, it is limited by aberrations of the image which affect the resolution of the optical system. An IR search and tracking system, for example, may be required to search over a wide angular field, while producing a maximum signal-to-noise ratio, in order to achieve detection at the greatest possible range. This problem is usually solved by a compromise; an optical system with a relatively narrow instantaneous field of view is mechanically scanned over the wide angular field of coverage required. In an IR pyrometer on the other hand, image aberrations can be tolerated, and the optical system can be designed with a wider instantaneous field of view. Images of extremely high quality together with very narrow fields of view are the requirements for IR microscopes and astronomical telescopes.

In all IR optical systems, high transmission of the received IR energy through the optical components is desirable. Transmission losses may be caused by absorption in lenses, prisms, windows, and other refractive components; by reflection at mirror surfaces; by dispersion or diffraction in prisms and gratings; or by interference in components such as filters.

In many applications, the use of a particular detector requires the IR optical system to limit its transmission of IR energy to a relatively narrow wavelength band in order to achieve optimum detectivity.   In addition to its other functions, therefore, the optical system may be required to operate as a filtering system.

IR optical systems used for air-borne and other applications may be required to withstand a wide range of ambient temperatures and large temperature gradients in exposed parts of the optical system such as windows or irdomes.   In applications of this nature, physical strength, light weight, and minimum size are additional requirements.

5-2. LIMITATIONS OF IR OPTICAL SYSTEMS

An IR optical system is invariably designed to fulfill the specific requirements of the IR device in which it is incorporated.   All IR optical systems are therefore specialized or *tailor-made* in nature.

In attempting to attain the desirable features discussed in the previous section, the IR optical designer faces major problems far more difficult than those encountered by the designer of optical systems for use in the visible-light spectral region.   First, the visible spectrum covers a wavelength band from 0.4 to 0.72 μ.   The IR spectrum covers the 0.72- to 1,000-μ wavelength band; in this band, the majority of present-day applications are limited to the 0.75- to 15-μ region.   This portion of the IR spectrum is approximately forty times wider than the visible spectrum.   Many optical systems are required to operate only in a relatively narrow waveband within these limits.   However, this wavelength band may still be much wider than the entire visible spectrum; consequently the attendant optical-design problems and limitations are increased.

Second, the availability of optical materials having suitable transmission properties even in this narrow section of the IR spectrum is very limited.   High transmission is required to obtain the utmost sensitivity from the IR system.   However, most IR materials exhibit selective absorption properties at certain wavelengths; this results in low transmission at these absorption bands, which may lie within the limits of those very wavelengths of radiation required to be received from the source.   Further dissipation of incoming IR energy is caused by surface reflection, since the majority of IR optical materials have relatively high refractive indexes.   The use of special low-reflection coatings is limited to narrow wavelength bands.   The problem of reducing surface reflections when a relatively wide wavelength band is to be received is often a major one.

Third, because the wavelength bands employed in many IR instruments are wider than those used in instruments for visible light, and the refractive indexes (and therefore dispersive properties of the optical materials employed) are high, the resulting aberrations of the optical image are much greater.   Under these conditions the design of a suitable optical system, with the high resolution often required, is a major problem.

Fourth, many of the IR optical materials which are otherwise satisfactory possess weak physical properties.   They may be attacked by organic solvents, acids, alkali solutions, or water.   They may distort under pressure.   This is particularly true of crystals, many of which tend to cleave under conditions of thermal shock and high pressure. Many IR optical systems are required to operate under conditions of severe vibration and shock.

Fifth, the high ambient temperatures often encountered in many IR optical systems impose additional design problems.   Heated optical systems may reradiate IR energy, causing the formation of undesirable false images.

Thus, the optical-design problems to be solved are difficult, while the available materials are limited.   Constant research on new and better optical materials for IR use is continuing, and is described in Chap. 6.

5-3. OPTICAL COMPONENTS

The several optical elements that, singly and in combinations, are used in the design of IR systems from the very simplest to the most complicated, are mirrors, lenses, prisms, gratings, windows and irdomes, filters, optical stops, and reticles, choppers, and other scanning devices. In integrating combinations of these components into an IR optical system designed to fulfill a particular purpose, the well-established principles of physical and geometrical optics are employed.

The following sections examine these optical elements individually; the various types of components commonly used in IR systems, their advantages and disadvantages, their aberrations and how these are corrected or reduced, often by using combinations of two or more components, are examined.

5-4. MIRRORS

The various types of mirror commonly used in IR systems are illustrated in Fig. 5-1. *Plane* and *corner-reflecting* mirrors are used in IR spectrometers and spectrographs, in monochromators, bichromators, and IR analyzers to direct beams of the radiation and to increase path length and hence dispersion. *Littrow mirrors* are plane mirrors pivoted about an axis of rotation. The angle of rotation or tilt may be quite small, and the mirror can be rapidly oscillated. These mirrors are used extensively in IR spectroscopic instruments to isolate preselected wavelengths. Plane mirrors with a hole in the center are used in Pfund-type spectrometers and spectrographs. Plane mirrors are also used in many

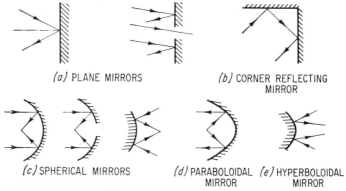

(a) PLANE MIRRORS   (b) CORNER REFLECTING
                                    MIRROR

(c) SPHERICAL MIRRORS   (d) PARABOLOIDAL (e) HYPERBOLOIDAL
                                MIRROR   MIRROR

Fig. 5-1. Types of mirrors.

other IR instruments; such as cameras and search and tracking detectors, to direct beams of IR radiation and to scan over wide angles of view. Examples of these and other applications are profusely illustrated in succeeding chapters, particularly in Chap. 9.

Spherical and Paraboloidal mirrors are used in IR telescopes, microscopes, spectrometers, and other instruments to concentrate and focus beams of IR radiation. Both concave and convex shapes are employed. These mirrors have the following advantages over lenses and other refracting elements; they do not show selective absorption of IR radiation, and they are free from chromatic aberrations; mirrors can also be made in larger sizes.

Spherical mirrors do, however, produce defects in the optical images; these are caused by spherical aberration and astigmatism.

Spherical aberration is illustrated in Fig. 5-2. Paraxial rays which lie very close to the optical axis and make very small angles with it are brought to a focus on the paraxial focal plane. Nonparaxial or oblique rays are brought to a focus at different points between the paraxial focal plane and the mirror. Instead of a point image of a distant object, a circular image is formed whose diameter varies with its distance from the paraxial focal plane. At a certain point this blur circle has a minimum diameter and is called the *minimum circle of confusion*

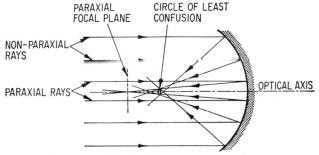

FIG. 5-2. Spherical aberration of a mirror.

or *minimum blur circle*. Spherical aberration can be corrected by combining a spherical mirror with a special correcting lens placed at the center of curvature of the mirror. This *Schmidt* system is discussed in Sec. 5-6. Spherical aberration can also be corrected by the Mangin mirror, another type of lens-mirror combination, discussed in Sec. 5-6. Both these optical systems are also employed to correct the second focusing defect of spherical mirrors, that of astigmatism.

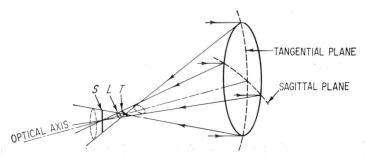

FIG. 5-3. Astigmatism of a concave mirror. (*After Jenkins and White, "Fundamentals of Optics," 2d ed., p. 91, McGraw-Hill Book Company, Inc., New York, 1950.*)

Astigmatism becomes increasingly evident in a spherical mirror as the angle between the optical axis and the incident radiation increases. Instead of forming a point image, radiation reflected in the vertical or *tangential plane* is brought to a focus at T as a line image, while radiation reflected in the horizontal or sagittal plane is focused as a line image at S. Figure 5-3 shows this effect, greatly exaggerated.

Between the focal surfaces T and S, which are very close together and mutually perpendicular, at the mean position L at the center of curvature of the mirror the image size is a minimum and lies on an almost spherical surface.[33]

If the mirror is a paraboloid of revolution no spherical aberration is present, even for large apertures. *Parabolic mirrors*, however, show large astigmatic effects for oblique rays. For this reason they are used in IR instruments to produce parallel or very narrow collimated beams. IR searchlights and astronomical telescopes employ parabolic mirrors.

All single mirrors reverse the image, an undesirable effect in IR fire-control devices, for example. Two mirrors are required to prevent this and several examples will be found in this and later chapters. Correction of both the aberrations described requires the use of a refractive component such as a lens, and thereby introduces still other aberrations. For this reason, the applications of spherical and paraboloidal mirrors in IR devices are more limited than those of lenses.

For high resolution, that is, the ability to distinguish between two point sources with a very small angular separation, high-quality mirrors and a narrow field of view are required. Aberrations, if excessive, may have to be reduced by incorporating a correcting mirror or lens into the optical system. If high resolving power is not required, relatively poor image quality may be acceptable, depending upon the nature of the detector used, and the background radiation from which the target is to be discriminated. In this case it is cheaper to use spherical mirrors.

5-5. LENSES

As with mirrors, all nonparaxial or oblique rays passing through a lens produce a blurring of the image caused by lens aberrations. Consider an oblique ray making an angle θ with the optical axis of the lens. By Maclaurin's expansion

$$\sin \theta = \theta - \frac{\theta^3}{3!} + \frac{\theta^5}{5!} - \frac{\theta^7}{7!} + \cdots \tag{5-1}$$

In the case of paraxial rays θ is very small, and all terms but the first may be neglected to a very good approximation. This first-order or Gauss theory is commonly used in the ray tracing of paraxial rays.[34]

With oblique rays, however, the higher-order terms must be considered. For a given wavelength and refractive index the aberration of an oblique ray can be expressed by what are known as the five *Seidel sums*. If all of the Seidel numbers are simultaneously zero the lens has no aberration.   The five *monochromatic* aberrations are: *spherical aberration* (S_1), *coma* (S_2), *astigmatism* (S_3), *curvature of the field* (S_4), and *distortion of the image* (S_5).[35]   Thus if S_3, S_4, and S_5 are zero, the lens still suffers from spherical aberration and coma.   In addition, since a lens has a refractive index greater than unity, there are two *chromatic* aberrations.   In discussing briefly these seven lens aberrations we shall introduce the principal lenses and their combinations used in IR optical systems.

Spherical Aberration.   As in the case of mirrors, oblique or non-paraxial rays are brought to a focus at different focal points, causing

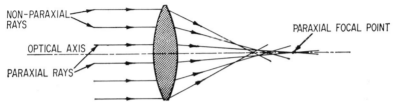

FIG. 5-4. Positive spherical aberration of a lens.

a blurred image.   For a convex lens the focal point moves closer to the lens as the zone diameter of the lens is increased.   This is shown greatly exaggerated in Fig. 5-4.   In this case, spherical aberration is positive for a convex lens.   With a concave lens, the focal point moves away from the lens as the zone diameter is increased, producing negative spherical aberration.

In a single lens, spherical aberration can be eliminated for one object distance by changing the curvatures of the zones on either or both lens surfaces.   This process is known as *aspherizing*.   The resultant lens surfaces are called *aspheric surfaces*.   Spherical aberration is still present, however, for other object distances.

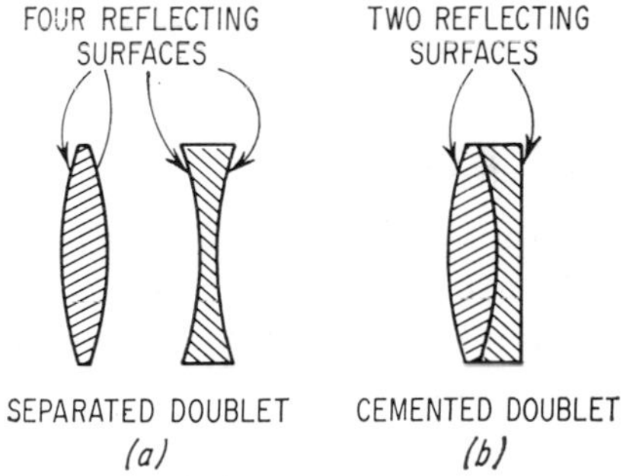

FOUR REFLECTING SURFACES   TWO REFLECTING SURFACES

SEPARATED DOUBLET *(a)*   CEMENTED DOUBLET *(b)*

FIG. 5-5. Doublets.

If a convex or positive lens is combined with a concave or negative lens with equal and opposite spherical aberration as in a *doublet* or a *cemented doublet* (Fig. 5-5), complete elimination of spherical aberration can be accomplished.

Coma.   An off-axis point object produces an image in the form of a series of circles formed by each zone of the lens.   These *comatic circles*, as they are called, are each produced by opposite pairs of rays passing through a particular zone of the lens.   The intersections of only two pairs of rays, those passing through the tangential and sagittal planes, are illustrated in Fig. 5-6, for two zones.[36] These comatic circles are located in the focal plane of the lens; their location and diameter vary with the zone. The illustration shows *positive coma*, where greater magnification is produced by rays from an outer zone than by rays from an inner zone. Superposition of the various comatic circles on one another gives a comet-shaped appearance to the image of a point object, hence the name *coma* for this aberration.

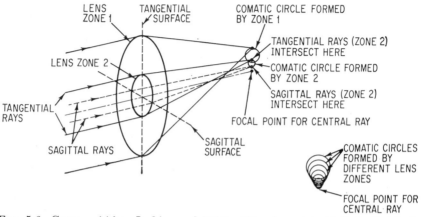

FIG. 5-6. Coma. (*After Jenkins and White, "Fundamentals of Optics," 2d ed., p. 133, McGraw-Hill Book Company, Inc., New York, 1950.*)

Fortunately the shape of a lens that produces minimum coma is very similar to that required to produce minimum spherical aberration. A contact-doublet lens with the correctly shaped aspheric surfaces has neither coma nor spherical aberration. Such a lens or optical system is termed *aplanatic*. The first two Seidel sums are zero.

Astigmatism. In the case of an off-axis object point, if the third Seidel sum is not zero, instead of a point image a blurred image is formed, due to astigmatism. This is illustrated for a lens in Fig. 5-7. Consider the rays from an off-axis object point, *O*, passing through the tangential and sagittal planes of the lens. Rays passing through the tangential plane intersect in a *focal line* perpendicular to the tangential plane; similarly, rays passing through the sagittal plane intersect in another focal line, perpendicular to the sagittal plane. The distance between these two focal lines, measured along the central ray, is a measure of the astigmatism. Only part of the object is in focus at either of the focal lines, which lie on paraboloidal surfaces. At a point on the central ray lying between these two focal lines the image is a minimum size at *C*.

Astigmatism is a more difficult aberration to correct.   A doublet, similar to that illustrated in Fig. 5-5a, with properly shaped lens surfaces and spacing, can be designed so that the tangential and sagittal focal surfaces coincide in a single paraboloidal surface, called the *Petzval surface*, on which point images of a single point object are

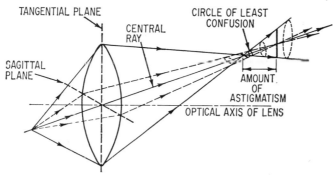

FIG. 5-7. Astigmatism in a convex lens.   (*After Jenkins and White, "Fundamentals of Optics," 2d ed., p. 139, McGraw-Hill Book Company, Inc., New York, 1950.*)

formed.[37]   The curvature of these astigmatic image surfaces can be altered, and considerable reduction of the astigmatism can be effected by the correct spacing of lens elements and by the introduction of an optical stop or another lens.   Lens systems of this type are known as *anastigmats*.

Curvature of the Field.   If a lens system is designed so that the first three Seidel sums are all zero, that is, the system completely corrects for spherical aberration, coma, and astigmatism, then point objects form images which lie on the curved Petzval surface (Fig. 5-8). If an image is formed on a flat screen at A, the center of the field lying near the optical axis will be sharply focused, while the edges are increasingly blurred as the distance off the optical axis increases.   For an image formed on a flat screen at B, however, the image is sharply

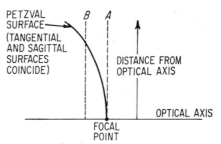

FIG. 5-8. Curvature of the field.   (*After Jenkins and White, "Fundamentals of Optics," 2d ed., p. 141, McGraw-Hill Book Company, Inc., New York, 1950.*)

focused about halfway out while the center and edges are blurred.[37]

Curvature of the field can be corrected by the careful design of anastigmats employing separated components and by the judicious use of a stop.

Distortion of the image will occur if magnification by the lens system is not uniform in all lateral directions over the whole field. The image of a square object, for example, suffers *pincushion distortion* when increased magnification occurs in the outer field, and *barrel distortion* when reduced magnification is produced by the optical system in the outer field, as illustrated in Fig. 5-9. A thin lens will cause, of course, less distortion than a thick lens.

Distortion is corrected by using two lenses, arranged symmetrically as far as possible, with a stop located between them.[38]

In all the aberrations just described we have been considering effects with monochromatic or single-wavelength radiation. We must now consider the effects produced by optical systems when nonmonochromatic radiation within definite wavelength bands is employed.

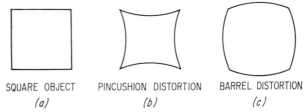

SQUARE OBJECT   PINCUSHION DISTORTION   BARREL DISTORTION

(a)   *(b)*   *(c)*

FIG. 5-9. Distortion. (*After Jenkins and White, "Fundamentals of Optics," 2d ed., p. 143, McGraw-Hill Book Company, Inc., New York, 1950.*)

Chromatic Aberrations. In refractive optical systems employed in IR devices, wavelength bands which may vary in width from a fraction of a micron to several microns are encountered. Variation of the refractive index of the optical material with wavelength must be considered. Because of this variation, a refractive element such as a lens focuses the images of various colors in the visible spectrum, or wavelengths in the IR spectrum, at different points along or off the optical axis. The amount of bending of a ray by the refractive element is called its *deviation*. The deviation is greater for a ray of short wavelength (blue in the visible spectrum), than that for a ray of long wavelength (red in the visible spectrum). The difference in the amount of bending of two rays of different wavelengths is called the *dispersion*. Some glasses or optical materials have greater *dispersive power* than others. Thus, flint glass has greater dispersive power than crown glass.

Two kinds of chromatic aberration are encountered. In a convex lens, dispersion causes the IR radiation of shorter wavelengths to be focused at points nearer to the lens. With a concave lens, the opposite effect is produced. The result is that along the optical axis of the system there is a horizontal spread between the images produced for differ-

ent wavelengths.   This effect, shown exaggerated in Fig. 5-10, is
known as *longitudinal chromatic aberration*.   The effective focal length
of the lens, and thus its magnification, varies, therefore, with wavelength.   The effect produced on off-axis radiation is that of vertical
differences in the images formed at different wavelengths.   This effect,
shown exaggerated in Fig. 5-11, is known as *lateral chromatic aberration*.

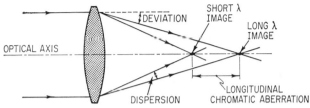

FIG. 5-10. Longitudinal chromatic aberration in a lens.   (*After Jenkins and White,*
"Fundamentals of Optics," 2d ed., p. 145, McGraw-Hill Book Company, Inc., New
York, 1950.)

Many optical materials used in IR systems have high refractive
indexes.   Examples are arsenic trisulfide glass (2.6), KRS-5 (2.63),
silicon (3.5), germanium (4.1), sapphire (1.76), and silver chloride (2.1).
Chromatic aberrations may therefore be quite large.   Their correction
becomes of primary importance in optical systems where high resolution is required.   Such IR systems are microscopes, astronomical telescopes, and telescopes used for search, detection, and tracking purposes.

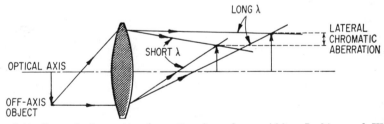

FIG. 5-11. Lateral chromatic aberration in a lens.   (*After Jenkins and White,*
"Fundamentals of Optics," 2d ed., p. 145, McGraw-Hill Book Company, Inc., New
York, 1950.)

Chromatic aberrations are corrected by employing combinations of
two lenses, or doublets, of different optical materials with different
refractive indexes.   This fact is true in the IR as well as in the visible
spectrum, and is used to correct chromatic aberration by means of
achromatic lenses.   These lenses were first produced in 1730 in England
by C. M. Hall, who combined glasses of different dispersive power.   A
few years later John Dolland revolutionized telescope design by the

development of achromats of the type illustrated in Fig. 5-12.   The color dispersion of a converging or positive lens of crown glass was reversed and thereby cancelled by that of a diverging or negative lens of flint glass.   The net result of the difference in refractive index of the two glasses was a converging lens.

This type of lens is known as an *achromatic doublet*.   In practice the two lenses are usually cemented together and coated with a low-reflection coating.   These lenses are commonly used in telescope objectives. A doublet does not give perfect color correction since, for most refracting optical materials, the deviation is not proportional to the wavelength.   The curve for refraction versus wavelength plotted for flint glass does not have the same shape as the corresponding curve for

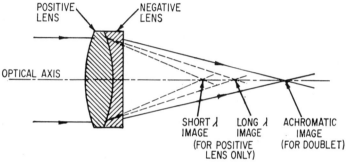

Fig. 5-12. Principle of achromatic doublet.

crown glass.   However, a doublet can be designed for the exact correction of two chosen wavelengths, with imperfect correction for intermediate wavelengths.   Wavelengths shorter or longer than the corrected waveband may deviate seriously from the common focus.   At the Yerkes Observatory, for example, the 40-in. achromat is corrected for red and blue; yellow-green light is focused at about 1 cm nearer the lens.

Another combination consists of two separate thin lenses of the same optical material, their distance apart being one-half the sum of their focal lengths; this is called a *separated doublet*.   When thick lenses of high power and short focal length are used, lateral chromatic aberration becomes increasingly difficult to correct.

Three different kinds of optical material may be combined to bring three different wavelengths to a common focus.   Lenses of this type are called *apochromats*.   They are costly and difficult to make.

Speed of a Lens.   The light- or radiation-gathering capacity of a lens is a function of both the area of its entrance pupil and its focal length.   These determine the solid angle of the converging beam of radiation which forms a point on the image.   The ratio of the focal length of the lens to the diameter of its entrance pupil, which is often determined by a stop placed in front of the lens, is the *focal ratio* or *f* value of the lens.[39]

$$f \text{ value} = f/a \qquad (5\text{-}2)$$

where f = focal length of lens
$\quad a$ = diameter of entrance pupil
The *speed* of a lens is inversely proportional to the square of its f value.[39]

$$\text{Speed} = \frac{\text{constant}}{(f \text{ value})^2} \qquad (5\text{-}3)$$

For example, an $f/1$ lens is *faster* than an $f/3.5$ lens by $(3.5/1)^2$, or a ratio of 12.25:1.   In some IR optical systems both high speed and high resolution are desirable.   High speed is required to concentrate as much radiation as possible on the sensitive area of the detector and may also be dictated by the requirement for a short focal length.   If at the same time high resolution is also a requirement, as in the case of IR microscopes and many tracking devices used in fire-control systems, design is a matter of compromise.   High speed requires a relatively large ratio of aperture to focal length; aperture size is limited by the degree of aberration that can be tolerated; and to a certain degree high resolution also limits the minimum focal length that can be employed without exceeding the aberration limitations imposed by the requirements on resolution.

The *entrance pupil* of an optical system is in the object space, that is, lying between the optical system and the object.   The *exit pupil* lies in the image space, or between the optical system and the image plane.   Both can be affected by stops or diaphragms.

Optical Effects of Stops.   We have already seen that a stop can be used to reduce certain aberrations in an optical system.   The outer

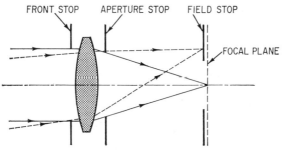

FRONT STOP   APERTURE STOP   FIELD STOP

FOCAL PLANE

FIG. 5-13. Effects of stops.   (*After Jenkins and White, "Fundamentals of Optics,"* *2d ed., p. 94, McGraw-Hill Book Company, Inc., New York, 1950.*)

rims of lenses and mirrors are naturally occurring stops which are always present in an optical system.   These and other stops control both the field of view and the image brightness.   Image brightness is controlled by a stop placed close to a lens, called an *aperture stop*.   If placed in the object space just in front of the lens it is known as a *front stop*. If placed just in front of the focal plane of the lens or optical system it is called a *field stop*, since, by limiting the incidence angles of radiation reaching the focal plane, the stop limits the extent of the field displayed in the image.   These effects are illustrated in Fig. 5-13.

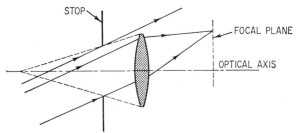

FIG. 5-14. Vignetting.   (*After Jenkins and White, "Fundamentals of Optics," 2d ed., p. 111, McGraw-Hill Book Company, Inc., New York, 1950.*)

In optical systems having relatively wide fields of view, such as in certain cameras, stops may cause a reduction in brightness for off-axis radiation (Fig. 5-14).   This effect is known as *vignetting*.

5-6. SPECIAL COMBINATIONS OF LENSES AND MIRRORS

Many IR optical systems used in practice combine the advantages, and disadvantages, of both reflective and refractive optics.   For example, many of the primarily reflective optical systems illustrated in this book incorporate some refractive optics in the form of a telescope objective, field lens, prism, or corrector lens to reduce aberration.   Many of the primarily refractive optical systems make use of reflecting mirrors to obtain a folded optical path and save space.   Numerous examples of these systems will be found in Chap. 9 and other chapters.   A brief discussion of the more important combinations used in many IR optical systems, particularly in IR telescopes and microscope objectives and field lenses, follows.

Reflecting Systems.   Various types of reflecting telescope objectives in common use are illustrated in Fig. 5-15.   These employ simple plane mirrors, and spherical, parabolic, and hyperbolic mirrors in both convex and concave shapes.   Folded reflecting systems consisting of two or more mirrors often employ pierced primary mirrors (Fig. 5-15c and d) to limit aberrations caused by off-axis rays.   This system, however, introduces the disadvantage caused by masking the center of the radiation beam by the secondary mirror.   This *blocking effect* reduces the optical gain, or radiation-gathering efficiency, of the optical system. An advantage of the folded reflecting system, however, is that relatively long focal lengths can be attained in a small space.   The optical system itself may be required to cover a much larger over-all field of view, or search field.   This is achieved by various types of *mechanical*

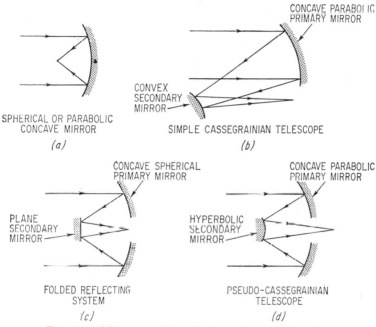

SPHERICAL OR PARABOLIC
CONCAVE MIRROR
(a)

CONCAVE PARABOLIC
PRIMARY MIRROR

CONVEX
SECONDARY
MIRROR

SIMPLE CASSEGRAINIAN TELESCOPE
(b)

CONCAVE SPHERICAL
PRIMARY MIRROR

PLANE
SECONDARY
MIRROR

FOLDED REFLECTING
SYSTEM
(c)

CONCAVE PARABOLIC
PRIMARY MIRROR

HYPERBOLIC
SECONDARY
MIRROR

PSEUDO-CASSEGRAINIAN
TELESCOPE
(d)

FIG. 5-15. Mirrors used in reflecting-telescope objectives.

scanning systems.   Many ingenious mechanical scanning systems have been devised and are in use in various types of IR detection systems. They may involve eccentric rotation, rotation plus nodding of the primary mirror, a rotary-nodding motion of the secondary mirror, or a conical scanning motion of the entire telescope assembly, which is mounted in gimbals.   The primary considerations in the design of these scanning systems are simplicity, physical strength combined with lightness, and freedom from small errors such as those introduced by backlash in gearing.   In this type of reflecting system, however, mounting and alignment problems are encountered.   Environmental temperature changes and temperature changes through the optical system can have serious effects.

Reflection losses are reduced by high-reflection coatings applied to the front surface of a mirror.   The materials used for this purpose are discussed in Chap. 6.

The advantages and disadvantages of reflecting optics are summarized in Table 5-1.   Numerous examples of mirror optical systems employed in IR instruments of various types will be encountered throughout this book, particularly in Chaps. 9, 10, and 11.

TABLE 5-1. ADVANTAGES AND DISADVANTAGES OF REFLECTING AND
REFRACTING OPTICAL SYSTEMS

Type of optics	Advantages	Disadvantages
Reflecting......	No selective absorption of IR radiation; high transmission Very high reflectivity of metal films No chromatic aberrations Less spherical aberration than for a single refracting element Long focal lengths possible in a compact optical system Axial aberrations can be reduced by suitably located stop	Reversal of image in single mirror Curved focal surface Field of view limited by off-axis aberrations Correction of aberrations requires introduction of refracting elements Blocking effect of secondary mirror reduces optical gain Mounting, environmental, and alignment problems Difficult to shield from stray radiation Window required to seal optical system introduces chromatic aberrations
Refracting......	More control of aberrations; greater freedom of design No blocking factor Better image quality possible Wider-aperture, faster lens systems possible Mounting problems simpler Sealing window not required Less sensitive to thermal effects Alignment and focusing simpler	More reflecting surfaces Selective absorption effects Wavelength transmission limitations of available materials Chromatic aberrations

Refracting Systems.   Basically, the refracting system consists of an objective, to gather and condense incoming IR radiation, and a field lens, to focus radiation on the sensitive surface of the detector.   Objective and field lenses may be either simple single lenses, or complex multiple lens systems, depending upon the degree of resolution, the corrections required for various aberrations, the focal length, and instantaneous field of view required of the optical system. A simple refractive system may consist, as in the case of some radiometers, of merely a single convex or meniscus lens with a low-reflection coating on each outside surface. More complex optical systems may involve multiple objective and field-lens combinations of meniscus, doublet, telephoto, equiconvex, achromat, or other lenses.

Refractive optical systems have certain inherent advantages over reflective systems and are necessary in some applications in which these features require full exploitation. First, no masking of the center of the incoming beam of radiation occurs. Generally speaking, refractive optics are less bulky, unless very long focal lengths are required. Also, because superior correction for an off-axis image can be achieved, refractive optics make it possible to obtain both wider fields of view and faster optical systems.

Among the disadvantages are the higher energy losses caused by absorption and reflection in the optical elements. A refractive element requires two low-reflection coatings—one on each surface—in comparison with a reflective optical element which requires only one. Chromatic aberration is also a problem. These difficulties are enhanced by the limited number of available materials with suitable optical and physical properties in the IR spectral region. Manufacturing difficulties and high costs are also factors to be considered.

The variation of refractive index with wavelength, causing high dispersion and hence chromatic aberration, is a mixed blessing. In spectrometers, monochromators, and allied IR instruments, this property is exploited by employing high-dispersion prisms in conjunction with Littrow mirrors to obtain multiple-path, beam-shifting, and high-resolution effects (see Chaps. 9, 10, and 11).

Wider angular coverage in refractive systems may be obtained by using multiple-lens systems, each objective lens covering a certain angular field and overlapping that of its neighbor, rotating about a common axis. Alternatively the entire telescope may be mounted in gimbals and scanned over the desired search field. Other scanning methods sometimes employed use rotating wedges or prisms.

Various types of refracting objectives and field-lens systems are illustrated in Fig. 5-16. Numerous other examples will be found in later chapters of this book. Figure 5-16c and d illustrates the use of *immersion optics*. Both the hyperhemisphere and the truncated cone are cemented to the front surface of the detector-cell. They function as *light pipes* by concentrating incident radiation on the small sensitive area of the detector cell by means of internal reflections. The over-all optical gain accomplished is equal to the refractive index, n, of the optical material employed. Alternatively, a reduction of $1/n$ in the linear dimension of the sensitive surface of the detector cell can be achieved, resulting in a reduction in cell noise.

The advantages and disadvantages of purely refractive optical systems are summarized in Table 5-1.

Combined Reflecting-Refracting Systems. These are employed to provide improved correction of aberrations over wider angular fields of coverage. They are known as *catadioptric systems.*

Schmidt Systems which combine a correction plate or aspherical lens with a concave spherical mirror are widely used for the correction of

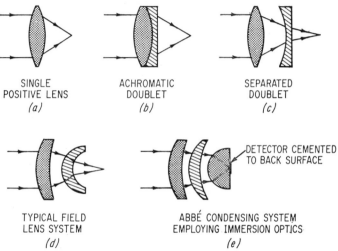

SINGLE   ACHROMATIC   SEPARATED
POSITIVE LENS   DOUBLET   DOUBLET
(a)   (b)   (c)

DETECTOR CEMENTED
TO BACK SURFACE

TYPICAL FIELD   ABBÉ CONDENSING SYSTEM
LENS SYSTEM   EMPLOYING IMMERSION OPTICS
(d)   (e)

Fig. 5-16. Types of refracting objectives and field lens systems.

aberrations in reflecting systems. The Schmidt corrector plate operates on the following principle:

The difference in curvature of the two surfaces of the plate or lens and the refractive index of the glass used determine the focal length. Both radii of curvature may be changed, but the difference in curvature is kept constant by bending the lens. In this way, all distortion of the optical image due to coma can be canceled, and practically all the spherical aberration can be eliminated. The correcting lens is placed at the center of curvature of the spherical mirror. These systems produce a spherical focal surface, and when they are used for cameras the film must be curved to fit this focal surface. By interposing a spherical convex mirror at the focal surface, a Schmidt autocollimator is formed (Fig. 5-17), the emergent rays being parallel. Schmidt systems with speeds as low as $f/0.5$ have been made.   This type of optical system is used in astronomical telescopes and was initially employed in World War II for objectives in a wide variety of IR devices.   Schmidt correctors require skilled workmanship and are expensive to make.

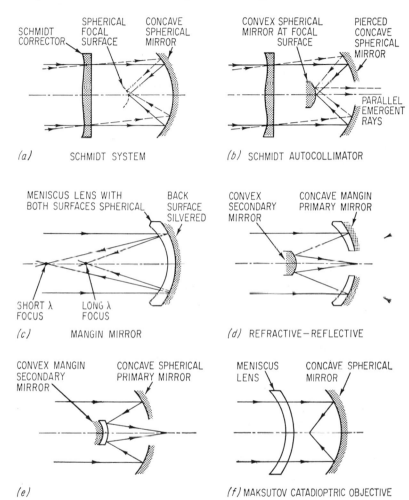

Fig. 5-17. Combined reflecting-refracting optical systems (catadioptric systems).

The Maksutov system is very similar to the Schmidt type, employing a concave spherical mirror with a meniscus lens as the correcting element (Fig. 5-17f).

The *Mangin mirror* consists of a meniscus lens with spherical surfaces, the back surface being silvered to form a concave or a convex mirror (Fig. 5-17d and e), which can be used in a telescope objective. As illustrated in Fig. 5-17c, the focal length of a Mangin mirror is greater for radiation of short wavelengths than for that of longer wavelengths.   This is the opposite of that for a convergent or positive lens. When combined with such a lens, the Mangin mirror may be used to correct chromatic aberration, which in fact can be practically eliminated over the entire photographic spectral range.   Astigmatism and spherical aberration can be reduced, but not eliminated.   By a suitable choice of the radii of curvature used in the objective lens and in the Mangin mirror, the image and object can be equalized for a mean wavelength, thus practically eliminating coma.   Several modern types of IR optical systems incorporate a Mangin mirror.

5-7. PRISMS

Since prisms of various shapes and optical materials are used extensively in IR monochromators, analyzers, spectroscopes, spectrographs, binoculars, and many other instruments, a description of the more common types of prism and their properties is appropriate.

Consider first the equiangular prism illustrated in Fig 5-18.   A ray passing through the prism is refracted or deviated once on entering and again on leaving the optical material.   The *total deviation* δ is the sum of the deviations δ_1 and δ_2 at the two faces.   If within the prism the ray

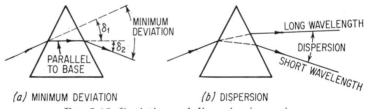

(a) MINIMUM DEVIATION   (b) DISPERSION
Fig. 5-18. Deviation and dispersion in a prism.

is parallel to the base, δ is a minimum and is known as the *angle of minimum deviation* (Fig. 5-18a).   In this case, $\delta_1 = \delta_2$, that is, the incident and exit angles of the ray are equal.   At minimum deviation there is no astigmatism.   At any other angle, astigmatism of the image is caused by refraction unless the incident radiation is in the form of a parallel beam.

Therefore, when prisms are employed in IR spectroscopic instruments, they are set as nearly as possible at minimum deviation in order to avoid astigmatic effects.   Alternatively the incident beam of radiation is collimated by means of a lens into a parallel beam; then the dispersion can be increased by using the prism out of minimum deviation.[40]

If the incident beam of radiation is nonmonochromatic, since refractive index increases as the wavelength decreases, the shorter-wavelength radiation is deviated more than the longer-wavelength radiation. The difference in deviation between the short and long wavelengths of the emergent beam is called the *dispersion* (Fig. 5-18*b*). Dispersion is almost constant from grazing incidence up to the angle of minimum

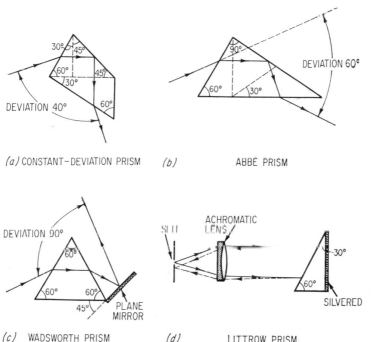

(a) CONSTANT–DEVIATION PRISM   *(b)*   ABBÉ PRISM

(c)   WADSWORTH PRISM   *(d)*   LITTROW PRISM

FIG. 5-19. Dispersing prisms.   (*After Jenkins and White, "Fundamentals of Optics,"* *2d ed., p. 30, McGraw-Hill Book Company, Inc., New York, 1950.*)

deviation. At angles greater than minimum deviation it rapidly increases, until at grazing emergence it is infinite.[40]

For a particular prism, dispersion is therefore greater in the near-IR spectral region than in the far-IR spectral region, and for both it is smaller than that occurring in the visible region.

Prisms employed in modern spectrographs are made of materials with such refractive indexes that they give high dispersion in the wavelength region under investigation. Prisms of various shapes are designed either to give constant deviation for a wide range of incidence angles or to operate at the angle of minimum deviation. Examples of prisms of this type in common use in IR spectroscopy are illustrated in Fig. 5-19. These prisms produce constant deviation. The *Wadsworth prism*,[41] operating at minimum deviation, is used extensively in IR monochromators, where for a constant angle between the collimator and the telescope, astigmatism-free images can be obtained at various wavelengths by rotating the prism. The *Littrow prism*[41] is widely used in spectrographs and spectroscopes to produce an autocollimated beam (Fig. 5-19*d*).

5-8. DIFFRACTION GRATINGS

These optical elements are employed in IR instruments used for spectroscopic analysis because of their great resolving potentialities. They require the use of an IR monochromator to provide monochromatic radiation from a slit source; this radiation is then resolved by the grating into individual spectral lines which are focused either on a photographic plate or on a detector whose output produces a trace on a

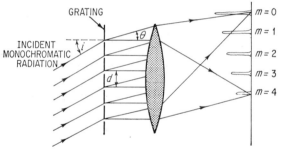

Fig. 5-20. Diffraction grating. (*After Jenkins and White, "Fundamentals of Optics," 2d ed., p. 327, McGraw-Hill Book Company, Inc., New York, 1950.*)

moving chart. The grating produces the same effect as many thousands of very fine parallel equidistant slits of the same width, forming spectral lines at angles given by [42]

$$d(\sin i + \sin \theta) = m\lambda \tag{5-4}$$

where d = separation distance between successive slits

i = incidence angle of monochromatic radiation illuminating slits

λ = wavelength of monochromatic radiation

m = order of principal intensity maximum, as illustrated in Fig. 5-20

Gratings are mechanically made on high-precision ruling machines which rule many thousands of equally spaced, fine grooves per inch by means of a diamond point.   In a *transmission grating*, these grooves or *lines*, ruled on a plane glass surface, are opaque and scatter the incident radiation.   The clear portions of the glass surface transmit the radiation, behaving therefore like very narrow slits.   In a *reflection grating*, the grooves are ruled on a polished metal surface, usually evaporated aluminum, where the unruled portions reflect radiation.

Gratings are produced in various widths up to 10 in. or more.   For a given width the resolving power increases directly as the number of lines.   Thus a 1-in. grating with 20,000 lines has twice the resolving power, for a given order, as a 1-in. grating with 10,000 lines.

Echelette Gratings.   In *echelette gratings*[43] (Fig. 5-21), the grooves are ruled with one face optically flat.   This face is inclined at an angle

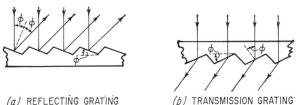

(a) REFLECTING GRATING   *(b)* TRANSMISSION GRATING

Fig. 5-21. Echelette gratings.   *(After Jenkins and White, "Fundamentals of Optics," 2d ed., p. 338, McGraw-Hill Book Company, Inc., New York, 1950.)*

ϕ, to reflect—in the case of a reflection grating—or refract—in the case of a transmission grating—most of the incident radiation in a desired direction.   In this way, radiation can be concentrated in a particular order, producing a brighter image.   Large, plane, reflection gratings are usually mounted in a *Littrow mounting*.[44]   The incident radiation from the slit is collimated by an achromatic lens which also focuses the diffracted radiation onto the photographic plate or detector (Fig. 5-22).

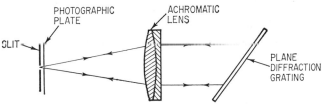

Fig. 5-22. Littrow mounting for plane diffraction grating.   *(After Jenkins and White, "Fundamentals of Optics," 2d ed., p. 341, McGraw-Hill Book Company, Inc., New York, 1950.)*

Concave Gratings.   These are ruled on concave spherical metal mirrors.   They have the advantage of focusing the radiation, thus eliminating the necessity of lenses which introduce aberrations.   The locus of points where the diffracted image is in focus is a circle, tangent to the grating, called the *Rowland circle*,[44] the diameter of which is the radius of curvature of the grating, and on which the slit source is mounted. Concave gratings exhibit quite large astigmatic aberrations. All the mountings commonly used for concave gratings in IR spectroscopy position the slit and the plate or detector on the Rowland circle (Fig. 5-23).

Rowland Mounting. In the *Rowland mounting*[44] (Fig. 5-23a), the grating and plate holder are mounted on a rigid beam which is a diameter of the Rowland circle. The ends of the beam are pivoted to two trolleys which move along two tracks perpendicular to each other. The slit is mounted at their intersection on the Rowland circle. Moving the beam around the Rowland circle effectively changes the angle

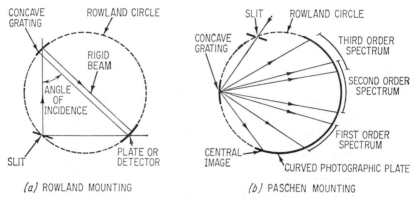

(a) ROWLAND MOUNTING   *(b)* PASCHEN MOUNTING

FIG. 5-23. Mountings for concave gratings. (*After Jenkins and White, "Fundamentals of Optics," 2d ed., pp. 340, 341, McGraw-Hill Book Company, Inc., New York, 1950.*)

of incidence and brings different portions of the spectrum to a focus on the photographic plate.

Paschen Mounting. In the *Paschen mounting*[44] the photographic plate itself is mounted in an arc of the Rowland circle so that several orders can be photographed simultaneously (Fig. 5-23b).

Ruling Errors. The ruling machines used to scribe the lines or grooves on a grating may, because of a faulty driving mechanism, suffer from ruling errors. The most common ruling error is *periodic* in nature. The grating then produces false lines or "ghosts" near each principal maximum. *Rowland ghosts*[43] are produced by a single periodic error and are false lines about the principal maxima which are symmetrical in intensity and in spacing. *Lyman ghosts*[43] occur less frequently, when a single error of very short period or two ruling errors of different periods are present, and may be widely separated from the principal maxima.   A *continually increasing* ruling error in one direction causes convergence or divergence in the diffracted beam.   *Random* ruling errors cause continuous background radiation around the principal maxima.

5-9. WINDOWS AND IRDOMES

In many IR instruments the high-precision optical system and the sensitive detector must be protected from thermal and atmospheric conditions pertaining to the immediate environment.   This requires the complete enclosure of the optical and detection system by means of a jacket.   Many IR instruments used in spectroscopy require sealing in a vacuum or an inert gas.   Some kinds of air-borne IR equipment require a cooling jacket.   The radiation-receiving end is sealed by an IR-transmitting *window* which may be flat or curved.   Windows often

Fig. 5-24. A small hemispherical irdome of synthetic sapphire.   (*Courtesy Linde Company, Division of Union Carbide Corporation, New York.*)

function additionally at filters.   They may be formed of various crystalline materials or glasses, described in Chap. 6.

A special type of window, essential in air-borne applications of IR in aircraft and missiles, is the *irdome*.   It is generally hemispherical in shape, but may also be in the form of an ogive or conical, either rounded or with several flat sides.   A typical hemispherical irdome for air-borne use is illustrated in Fig. 5-24.

The function of an irdome is to protect the IR system from air, dust, precipitation, and thermal effects in a high-velocity air stream.   At the same time, it must transmit IR radiation from the source with a minimum of absorption loss, reflection, and optical distortion.

In addition to these desirable optical properties, the irdome material must be able to withstand both a wide range of environmental temperatures and the rapidly changing surface temperatures encountered in high-speed maneuvers and flight through clouds composed of water droplets and ice crystals.   Temperature gradients across the irdome wall between front and rear surfaces may be very high and may also change rapidly.   Irdome materials with high physical strength and with good thermal properties are necessary to prevent distortion and fracture under these severe environmental conditions.   For supersonic flight at high Mach numbers, artificial cooling of both the internal and external surfaces of the irdome may be required.

Pitting of the external surface of the irdome, caused by erosion by rain, ice, or dust particles at high speed, tends to weaken the irdome structure, and also creates local IR-radiation sources or *hot spots* which interfere with the target image by the formation of *ghost images*.   In order to prevent this, the irdome material must not only possess the necessary hardness, but its outside surface must be highly polished. To achieve the high degree of surface polish required, and at the same time maintain uniform wall thickness, is a major production problem.

The irdome designer, therefore, faces many difficult problems.   He is severely limited by the scarcity of suitable optical materials possessing the requisite optical and physical properties over the wavelength bands encountered in this type of work.   The various optical materials available and their properties are discussed in greater detail in Chap. 6.

5-10. SPECTRAL FILTERING BY OPTICAL FILTERS

Optical filters are required in most IR systems in order to pass IR radiation of a particular wavelength or within a particular wavelength band through the optical system to the sensitive surface of the detector. This process is known as spectral filtering.   For this purpose *transmitting, reflecting*, or *interference* filters of various optical materials and metal surfaces are employed.   *Long-wavelength-cutoff filters* pass IR radiation only up to a particular wavelength.   *Short-wavelength-cutoff filters* block all IR radiation below a certain wavelength.   *Bandpass filters* or combinations of filters transmit IR radiation only within specific wavelength limits.   It is most desirable that the wavelength-cutoff region of a filter be very sharp.   Since their properties are very dependent upon the optical material and method of construction employed, IR optical filters are discussed more fully in Chap. 6.

5-11. SPACE-FILTERING AND SCANNING DEVICES

The purpose of a scanning system depends a great deal upon the particular design and function of the IR device of which it is a part. A scanning system may be used to increase the total search coverage of an IR detector; or predominantly for tracking purposes, by providing target-position information; or to improve responsivity of the detection system and improve background discrimination.

Scanning systems may be classified into four basic types: (1) the simple system, (2) the scanning-spot system, (3) the reticle or chopper scanning system, and (4) the mosaic system.

In addition, there are numerous combinations of these four main types of systems. In the discussion which follows, the methods of operation and the properties of the four basic types of scanning systems will be described.

1. The Simple System. The simple system is merely a reflective, refractive, or catadioptric optical system, designed to collect IR energy from a fixed field of view and focus it on a detector. Such systems are useful for detecting IR intensity variations. They are employed in such applications as IR pyrometers, communication systems, and beacons.

2. The Scanning-spot System. A rotating or nodding mirror, prism, or lens system is used to position a small instantaneous field of view in a particular scan pattern over the entire search field. Scan patterns may be of the circular, cycloidal, interlacing, raster, or other forms. After one complete coverage of the search field, the scan pattern is repeated. The repetition rate is called the *frame rate*.

Scanning systems of this type are used to cover large search fields. For maximum sensitivity and efficient background discrimination, the size of the scanning spot should be no greater than the size of the circle of least confusion of the IR image. Wide passbands are generally used with this type of system.

3. Reticle Scanning Systems. These are among the most widely used types of scanning systems in use at the present time. A reticle with areas which are alternately clear and opaque to IR radiation is situated just in front of the sensitive surface of the detector cell and as close as possible to the principal focal plane of the optical system.

Most IR devices employing reticle scanning systems have a single detector cell. Their optical field of view is limited to relatively small solid angles to limit off-axis aberrations.

An infinite number of variations in the reticle pattern is possible. The reticle pattern is first drawn to a large scale, projected on a reticle blank of optically flat glass of suitable IR-transmitting properties, and photographed.   Using photographic reduction techniques, reticles can be made extremely small in size.   They may be stationary, with the target image rotating, or rotating near the focal plane of the target image.   In the latter case, their speed of rotation is controllable over a wide range.

Reticle-pattern designs and rotation speeds are tailored to perform the following basic functions: First, reticles are eminently suitable for *space filtering* by which the target may be discriminated against the background radiation.   Second, according to the time constant of the detector being used, the reticle design and speed of rotation are chosen to modulate the IR signal at that frequency which ensures maximum detector performance.   Third, the reticle may be designed to modulate the IR signal in two modes, so that its angular position in the field of view may be displayed.

For a better understanding of these functions, a brief discussion of reticle design and operation follows.

Concentric Reticle.   This reticle, in which the axis of rotation coincides with the optical axis of the IR system, is shown in Fig. 5-25.   Concentric reticles have a central *dead spot*, formed by the axis or by the center of the reticle pattern, which masks off IR radiation around the optical axis.   The reticle is rotated, by means of a small electric motor equipped with a belt drive or gear train.   These reticles are usually very small in diameter, and are mounted in a ball-bearing race around their circumference for accurate positioning and high-speed rotation.

Many detectors, particularly those with chemically deposited or evaporated sensitive surfaces, and semiconductor types, require as small a sensitive area as possible to minimize cell noise.   The majority of detector cells of this type have extremely small sensitive areas; in some cases on the order of a few square millimeters.   The size of a concentric reticle is approximately the same as that of the detector-surface area, since it is positioned immediately in front of the detector.

The Eccentric Reticle.   Commonly referred to as a *chopper*, this reticle has an axis of rotation parallel with but to one side of the optical axis (Fig. 5-25).   This type of reticle can be made in much larger diameters, and there is no *dead spot* in the optical path of the IR radiation.   Production methods for choppers are similar to those for concentric reticles, if they are made on optical flats.   Choppers may also consist of slits or holes in a rotating metal plate.

Reticles are usually in the form of thin plates, the optical material being chosen for its good transmission properties in the IR wavelength band required for the particular IR system.   They may, however, be spherical or cylindrical in form, and instead of rotating, may oscillate, nutate, or combine these motions.

All rotating reticles are loosely referred to as *choppers*, since they literally chop the incident IR radiation passing through them into pulses of radiation. Strictly speaking, the term chopper should be applied only to rotating eccentric reticles.

Let us now consider the modulation effects produced by a few simple reticle patterns. First, consider a reticle in the form of the transparent

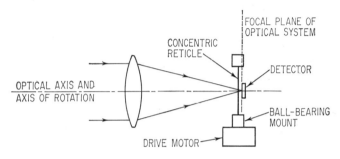

(a) CONCENTRIC ROTATING RETICLE

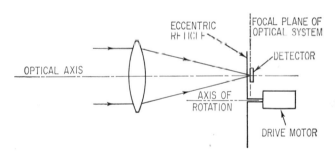

(b) ECCENTRIC RETICLE OR CHOPPER

FIG. 5-25. Concentric and eccentric rotating reticles.

spiral illustrated in Fig. 5-26a. The width of the spiral is one-half of the diameter of the source image on the reticle face. At the center of the reticle is a transparent circle of exactly the same diameter as the source image. When the source image is exactly centered, transmission through the reticle, assuming no absorption or reflection losses, is 100 per cent. As the source image moves off the center of the field of view, transmission through the reticle falls to zero, rising again to a peak of 50 per cent when crossed by the full width of the spiral. With the source image in the position shown, this would occur at one-half revolution of the reticle, measured from A.

Consider now the concentric reticle illustrated in Fig. 5-26b.   It is formed of alternating dark and clear concentric circles.   The width of each dark and clear area is exactly one-half the diameter of the source image on the reticle face.   The output signal will be constant at 50 per cent transmission.   Some background discrimination against large source areas such as bright clouds will result.

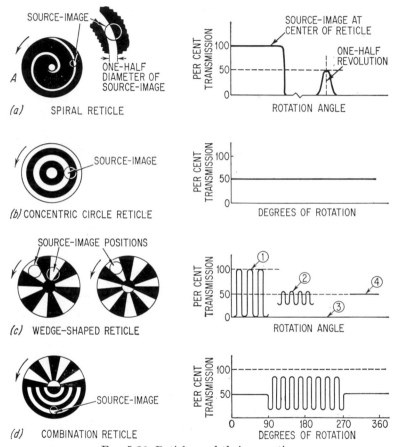

FIG. 5-26. Reticles and their operation.

Now let us look at Fig. 5-26c, representing a concentric reticle formed of pie-shaped wedges with a dark circular center of the same diameter as that of the source image on the reticle face.   At the circumference of the reticle the width of the dark and clear wedges is slightly greater than this diameter.   With the source image located near the circumference, position 1, modulation is 100 per cent, assuming no transmission or reflection losses in the reticle, and the signal amplitude is a maximum. If there are n clear wedges, then one complete rotation of the reticle produces n signal pulses. As the source image moves inward, position 2, the pulse rate is unaltered, but modulation is less than 100 per cent, and the signal amplitude is reduced. When the source image coincides with the center of the reticle there is no signal, position 3. The center of the reticle is therefore a *dead spot*. This can be eliminated by a center consisting of one clear and one dark semicircle of the same diameter as that of the source image (Fig. 5-26c, position 4). This would give a steady 50 per cent signal when the source image is centered. It is clear that for this type of reticle, the signal amplitude indicates the off-center distance of the source image.

Now consider a combination of one-half of the reticle in Fig. 5-26b and one-half of the reticle in Fig. 5-26c, as illustrated by Fig. 5-26d. With the source image located in the lower hemisphere in the position shown, modulation is constant at 50 per cent. After a 90° rotation the signal is pulse-modulated by the wedge-shaped half of the reticle for the duration of one-half revolution. The *amplitude* of the pulses indicates the *radial* location of the source image with maximum amplitude occurring at the circumference. If the position of the source image changes in *azimuth* by $\theta°$, then the commencement and ending of pulse modulation change by $\theta°$ in *phase*.

Thus we see that by designing a reticle to yield both phase and amplitude information, the azimuth and radial location of the source image are given in the form of voltage-output signals. This information can be used to center the image in the field of view through a servo loop which controls movement of the scanner head. At the same time, a certain amount of background discrimination is provided by this reticle design. The target source image is approximately the same diameter as the width of the clear areas and is transmitted through the reticle with no more than 50 per cent attenuation. A large, bright background image, such as the edge of a cloud, is split up by the reticle pattern into several small areas of lesser brightness.

4. Mosaic Systems. These systems employ a number of detectors, each of equal and very small sensitive surface area, arranged in the form of a pattern or mosaic. Figure 5-27 shows a 100-element thermistor mosaic.

Each detector may have its own signal channel for the amplification and transmission of received signals to the display. The modern technique is to integrate and commutate the output at the cell-output-signal level, thus eliminating the need for individual signal channels, and saving weight and space. Mosaic IR image-converter tubes carry this principle a step further.

In this type of system some difficulties encountered are due to the varied response of individual cells in the mosaic and to the effects on them of thermal gradients. Systems of this type, however, are still in an early stage of development, as compared with the older forms of IR detectors. They are useful in surveillance and tracking devices because of the wide fields of view that can be attained, and the saving in space and weight resulting from the elimination of complex mechanical scanning systems.

Numerous combinations of the four basic types of scanning systems are possible.

Fig. 5-27. Photograph of 100-element thermistor mosaic detector. (*Courtesy Barnes Engineering Company, Stamford, Conn.*)

In mosaic systems, radiation from the source is focused, by means of a high-quality optical system, on the sensitive surface of the mosaic as a tiny spot image. The optical system itself may be nutated or rotated about an off-center axis so that the target image is scanned across the mosaic surface in a repetitive pattern. In some image-conversion tubes, the scanning is done by an electron beam which moves in a television-tube type of scanning pattern. The total time taken to complete one scan pattern is known as the *frame time*.

5-12. OPTICAL GAIN

The optical system is designed to concentrate on the detector the maximum amount of IR energy possible in the wavelength band employed by the IR system. In performing this function, losses are incurred at the irdome, in the mirrors and lenses, in the chopper, and at the surface of the detector itself.   These radiation losses are due to reflection, absorption, optical distortion, chopping losses, and reduction in the effective aperture or vignetting.   The over-all efficiency of the optical system after allowance for these losses is made is called its *optical gain*.   This may be defined as

$$\text{Optical gain} = \frac{\text{IR energy incident on detector-cell surface}}{\text{IR energy incident on cell in absence of optics}}$$

Alternatively, optical gain may be defined as the ratio of the effective telescope aperture to the effective cell area, corrected for the loss factors incurred by the optical system.

For example, let us assume that, for a given IR device, the ratio

$$\frac{\text{effective aperture of optical system}}{\text{effective cell area}} = 400$$

An area obscuration of 25 per cent due to vignetting losses would reduce this optical gain to 300.   Let us further assume the following transmission factors due to reflection and absorption in the refractive optical components: objective, 80 per cent; field lens, 90 per cent. The reticle cuts down transmission in three ways: The reticle pattern blocks out a percentage of the incident radiation, resulting in a transmission factor of, say, 50 per cent.   A chopping effect occurs if the target-image size on the reticle is larger than the smallest clear area in the reticle pattern, resulting in a transmission factor of, say, 80 per cent.   Absorption in the optical blank on which the reticle pattern is photographed cuts transmission through the clear areas to, say, 90 per cent.

The original optical gain has now been reduced as follows:

Optical component	Transmission factor	Optical gain
Effective aperture of optics / Effective cell area	. . . .	400
Obscuration.	75 per cent	
Objective.	80 per cent	
Field lens.	90 per cent	
Reticle, optical material.	90 per cent	
Reticle pattern.	50 per cent	
Reticle chopping effect.	80 per cent	
Product of above factors.	$0.75 \times 0.8 \times 0.9 \times 0.9 \times 0.5 \times 0.8 = 0.1944$	77.8

Unless immersion optics are used, yet another energy loss occurs at the sensitive surface of the detector cell.   For example, at an air-to-lead sulfide surface the refractive index changes from 1.0 to 4.0 approximately.   This means that 35 per cent of the incident IR radiation is reflected at the cell surface, resulting in an effective transmission factor at the cell surface of 65 per cent.   Applying this to the above figure of optical gain reduces our original figure of 400 to a final optical gain of only 58.   This does not take into account any losses incurred in the irdome if one is employed, or due to environmental heating effects in the optical system.

5-13. OPTICAL-ELECTROMAGNETIC SYSTEMS

The fourth type of IR optical system is exemplified by the various forms of image-conversion tubes which have been developed in the last few years.   These systems employ refractive optics in the form of objective and ocular lenses, in combination with electromagnetic and electrostatic focusing and scanning techniques.

The general principles of operation of these devices are illustrated by three examples of image-conversion tubes which have been extensively used for several years.   The common television tube employs the same physical principles for its operation.   The three examples given all operate in the near-IR spectral region.   Later developments in image-conversion tubes have extended their operation into the middle-IR spectral region.   The majority of the newer developments in this field, however, are either of a proprietary nature or are still classified and therefore cannot be discussed in a book of this type.   A comparison of types of image-forming receivers is given in Table 5-2.

TABLE 5-2. COMPARISON OF IMAGE-FORMING RECEIVERS

Type of receiver	Physical process	Long-wavelength threshold, μ	Response time, sec	Relative comparative efficiency
Cesium cathode-image tube	External photoeffect	1.2	10^{-6}	1.00
Phosphorescent image tube	Quenching of the phosphor	1.2	0.1 to 10^{-4}	0.005
IR photography	Photographic	1.2	$\frac{1}{60}$	0.002
Evaporation from a surface at low pressure (evaporograph)	Thermic absorption process	16	$\frac{1}{60}$	0.001

Bildwandler Image-converter Tube. This tube[3] was developed and produced in Germany during World War II. Use is made of the external photoeffect to reproduce a visual image of the IR target viewed. Incident IR radiation from the target is focused by refractive optics on a cesium-coated cathode (Fig. 5-28). Photoelectrons released by the IR radiation are accelerated through the body of the tube and strike the anode, which is coated with a mixture of zinc sulfide and zinc selenide phosphors, where a visual image is generated. This is viewed through an eyepiece.

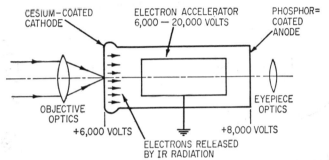

FIG. 5-28. Schematic of *Bildwandler* IR image-converter tube. (*After Reference 3.*)

The optics were specially designed for maximum tube resolution and sensitivity in the near-IR waveband used (out to 1.3 μ). A resolution of 50 lines per millimeter and a sensitivity on the order of that of the human eye in the visible spectrum were achieved.[3] This tube was restricted to use in the near-IR spectral region, that is, for relatively high-temperature source detection. It was extensively used by the German armed forces during the latter part of the war for target detection at night.

The Unipotential IR Image Tube. This somewhat simpler type of IR image tube was also developed and produced in Germany during the war.[45] Its imaging function was achieved by the shape of the electrodes. No adjustment of electrode voltages was required. Incident IR radiation is focused on a curved, cesium–silver oxide photocathode where it is converted to an electron image. Electrons released at the photocathode are accelerated and focused on a phosphor screen (Fig. 5-29).

This tube was used in the German *Vampire* device, an IR viewing device mounted on a rifle fitted with a filtered tungsten-source searchlight, similar to the United States sniperscope. A similar but larger IR image-conversion tube, operating at 17 kv, was used in their *Spanner* and *Adlergerate* devices for mounting on antiaircraft and field guns on

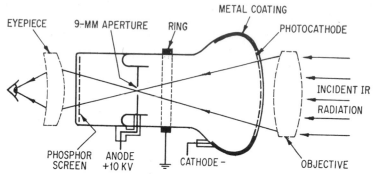

FIG. 5-29. Schematic of German unipotential IR image tube.   (*After Reference 45.*)

tanks fitted with IR searchlights for use at night.   A typical tank- and field-gun operation using this equipment is illustrated in Fig. 11-6.

RCA Type 6929 IR Image-converter Tube.   The type 6929 tube is a modern self-focusing image-converter tube developed and manufac-

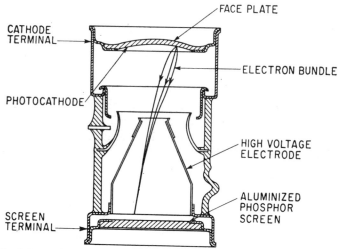

FIG. 5-30. Schematic arrangement of RCA type 6929 IR image-converter tube. (*Courtesy Radio Corporation of America, Harrison, N.J.*)

tured by the Radio Corporation of America.   It is illustrated schematically in Fig. 5-30.   The scene to be viewed is focused by means of an optical objective on a semitransparent photocathode.   Electrons from the image on the photocathode are electrostatically focused on the fluorescent screen at the other end of the tube by electron-optical methods to form a reduced image, which can be viewed with an optical magnifier.

The 6929 tube operates with only a single voltage applied between its two terminals, and remains in focus with any applied voltage in the operating range from 2,000 to 12,000 volts. Features include a high ratio of light output to IR-energy input, minimum resolution of 25 line pairs per millimeter at the center of the photocathode, low pincushion distortion, low power requirements, and small size. These features make the 6929 tube especially useful in portable equipment for viewing a scene irradiated with near IR radiation.

Image-conversion tubes of these types were used for such active applications as the landing of aircraft at night without visual landing lights, entering harbours in darkness, night driving of vehicles without the use of visible headlights, and for fire-control and detection purposes. Passive applications such as the observation of troops and vehicles at night, recognition, missile homing, and fire-control devices were numerous.

Several other types of image tubes exist or are in the process of development. In these tubes, the target image is formed on a focal plane, and either observed visually on a phosphorescent screen, or scanned electronically as in a television tube. Various types of sensitive deposits or film are used for the surface which is scanned by the electron beam.

Mosaic Tubes. Mosaic tubes use a linear array or mosaic of small detector cells. These mosaics are fabricated in special evaporators which deposit very thin layers of the sensitive detector material in an intricate mosaic pattern. The detector mosaic together with the integration networks are enclosed in an evacuated glass envelope and scanned by a low-velocity electron beam.

Some image tubes use a thin, conductive film whose resistance varies with the thermal gradients of the images formed on its surface. Other image tubes employing photothermionic, ferroelectric, or thermal principles have been constructed. Further examples of image tubes will be discussed in Chap. 7.

The great advantages of these optical systems are, of course, the elimination of complex mechanical scanning devices and the rapid scanning which makes it possible to observe transient phenomena.

Because of the relatively wide fields of view employed in these tubes, refractive optics are required. To reduce chromatic aberration, achromatic lens combinations are generally required for the objective and eyepiece optics.

REFERENCES

33. Jenkins, F. A., and White, H. E.: "Fundamentals of Optics," 2d ed., p. 90, McGraw-Hill Book Company, Inc., New York, 1950.
34. *Ibid.*, pp. 119, 120.
35. *Ibid.*, p. 123.
36. *Ibid.*, p. 133.
37. *Ibid.*, pp. 140, 141.
38. *Ibid.*, p. 143.
39. *Ibid.*, pp. 156, 157.
40. *Ibid.*, pp. 26, 27, 28.
41. *Ibid.*, p. 30.
42. *Ibid.*, p. 330.
43. *Ibid.*, pp. 338, 339.
44. *Ibid.*, p. 341.
45. Canada, A. H.: Infrared Military and Peacetime Uses, *General Electric Company Data Folder* 87516, 8th printing, December, 1947.
46. Morton, G. A., and Flory, L. E.: An Infrared Image Tube and Its Military Applications, *RCA Rev.*, vol. 7, p. 385, 1946.

6

Optical Materials

The properties of various IR optical materials are discussed. Desirable materials for use as irdomes, windows, filters, prisms, and lenses are described. Tables and charts of the properties and IR-transmission limits of various optical materials are given.

6-1. DESIRABLE PROPERTIES OF IR OPTICAL MATERIALS

Since the 1930s a great deal of effort has been expended in the search for materials with optical and physical properties suited for IR applications. Before describing some of these materials it is appropriate at this stage to summarize the properties required, bearing in mind that IR systems today are being applied to longer-wavelength regions of the spectrum, and are being used under increasingly harsh environmental conditions.

Optical Properties. The primary requirement of an IR optical material is that it shall afford maximum transmission of IR radiation in the desired wavelength band. Some materials occur naturally and others can be made synthetically which incur minimum absorption losses within a given spectral region.

In all refractive materials, the refractive index must be considered for various applications. In lenses designed for high magnification or for wide fields of view, materials with a high refractive index are desirable. However, a penalty is paid in higher reflection losses at surface-to-air interfaces, requiring the use of a low-reflection coating on the exposed optical surface. The availability of optical materials with a wide range of refractive indexes is desirable for the correction of aberrations, as we have seen in the previous chapter.

In prisms, a high refractive index is generally a most desirable feature, since maximum dispersive power is usually required. All optical materials should have a high degree of homogeneity and of freedom from birefringence. In materials used for mirrors the ability to take a high polish and high reflectivity are desirable features. Emissivity of the optical material is an important consideration where high environmental temperatures are encountered. In irdomes and windows used in missiles and high-speed aircraft, for example, aerodynamic heating may cause the emission of IR radiation due to

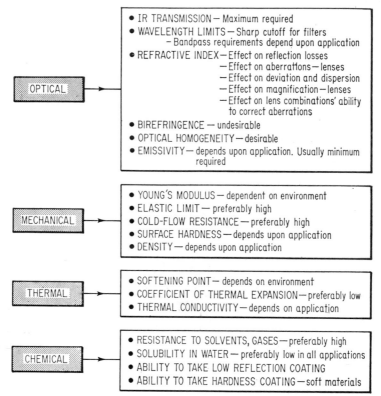

FIG. 6-1. Properties to be considered in IR optical materials.

molecular heating of the optical material. This can become so serious that unless the irdome is artificially cooled, saturation of the detector occurs.

Mechanical Properties. Particularly in the case of optical materials employed for IR air-borne and missile applications, where severe vibration and shock conditions exist, mechanical strength is essential. This involves consideration of such properties as Young's modulus, the elastic limit, the tensile, compression, and torsional strengths, and the

TABLE 6-1. PROPERTIES OF IR CRYSTALLINE MATERIALS

Material	Description	Wavelength limits, μ	Index of refraction	Cold-water solubility g/100gH₂O	Melting point, °C	Young's modulus 10⁶ psi	Knoop hardness	Density g/cm³	Coeff. of thermal expansion 10⁶/°C	Maximum size	Relative cost
Artificial sapphire	Hexagonal crystal; hard to scratch; no cleavage; excellent mechanical strength (see Table 6-2)	0.17–5.3	1.77 at 1.0μ	9.8×10^{-5}	2030	53	1,370	3.98	6.7 (parallel) 5.0 (perp.)	4½ in. diam.	high
Fused quartz (SiO₂)	Isotropic; good mechanical properties	0.2–4.0	1.45 at 1.0μ	0	1700	10.1	470	2.21	0.5	limited by practical optical homogeneity	moderate
Silicon	Steel-gray cubic crystal; transmission decreases above 300°C; soluble in HF, HNO₃ (see Table 6-2)	1.2–15	3.4 at 10μ	0	1420	1.9×10^{12} dyne/cm²	1,150	2.33	4.2	approx. 7 in. diam.	high
KRS-5 (TlBr-TlI)	Red cubic crystal; toxic; no cleavage; difficult to polish; scratches easily; strains easily	0.6–38	2.37 at 10μ	0.05	415	2.3	40	7.27	58	approx. 5 in. diam.	high
KRS-6 (TlBr-TlCl)	Colorless cubic crystal; toxic	0.4–30	2.18 at 10μ	0.32	424	3.0	35	7.2	51	approx. 7.5 in. diam.	high
Cesium bromide (CsBr)	Colorless cubic crystal; Hygroscopic; Soft; soluble in alcohol.	0.2–40	1.66 at 10μ	124	636	2.3	.....	4.5	48	approx. 2 in. diam.	moderate
Potassium bromide (KBr)	Colorless cubic crystal; soft; hygroscopic; cleaves	0.2–32	1.53 at 10μ	66	728	3.9	6	2.75	41	approx. 7½ in diam	moderate
Periclase (MgO)	Hard isotropic crystal; cleaves (see Table 6-2)	0.25–7	1.71 at 2.0μ	1.2×10^{-6}	2800	36	690	3.59	13	approx. 3 in. diam.	high
Rutile (TiO₂)		0.4–5.2	2.6 at 1.0μ	0	1830	....	880	4.25	9 parallel 7 perp.		

TABLE 6-1. PROPERTIES OF IR CRYSTALLINE OPTICAL MATERIALS (*Continued*)

Material	Description	Wave-length limits, μ	Index of refraction	Cold-water solubility g/100gH$_2$O	Melting point, °C	Young's modulus 10^6 psi	Knoop hardness	Density g/cm^3	Coeff. of thermal expansion 10^6/°C	Maximum size	Relative cost
Potassium chloride (KCl)	Colorless cubic crystal; soft; hygroscopic; cleaves; soluble in glycerin; ether; alkali	0.21-25	1.46 at 10μ	35.5	768	4.3	8	1.99	36	approx. 7½ in. diam.	moderate
Potassium iodide (KI)	Colorless cubic crystal; cleaves; very soft; very hygroscopic; soluble in alcohol, ammonia	0.2-31	1.67 at 10μ	127	....	....	......	....	....	approx. 7½ in. diam.	moderate
Cesium iodide	Cubic crystal; soft, hygroscopic; cleaves	0.24-52	1.74 at 10μ	44	621	0.8	......	4.53	50		
Lithium fluoride (LiF)	Colorless cubic crystal; soft; cleaves; soluble in acid	0.12-7	1.38 at 2.0μ	0.26	870	11	110	2.6	36	approx. 5 in. diam.	moderate
Calcium fluoride (CaF$_2$)	Colorless cubic crystal; easily scratched; cleaves; soluble in ammonium salts	0.13-9.5	1.42 at 2.0μ	1.5×10^{-3}	1400	15	158	3.18	23	approx. 6 in. diam.	moderate
Lead fluoride (PbF$_2$)	....	0.25-12	1.75 at 1.0μ	....	822						
Barium fluoride (BaF$_2$)	....	0.15-13	1.6 at 12μ	0.16	1280	8	82	4.9			
Germanium	....	1.8-15+	4.1 at 10μ	....	942	15	......	5.33	6.1		
Spinel (MgO·Al$_2$O$_3$)	....	0.3-5	1.73 at 1.0μ	0	2050	....	1,140	3.62	6		

hardness of the optical material. For windows and irdomes exposed to the severe erosion problems which occur in air-borne applications, the surface hardness of the material is an important factor. Certain optical materials require special surface coatings to prevent scratching and erosion, which cause pitting of the polished surface, forming local "hot spots" or sources of radiation which produce false target images and sharp background-radiation gradients.

Thermal Properties. For applications of this nature, consideration must also be given to the melting point, the thermal coefficient of expansion, and the thermal conductivity of the material, which may be exposed to excessive environmental temperature ranges, and to severe thermal-shock conditions.

Under severe environmental conditions, weakening of the exposed optical surface may occur, leading to possible fracture because of high-temperature gradients existing between the exposed outer surface and the inner surface of the optical material. A high softening point, a low thermal coefficient of expansion, and good thermal conductivity are desirable properties under these conditions.

Chemical Properties. In the optical materials used for many industrial applications of IR, such as pyrometers, process-stream analyzers, etc., the material's chemical resistance to the various solvents and gases encountered in industrial processes must be considered. In windows and irdomes exposed to atmospheric environments, optical materials used should be nonhygroscopic or possess a low cold-water-solubility factor.

The different properties of IR optical materials that require consideration when selecting a suitable material for a particular application are summarized in Fig. 6-1. Optical, mechanical, thermal, and chemical properties are listed in Tables 6-1 and 6-2.

IR optical materials may be broadly classified into the following two groups: (1) crystalline materials, (2) glasses. A third possible group, of which too little is known at the present, includes the perfluor-silicones and related compounds.

6-2. CRYSTALLINE IR OPTICAL MATERIALS

Brief descriptions of the more important materials follow. Curves plotting per cent transmission versus wavelength at room temperature are given in Figs. 6-2a and b for several uncoated crystalline materials in common use. Properties of these and other optical materials used in IR applications are listed in Table 6-1. Wavelength limits of IR transmission are illustrated in Fig. 6-3.[53] Variation of refractive index and dispersion with wavelength are shown in Figs. 6-4 and 6-5 respectively.

Rock Salt (NaCl).   This is a colorless cubic crystal, easily shaped, cheap, and available in quantity.   It is used in the laboratory or where environmental conditions can be controlled.   Its IR transmission is good out to a wavelength of 15 μ.   Disadvantages of this material are: (1) it is highly soluble in water and in glycerine; (2) it is subject to cleavage; and (3) it scratches easily.

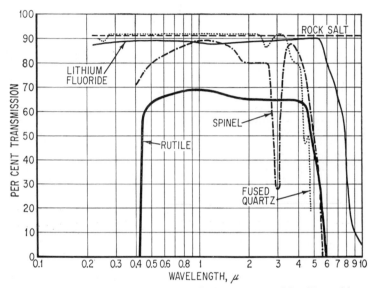

FIG. 6-2a. Optical transmission of crystals (not corrected for Fresnel losses).

Lithium fluoride (LiF)................. 0.152 cm thick
Rock salt (NaCl)..................... 0.544 cm thick
Synthetic spinel (MgO-Al$_2$O$_3$).......... 0.544 cm thick
Rutile (TiO$_2$)........................ 0.600 cm thick
Fused quartz (SiO$_2$).................. 0.099 cm thick

(Data from Richard W. Kebler, "Optical Properties of Synthetic Sapphire," pp. 12, 13, Linde Company, Division of Union Carbide Corporation, New York, 1959.)

Lithium Fluoride (LiF); Calcium Fluoride (CaF$_2$).   These materials are colorless cubic crystals which scratch easily and exhibit cleavage. Lithium fluoride transmits IR radiation out to about 6 μ, but is soluble in acids. Calcium fluoride transmits out to 9 μ, and is soluble in solutions of ammonium salts.   Both materials are moderate in cost and can be used for IR windows and lenses with diameters up to 5 in. for laboratory work.

Fused Quartz (SiO$_2$).   This material has excellent thermal, mechanical strength, and transmission qualities, is isotropic and nonhygroscopic.   Its long-wavelength-transmission limit is approximately 5 μ.

It is moderate in cost.   The maximum sizes of lenses and windows made from fused quartz are limited only by the degree of optical homogeneity practicable.   This material is discussed more fully in Sec. 6-4.

Magnesium Oxide (MgO).   This is an excellent IR optical material, possessing good thermal and physical properties.   Its long-wavelength-transmission limit is about 7 μ.   It is hard, with a high melting point (above 450°C), and has isotropic thermal expansion.   Although slightly superior to sapphire as an optical material in this wavelength

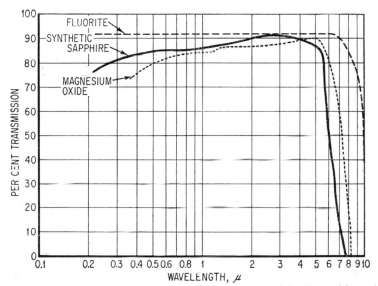

Fig. 6-2b. Optical transmission of crystals (not corrected for Fresnel losses).
Fluorite (CaF₂)............................ 0.544 cm thick
Synthetic sapphire (Al₂O₃)................. 0.094 cm thick
Magnesium oxide (MgO).................... 0.544 cm thick

(Data from Richard W. Kebler, "Optical Properties of Synthetic Sapphire," pp. 12, 13, Linde Company, Division of Union Carbide Corporation, New York, 1959.)

region, it is obtainable only in small sizes, and does exhibit some cleavage.   This optical material, also known as *periclase*, requires more research in production techniques to reduce costs and improve its availability, especially in larger sizes.   Because of this, its uses are at present limited to small windows and lenses.   Irdomes, up to a maximum base diameter of 2½ in., have been made of this material.   High-temperature properties of periclase are discussed in Sec. 6-5.

Synthetic Sapphire (Al₂O₃).   This also is an excellent IR optical material, with high mechanical strength and good thermal properties. It is a hexagonal crystal showing no cleavage, and has an extremely high surface hardness. Its long-wavelength-transmission limit is about 5.5 μ. It is nonhygroscopic.

Synthetic sapphire, in the form of a boule, is grown in a high-temperature furnace from a small seed of the pure crystal. At the

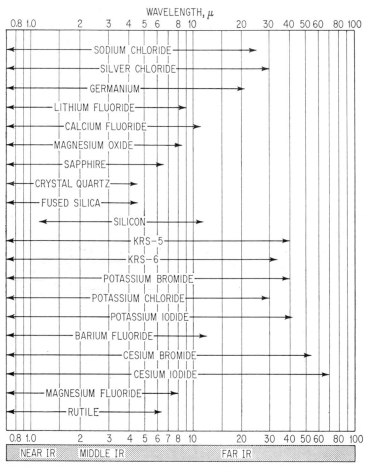

Fig. 6-3. Useful IR transmission regions of crystalline optical materials. For samples 2 mm thick, long-wavelength cutoff at 10 per cent external transmittance. (*After Reference 53; MgF₂ data courtesy Eastman Kodak Company, Rochester, N.Y.*)

present time, production sizes are limited to about 5 in. in diameter for windows and 3 in. in diameter for irdomes, but larger sizes will be available in the future. Production of this material in a crystal-growing furnace is discussed further in Sec. 6-3. Properties of synthetic sapphire are discussed more fully in Sec. 6-5.

It is still relatively expensive although costs have been greatly reduced in recent years. This material is used for windows and irdomes operating under severe environmental conditions, where high surface temperatures are encountered.

Silicon (Si). This is a steel-gray cubic crystal with a high melting point and a high index of refraction. Like synthetic sapphire, crystals of silicon are grown from a seed in a high-temperature furnace. Production, polishing, and coating techniques are discussed in Sec. 6-3; high-temperature properties in Sec. 6-5.

This material is nonhygroscopic. Due to its high refractive index, a low-reflection coating is required. Coated samples transmit over 90 per cent of incident radiation between 3.5 and 4.3 μ, and more than 30 per cent of incident radiation over the range from 3 to 11 μ. It is available in production quantities in various shapes up to 8 in. in diameter at present. This material is relatively inexpensive, and is used in a wide variety of IR applications.

Silver Chloride (AgCl). This material has excellent IR-transmission properties out to wavelengths beyond 20 μ. It is a

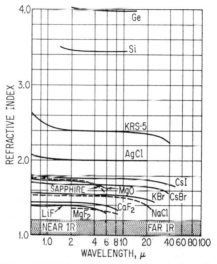

FIG. 6-4. Refractive index vs. wavelength of crystalline materials. (*After Reference 53; MgF₂ data courtesy Eastman Kodak Company, Rochester, N.Y.*)

colorless, cubic, isotropic crystal, which is nonhygroscopic and exhibits no cleavage. Disadvantages of this material are its relatively high cost and inferior strength; it is soft, malleable, and subject to cold flow. It is corrosive to most metals on contact. Reduced IR transmission occurs in sunlight and in artificial light due to photosensitive darkening of the material. This can be prevented by coating the surface with a film of stibnite (antimony trisulfide).

Germanium (Ge). The uncoated material has approximately 50 per cent transmission in the IR region to beyond 15 μ, because of high reflection losses due to its high refractive index. It is used for IR windows, up to temperatures of about 300°C. At higher temperatures, transparency to IR is reduced by the thermal-saturation effect. It is costly and is used for small windows and filters.

The Alkali Halides. These materials include *KRS-5*, a mixture of thallium bromide and thallium iodide, and *KRS-6*, a mixture of thallium bromide and thallium chloride. Developed in Germany during World War II, these materials have excellent long-wavelength-transmission qualities. KRS-5 transmits to about 45 µ, and KRS-6 transmits out to about 23 µ. Both materials also have fairly high indexes of refraction, and, therefore, good dispersive properties. They are practically nonhygroscopic. KRS-5 is a red cubic crystal exhibiting no cleavage. It is soluble in acids, is difficult to polish, and stains easily. It has a high coefficient of thermal expansion and is extremely

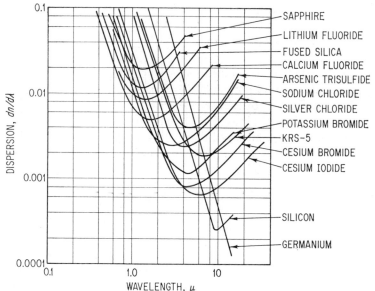

Fig. 6-5. Dispersion vs. wavelength for IR optical materials. (*After Reference 53.*)

toxic. KRS-6 is a colorless cubic crystal with similar properties. Both materials are extensively used for spectrometer prisms and bolometer and absorption-cell windows in the long-wavelength IR spectral region.

Potassium Bromide (KBr); Potassium Chloride (KCl). These are colorless cubic crystals. They are very hygroscopic. They also cleave easily, are very soft and difficult to polish, and are easily scratched. Potassium bromide transmits radiation out to about 27 µ. The long-wavelength cutoff for potassium chloride is at approximately 20 µ. Lenses up to about 7 in. in diameter are possible with these materials. They are used mainly for laboratory work under controlled environmental conditions. Their cost is moderate.

Potassium Iodide (KI). This material is also a colorless cubic crystal which cleaves easily and has a soft, easily scratched surface. It has a low refractive index in the 30- to 40-μ wavelength region, and therefore has low reflection loss. At wavelengths much longer than 35 μ, absorption becomes too high for its use in prisms. It is hygroscopic but cheap to produce. This material is used for thin absorption-cell windows for wavelengths up to 40 μ.

Barium Fluoride (BaF). This is a relatively new optical material. Its properties are similar to those of fluorite (calcium fluoride). It has a useful transmission range up to 13 μ and reasonably low reflection loss. Because it is easily worked and fairly nonhygroscopic it is used for windows and lenses. Costs and sizes are comparable to those for fluorite.

Barium fluoride is inert to most chemicals. Because of its good IR transmission when in the form of thin plates a few millimeters thick and its relative insolubility in water, this material is now widely employed in IR spectroscopy for windows of sealed absorption cells used for the study of liquids and water solutions of inorganic materials.[47]

Cesium Bromide (CsBr). This also is a fairly new optical material, with excellent transmission through the entire visible spectrum out to 40 μ in the far-IR spectral region. It is a colorless cubic crystal, with a soft surface that is easily worked, but is also easily scratched. Although very soluble in water, it is neither deliquescent nor hygroscopic. With a lower reflection loss, less toxicity, and a higher melting point than KRS-5, this material is used in place of KRS-5 for cell and thermocouple windows.

As a prism material it is superior in all respects except for moisture resistance. Prisms of cesium bromide are used in the 15- to 38-μ region in IR spectroscopy. Because its optical quality is superior to that of KRS-5, sharper images are formed at the second slit of the spectrometer. Dispersion and resolution are approximately twice as great as for KRS-5 in this spectral region.[48]

Cesium Iodide (CsI). This relatively new IR optical material with very good IR transmission out to about 50 μ is used for prisms and windows in far-IR spectroscopy. This cubic crystalline material is soft, subject to cleavage, and hygroscopic. Its melting point is quite high, about 620°C; so are its coefficient of thermal expansion and solubility in water. IR transmittance, for a plate 5 mm thick and not corrected for Fresnel losses, is 92 per cent at 40 μ, falling off quite rapidly to zero at about 76 μ.[49]

Its use in a far-IR reflection filter is described in Sec. 6-7.

Magnesium Fluoride (MgF₂).[53] Used for some time as a low-reflection coating for lenses, magnesium fluoride has excellent optical and physical properties for applications in IR work.   Polycrystalline magnesium fluoride can now be pressed into various shapes and sizes for optical components as a result of research carried out by the Eastman Kodak Company.   The material may be hermetically sealed to stainless steel.   It possesses excellent optical and physical properties at elevated temperatures, highly desirable characteristics in windows used for supersonic aircraft and missiles (see Sec. 6-5).

The physical properties of magnesium fluoride are given in Table 6-1. Its transmission and emissivity are shown in Fig. 6-6.

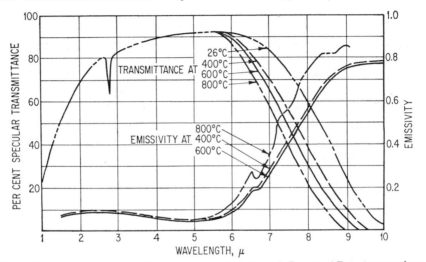

FIG. 6-6. Specular transmittance and emissivity of Irtran AB-1 (magnesium fluoride) 1.75 mm thick.   (*Data courtesy Eastman Kodak Company, Rochester, N.Y., October, 1959.*)

6-3. CRYSTAL-GROWING TECHNIQUES

Since so many important IR optical materials are crystals, a résumé of crystal-growing techniques is presented.   The difficulties and limitations associated with these techniques restrict the ultimate sizes of the crystals that can be grown.   There are four broad categories of growing techniques in use:[50]

1. Growth from solutions
2. Growth by vapor deposition
3. Growth from or within solids
4. Growth from melts

Growth from Solutions.   Growth occurs on small crystals suspended in a saturated solution of the material.[51]

Growth by Vapor Deposition. Some crystals are grown directly by vapor condensation. Quite large single crystals of cadmium sulfide have been grown by this method. For most materials, large single crystals are difficult to grow, the resulting porous mass of small crystallites being quite unsuitable for optical purposes.[50]

Growth from Solids. Single-crystal whisker growth, from the surface of metals, and grain growth of polycrystalline solids have both been observed. In the latter process, crystals several inches long have been grown by subjecting the material to a large deformation and a high annealing temperature.[50]

Growth from Melts. The following techniques are widely employed:[50] (1) Bridgeman method, (2) zone-leveling method, (3) floating-zone technique, (4) the Verneuil flame-fusion technique, and (5) Czochralski crystal-pulling method.

The *Bridgeman method* is applicable to crystalline materials for which a suitable container, with low contraction and expansion rates, that neither sticks to the frozen material nor reacts with it when in the molten state, is available.[50] A vertical molten column of the material is slowly moved through a thermal gradient so that freezing proceeds uniformly from one end of the container to the other. This method is used for many alkali halides and a large number of metals.[51]

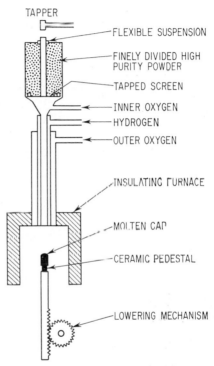

FIG. 6-7. Schematic diagram of Verneuil-type flame-fusion process for growing cylindrical crystals of synthetic sapphire. (*Courtesy Linde Company, Division of Union Carbide Corporation, New York, 1959.*)

In the *zone-leveling method* crystals are grown from a single-crystal seed at one end of a horizontal boat by slowly moving a narrow molten zone to the opposite end. This method is used to produce high-quality germanium crystals.[50]

In the *floating-zone technique*, the narrow molten zone is moved from one end to the other of a vertical rod of the material. This method is used for growing single crystals of materials such as silicon which react with the container walls when in contact.[50]

The *Verneuil flame-fusion technique,*[52] originally invented by the Frenchman Verneuil for synthesizing sapphire and ruby from purified alumina powder in a hydrogen-oxygen blowpipe flame, has been improved by the Linde Company, Division of Union Carbide Corporation, of New York for the production of single-crystal sapphires and artificial gems. The equipment used to grow cylindrically shaped crystals from very high-purity alumina powder is shown schematically in Fig. 6-7.

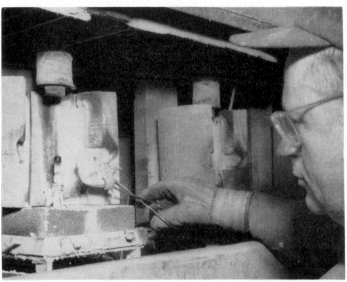

FIG. 6-8. Photograph of flame-fusion equipment after shutdown, showing boule of synthetic sapphire. (*Courtesy Linde Company, Division of Union Carbide Corporation, New York.*)

Linde's process differs from the original Verneuil process in that two independent oxygen flows are used for better control of the thermal gradients in the growth furnace. The powder dispenser has a fine wire-mesh screen bottom. When shaken by a mechanical tapping system, powder sifts through the screen and is carried by an oxygen stream down the inner tube of the oxyhydrogen burner. Hydrogen and additional oxygen are fed in to surround the flow of oxygen and powder. Leaving the burner tip, the gases interdiffuse and burn. The powder falling through the flame is heated and then deposited on a starting seed of a single crystal melted on its upper tip. Powdered material falling on the seed is added to and melted into the molten cap. Adjust-

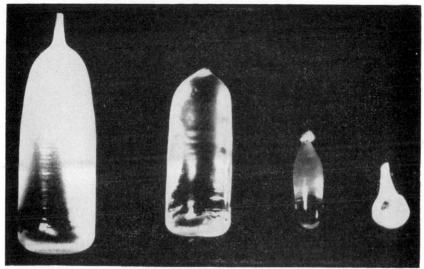

FIG. 6-9. Photograph showing stages in the growth of a boule of synthetic sapphire. (*Courtesy Linde Company, Division of Union Carbide Corporation, New York.*)

ment of the powder-feed rate and gas flows results in the growth of a cylindrical crystal which is continuously lowered vertically in order to maintain the molten cap in the same relative position in the furnace.

The entire operation is carried out in a refactory-ceramic furnace to prevent drafts from disturbing the flame and to help establish suitable temperature gradients. Upon completion of growth the powder feed and gases are cut off simultaneously and the furnace is allowed to cool normally. Figure 6-8 shows a photograph of the flame-fusion equipment after shutdown. The furnace is open to show the relative position of the grown crystal, known as a *boule*. Figure 6-9 shows stages in the growth of a boule.

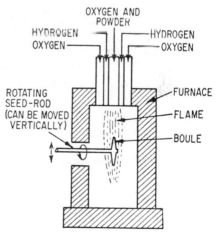

FIG. 6-10. Diagram of technique for growing large disk-shaped crystals of synthetic sapphire. (*Richard W. Kebler, Linde Company, New York.*)

The boule is then annealed in a specially designed oxygen gas-fired high-temperature furnace at 1900 to 1950°C to relieve growth strains and prevent fracture when it is subsequently sawed, ground, or lapped. Because of the hardness of sapphire, diamond-fabricating techniques must be employed.

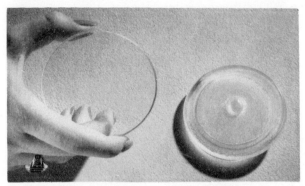

FIG. 6-11a. Photograph of disk-shaped boule and finished window of synthetic sapphire. (*Courtesy Linde Company, Division of Union Carbide Corporation, New York.*)

FIG. 6-11b. Photograph of conically shaped boule of synthetic sapphire for an irdome. (*Courtesy Linde Company, Division of Union Carbide Corporation, New York.*)

Boules grown by this technique are limited in size by built-in growth strains which cause fracture of the single crystal upon shutdown of the growth operation. Maximum sizes range from about 1-in. maximum diameter and 1-in. length, to 0.3-in. diameter and 14-in. length.

More recently a modification of the process by Drost and Kebler of the Linde Company (U.S. Patent 2,852,890) has made possible the growth of larger sapphire shapes.   A long seed rod of sapphire is inserted horizontally through the side of the furnace and under the flame.   Rotation of the seed about its cylinder axis starts crystal growth on the periphery of the seed rod.   Gas flows, powder-feed rate, and lowering are manipulated to build up a roughly disk-shaped crystal. This technique is illustrated schematically in Fig. 6-10.   If the seed rod is rotated at an angle other than the horizontal to the burner axis, a conical boule with a filled apex is grown.   Figures 6-11*a* and *b* show a flat window with the disk-shaped boule from which it was cut and polished, and an irdome made from a conical boule.   Windows up to 5½ in. in diameter and ¼ in. thick and hemispherical-section irdomes with chord diameters up to 4½ in. and depths to 1⅝ in. have been made by this process.   With further development of this technique it is anticipated that hemispherical irdomes of chord diameter up to 6 in. can be made.

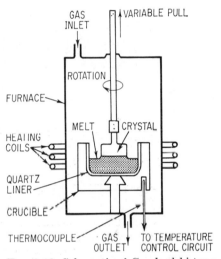

Fig. 6-12.   Schematic of Czochralski-type crystal-pulling furnace.   (*Based on a design by Teal and Little.*[50])

Czochralski's crystal-pulling technique,[50] illustrated schematically in Fig. 6-12, is used for growing larger single crystals of silicon.   The boule is grown from a single seed crystal, dipped in a pool of the molten material, rotated at spin rates which may vary from zero to several hundred rpm, and slowly withdrawn under controlled temperature conditions.   Silicon crystals are grown in a helium or argon atmosphere.   The original silicon charge in the crucible is melted by an induction heater, the temperature being regulated by a thermocouple and phase controller.   Temperature control and spin and withdrawal rates determine the rate of crystal growth along the upper surface of the melt.   For large diameters a lower spin rate is required.   Spinning the crystal in this fashion prevents freezing of the surface of the melt, circulates cooler liquid from the bottom of the crucible around the crystal, and causes symmetrical growth.   Silicon crystals up to 7 in. in diameter have been grown by this method.   A silicon crystal being grown by this method is shown in Fig. 6-13.

FIG. 6-13. Photograph of silicon crystal-pulling furnace. (*Courtesy Raytheon Manufacturing Company, Waltham, Mass.*)

6-4. GLASSES

In this class of optical materials, a limited number of special glasses are available for IR use in the longer-wavelength regions of the spectrum. As IR optical materials, glasses have several advantages. Unlike many crystals, they are not subject to cleavage and therefore have superior shock resistance. They can be produced with relative ease and speed. Larger sizes of windows, lenses, and prisms can be produced. They are easily shaped and polished, and generally have superior surface hardness and thermal and mechanical properties. They also possess superior moisture resistance. Useful IR transmission regions of several optical glasses are shown in Fig. 6-14.

Fused Silica Glass. Homogeneous, colorless, and nontoxic, this glass is easily fabricated at moderate cost. It is moisture-resistant and has good thermal properties, with a melting point at 1700°C. Long-wavelength transmission is limited to approximately 3 μ.

Arsenic Trisulfide Glass. This is a homogeneous, nontoxic, non-corrosive, red glass that is easily formed, ground, and polished. Stable, it has long life and is not subject to plastic deformation. Since it has a coefficient of thermal expansion very nearly equal to that of aluminum, it is an excellent optical material for mounting in aluminum fixtures. IR transmission falls to 10 per cent at 0.6 μ and 12 μ. However, when coated, transmission can be increased to over 90 per cent for any wavelength between 1 and 8 μ. This glass begins to soften at 195°C, and is susceptible to thermal shock. It is readily available in irdome sizes up to 12 in. in diameter at moderate cost. This material is widely used for irdomes, windows, and lenses, and corrector plates, prisms, and wedges.

Kodak 80-20 Arsenic-modified Selenium Glass.[54] This relatively new glass is opaque to visible light but has good IR-transmission properties out to 25 μ. There is a strong absorption band between 12 and 13 μ (Fig. 6-15). Optical deterioration begins to occur at environmental temperatures above 70°C. This glass is vitreous and nonbirefringent. Insoluble in water, it is slightly attacked by some aromatics

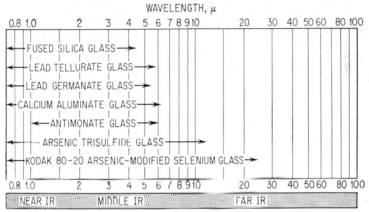

FIG. 6-14. Useful IR transmission regions of optical glasses. Approximate limits for long-wavelength cutoff at 50 per cent external transmittance. Arsenic trisulfide glass 5 mm thick; others 2 mm thick.

and chlorinated solvents. Its index of refraction varies slightly from 2.58 at 1.01 μ to 2.48 at 14 μ. Thermal conductivity is 3.3×10^4 cal/(cm^2)(sec)(cm). Its bulk electrical conductivity is less than 10^{-10} ohm/cm^3. Experimental hemispherical irdomes have been made in sizes up to 5 in. in diameter, and $\frac{1}{4}$ in. thick and have successfully withstood exploding pressures of 25 lb/in.^{2} This material is suitable for irdomes, windows, and image-forming and condensing optics for certain applications where temperatures are below 70°C.

Tellurate Glasses. These also are relatively new optical materials. They have a greater surfaces hardness than arsenic trisulfide glass, good moisture and weathering resistance, and superior thermal properties. The softening point is near 450°C. Transmission of IR radiation is good out to 6.5 μ, but there is a strong absorption band centered around 3 μ.

Calcium Aluminate Glasses.[55]   These glasses are also a relatively new development.   The long-wavelength-transmission limit is 6 μ, with a strong absorption band centered around 3 μ and due to the presence of water in the glass.   This, however, can be reduced by grinding and remelting in a vacuum.   These glasses have good thermal properties with the softening point occurring near 800°C.   They cannot be reheated and reformed like conventional glasses.   Shapes must

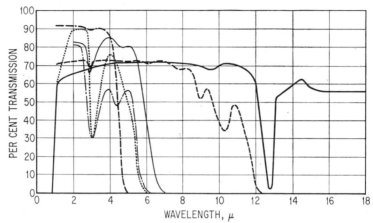

FIG. 6-15. IR spectral transmission of some uncoated optical glasses, at room temperature.

———	Kodak 80-20 arsenic-modified selenium glass.............	2.3 mm thick
– – –	Arsenic trisulfide glass................................	4.7 mm thick
—·—	Lead germanate glass.................................	3.0 mm thick
———	Lead tellurate glass..................................	3.0 mm thick
—··—	Fused silica glass....................................	3.0 mm thick
......	Bausch and Lomb RIR-10 calcium aluminate glass......	4.0 mm thick

be cut from the melt.   Since calcium aluminate glasses are attacked by water, which rapidly causes a substantial reduction in IR transmission and destroys polished surfaces, they must be protected by evaporated coatings of magnesium fluoride.   This coating greatly improves the moisture resistance and the transmission properties.   Surfaces are polished by conventional methods prior to coating.   Cleaning with organic solvents is necessary.   These glasses are produced in various forms up to about 6-in. diameter, 1-in. thick irdomes by the Bausch and Lomb Optical Company in the United States, and by the British-Thompson-Houston Company in the United Kingdom.   The IR transmission of a sample of Bausch and Lomb RIR-10 glass is shown in Fig. 6-15.

6-5. HIGH-TEMPERATURE OPTICAL MATERIALS

Optical materials used for windows and irdomes on high-speed missiles and aircraft must be able to withstand very severe environmental conditions, in some cases for extended periods of time.

As the speed of the vehicle increases, the temperature of the outer surface of a window or irdome exposed to the air stream increases because of aerodynamic heating. Optical materials employed should be stable at elevated temperatures which may reach several hundred degrees centigrade. The optical surface, mechanical strength, and IR-transmission properties should not deteriorate with increase in temperature. Glasses should be immune to devitrification. In silicon, for example, a marked reduction in IR transmission occurs at temperatures exceeding about 300°C.

In addition, high percentage transmission is required for the relatively thick sections of optical material which may be necessary in order to achieve mechanical strength. The ability to undergo abrupt temperature variations over a large range of temperatures, that is, a low thermal expansion coefficient, and a high thermal conductivity are required. The material should be nonphotosensitive, nontoxic, homogeneous to a high degree, and moisture-resistant. The ability to take low-reflection and surface-hardness coatings, if required, is an essential feature. Increasingly, requirements call for larger windows and irdomes in flat, hemispherical, conical, ogive, and other shapes.

Unfortunately, no glasses or crystalline materials are available which possess all these desirable features. The choice of an optical material for a particular application is therefore a matter of compromise for the designer.

The most promising optical materials for high-temperature applications are silicon, fused quartz, periclase, synthetic sapphire, rutile, magnesium fluoride, and certain glasses. Their properties are given in more detail in Table 6-2, and curves plotting their percentage transmission versus wavelength in Fig. 6-16. The emissivity characteristics of some IR optical materials used at high temperatures are compared in Fig. 6-17.

In addition to a reduction in IR transmission as the temperature increases, optical materials tend to radiate in the IR spectral region as their exposure time to a high-velocity air stream increases. This radiation from the irdome or window may reach such proportions that it saturates the detector. In such cases the window or irdome must be artificially cooled, either by an aerodynamic spike to divert the air

TABLE 6-2. PROPERTIES OF IR OPTICAL MATERIALS SUITABLE FOR HIGH-TEMPERATURE APPLICATIONS

Optical material	Properties			
	Optical	Thermal	Mechanical	Physical
Magnesium fluoride (MgF₂)	Absorption coef, 0.02 mm⁻¹ at 5.3μ; Refractive index, 1.371 at 2μ, 1.301 at 6.7μ; Homogeneity: scatters in visible, little or no scattering in IR region	Specific heat, 0.22 cal/(g)(°C); Thermal conductivity, 7.5 × 10⁻³ cal/(cm²)(sec)(°C)(cm); Melting point, 1396°C; Expansion coef (× 10⁻⁶/°C), 10.19 for 25–360°C, 13.13 for 25–650°C; Thermal shock tests: no fracture, 20–195°C and 8–260°C	Density, 3.18 g/cm; Hardness, 576 Knoop; 6 Mohs	Chemical and weather resistance: no deterioration or transmission loss for mil-std-605; inert to strong acids, and to all hydrocarbons; Working characteristics: pressable into special shapes; easily ground and polished by standard optical methods; accepts evaporated coatings; Sealing to metals: may be chemically bonded to 18-8 stainless steel insert during forming operations, to form a leaktight joint
Synthetic sapphire (Al₂O₃)	Absorption coef, 1.9 cm⁻¹ at 5.35μ, 7.6 cm⁻¹ at 6.3μ; Refractive index N₀, 1.62 at 5μ, 1.82 at 0.3μ; Homogeneity, excellent	Specific heat, 0.0249 cal/g at 91°K, 0.1813 cal/gm at 291°K; Thermal conductivity, 0.065 cal/(sec)(°C)(cm) at 100°C; Melting point, 2040°C; Expansion coef (parallel to C-axis), 6.66 × 10⁻⁶/°C from 20–50°C, 9.03 × 10⁻⁶/°C from 20–1000°C	Density, 3.98 gm/cm³; Hardness, 1525–2000 Knoop; 9 Mohs; Young's modulus, 50–56 × 10⁶ psi; Modulus of rigidity, 21–26 × 10⁶ psi; Modulus of rupture, 65–100 × 10³ psi	Chemical and weather resistance: excellent; Working characteristics: use diamond-finishing techniques; Sealing to metals: high- and low-temperature seals can be made to metals, glass, ceramics
Fused MgO	Transmission (3/16-in. thickness), 85% at 2–2.5 and 4.5–5.3μ; 86% at 3.5–4.3μ; zero at 9.0–14.5μ; Refractive index, 1.7226 at 1.014μ, 1.6853 at 3.033μ, 1.624 at 5.35μ; Emissivity (total), 0.60 at 400°C, 0.51 at 600°C; Cubic, isometric crystal	Specific heat, 0.276 g cal/g over range 20–800°C; Thermal conductivity [cal/(cm²)(sec)(°C)], 0.1 at 0°C, 0.048 at 300°C, 0.014 at 1300°C, min. at approx. 1500°C, 0.02 at 1800°C; Melting point, 2790°C; Expansion coef, 139 × 10⁻⁷/°C average over range 0–1000°C	Density, 3.5761 g/ml at 25°C; Hardness, 5½–6 Mohs; Compressive strength, 112,000 psi; Modulus of rupture, 20,000 psi; Young's modulus, 2.51 × 10¹² dynes/cm²	Chemical and weather resistance: slowly soluble in aqueous acids; resists aqueous and caustic alkali, fused alkali, alkaline vapor, anhydrous HF; Size limitations: about 1 in. diam. plates and windows

96 per cent silica glass (Corning Vycor Brand, no. 7905)	Transmittance (2 mm thickness at room temp.), 90–91 % at 1.3–3.1μ; 75 % at 3.4μ; 10 % at 3.6μ. Refractive index, 1.449 at 1.0μ, 1.443 at 1.5μ, 1.437 at 2.0μ, 1.428 at 2.5μ, 1.417 at 3.0μ, 1.405 at 3.5μ	. . . .	Density, 2.18 g/cc. Young's modulus (lb/in.^{2} at 25°C), 9.6 × 10^6 at 25°C; 10.64 × 10^6 at 800°C;	
Vycor 7900	. . . .	Specific heat [cal/(g)(°C)], 0.18 at 25°C, 0.229 at 200°C, 0.246 at 300°C, 0.258 at 400°C, 0.272 at 500°C, 0.282 at 600°C, 0.292 at 700°C, 0.301 at 800°C. Thermal conductivity [cal. cm/(cm^2)(sec)(deg)], 0.0035 at 25°C, 0.0042 at 300°C, 0.0045 at 600°C, 0.0047 at 800°C. Extreme temperature limit in service 1090°C. Expansion coef [in./(in.)°C × 10^{-7})], 4 at 25°C; 7.3 at 300°C; 7.0 at 600°C; 5.8 at 800°C	Modulus of rupture (psi × 10^3), 7.13 at 25°C, 8.52 at 300°C, 9.06 at 600°C, 9.16 at 800°C.	Chemical and weather resistance: excellent. Working characteristics: made and formed by conventional glass-working techniques; can be blown, pressed, spun; shaped, ground, and polished by standard optical techniques
Silicon	Absorption coef, 0.032 mm^{-1} at 3.0μ (25°C), 0.07 mm^{-1} at 3μ (350°C), 0.017 mm^{-1} at 6.0μ (25°C), 0.021 mm^{-1} at 6.0μ (350°C). Refractive index, 3.4975 at 1.357μ, 3.4176 at 11.04μ (at 26°C). Crystal structure, cubic (diamond)	Specific heat, 0.181 cal/(gm)(°C) at 18.2 to 91.1°C. Thermal conductivity, 0.2 cal/(sec)(cm)(°C) at 20°C. Melting point, 1420°C. Expansion coef (linear), 2.33 × 10^{-6}/°C at 27°C	Density, 2.33g/cm^3. Hardness, 1150 Knoop; 7 Mohs. Young's modulus, 1.9 × 10^{12} dynes/cm^2. Modulus of rupture (bending), 35 Kg/cm^2	Chemical and weather resistance: requires evap. coating (SiO). Working characteristics: shaped, ground, polished by standard optical techniques

TABLE 6-2. PROPERTIES OF IR OPTICAL MATERIALS SUITABLE FOR HIGH-TEMPERATURE APPLICATIONS (*Continued*)

Optical material	Properties			
	Optical	Thermal	Mechanical	Physical
Calcium aluminate glass	Transmission, 85 % at 0.7μ, 90 % at 2.0–2.75μ, 75 % at 2.75–3.2μ (water vapor absorption), 78 % at 3.75–4.5μ, 4.9μ cutoff for 2-mm thickness (Bausch and Lomb RIR-2 glass). Refractive index, 1.769 at 1.014μ, 1.746 at 2.577μ (Bausch and Lomb RIR-2 glass). Homogeneity, excellent	Specific heat. Thermal conductivity. Melting point. Expansion coef, $8.1 \times 10^{-6}/°C$ (B and L RIR-10 glass)	Density, 3.07 g/cm³ (B and L RIR-10 glass). Hardness, 594 Knoop (B and L RIR-10 glass). Young's modulus, 15.2×10^6 psi (B and L RIR-10 glass)	Chemical and weather resistance—RIR-10 glass (experimental); attacked by water vapor and water with substantial reduction in IR transmission, requires evaporated coating of MgF_2 or chemical treatment RIR-2 glass; excellent; immune to attack by water vapor (for 24-hour period), protective coating not required. Working characteristics: shapes cast directly from melt; can be reheated and molded; worked by standard optical techniques
Rutile (TiO_2)	Transmission (fully oxidized), 64 % at 0.7μ, 67 % at 1.0μ, 68–72 % at 1.3–4.8μ, 68 % at 5μ, 52 % at 6μ, 10 % at 7μ. Refractive index (perpendicular and parallel to C axis, fully oxidized), 2.548, 2.827 at 0.7μ, 2.483, 2.746 at 1.014μ, 2.451, 2.709 at 1.53μ. Reflection coef (fully oxidized), strong absorption edges parallel and perpendicular to C axis at 11μ, and perpendicular to C axis at 21μ reported	Specific heat, $0.169 + 0.000109 \Delta T$ cal/g. Thermal conductivity [cal/(cm-sec)(°C)], 0.0136 at 43.8°C, 0.0128 at 83.7°C, 0.0124 at 103.8°C. Melting point, $1820 \pm 20°C$. Linear coef of thermal expansion [cm/(cm)(°C)], parallel to C axis: $9.19 \times 10^{-6} + 22.5 \times 10^{-9} \Delta T$; perpendicular to C axis, $7.14 \times 10^{-6} + 11 \times 10^{-9} \Delta T$	Specific gravity, 4.26. Molecular weight, 79.9. Hardness (Knoop), 910 parallel to C axis, 900 perpendicular to C axis	Insoluble in acids, soluble in fused alkali; when heated to 600°C in hydrogen, rutile becomes an n-type semiconductor; normally rutile is an insulator

References: Properties of rutile; Industrial Crystals Bulletin F-908, Linde Company, Division of Union Carbide Corporation, April, 1958.

Data on MgF_2: Magnesium Fluoride as an Infrared Window Material, *Bull*. Eastman Kodak Co., Rochester, New York, November, 1958.

Data on synthetic sapphire: Properties and uses of Linde Sapphire, *Bull. F-1176*, and R. W. Kebler: "Optical Properties of Synthetic Sapphire," Linde Co., Division of Union Carbide Corporation.

Data on fused MgO: "Properties and References on Fused Magnorite (Fused MgO)," *Bull*. CP 8.4.3, Refractories Division, Norton Co., Worcester, Mass., January, 1958.

Data on silicon: Reference 50.

Data on calcium aluminate glass: *IR Progress Reports* 1, 2, Bausch and Lomb Optical Co, April, June, 1958.

Data on Vycor silica glass: Corning Glass Works, Corning, New York, 1959.

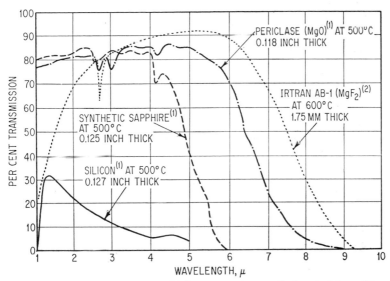

FIG. 6-16. IR transmission of some high-temperature optical materials. (*Courtesy Industrial Crystals Bulletin F-917, p. 4, Linde Company, Division of Union Carbide Corporation, June, 1958.*[1] *Eastman Kodak Co., Rochester, N.Y., November, 1958.*[2])

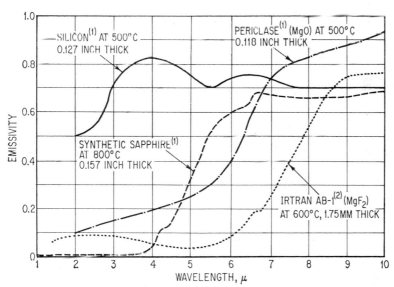

FIG. 6-17. Relative emissivities of optical materials at high temperatures. (*Courtesy Industrial Crystals Bulletin F-917, p. 5, Linde Company, Division of Union Carbide Corporation, June, 1958.*[1] *Eastman Kodak Company, Rochester, N.Y., March, 1959.*[2])

stream, or by cooling air forced over the outer surface or circulated in
the space between a double window.

TABLE 6-3. CHARACTERISTICS OF SOME USEFUL SEMICONDUCTOR IR
FILTER MATERIALS

Material	Refractive index	Thickness, mm	Transmittance, cutoff wavelength, μ
Si	3.5	1.5	1
Ge	4.0	1.0	1.7
InAs	3.2	0.125	3.8
InSb	4.0	0.08	7.4

After J. T. Cox and G. F. Jacobus.[63]

Properties of the newer optical materials mentioned in this section
are given in Table 6-2.

6-6. IR FILTERS

Optical filters are required in many IR instruments in order to
remove or reduce undesirable stray or background radiation or to
segregate certain wavelength regions. This is called *spectral filtering*
to distinguish it from *space filtering*, which was discussed in Sec. 5-11.
For example, in IR search equipment, filters are used to suppress scattered sunlight and other background radiation, and to isolate an atmospheric "window."

In grating spectrometers, filters are used for the elimination of high-
order images. In prism spectrometers, they are employed to reduce
stray radiation.

There are three basic classifications of IR optical filters: The *short-
wave-pass* filter transmits only radiation with a wavelength *shorter* than
the cutoff wavelength. The *long-wave-pass* filter transmits only those
wavelengths *longer* than the cutoff wavelength. *The bandpass* filter
cuts off transmission at both ends of a spectral band.

The wavelength cutoffs should be as sharp as possible. The ideal
short-wave-pass filter, for example, with a cutoff at, say, 4μ, would
transmit 100 per cent of incident radiation with wavelengths shorter
than 4μ, and zero per cent of incident radiation of 4-μ wavelength and
longer. The cutoff effect in a filter may be achieved by several methods, utilizing different physical properties of the optical material
employed. *Absorption cutoffs* by organic molecules, or by the lattice
of an inorganic crystal are used in long-wave-pass or broad-bandpass

filters.   Cutoff effects due to *scattering* are usually used in long-wave-pass filters.   *Reflection*-cutoff effects are employed in long-wave-pass or narrow-bandpass filters.   *Interference* cutoffs are used for long-wave-pass and for bandpass filters.   Many filters, of different optical materials, employing these mechanisms are available.

Figure 6-18 illustrates schematically the common forms of IR filter. *Short-wavelength-pass* filters have a sharp drop in transmission at a certain cutoff wavelength, wavelengths below this having a high transmittance.   *Long-wavelength-pass* filters have high transmittance for wavelengths longer than a particular cuton wavelength (see Fig. 6-18). These filters are also referred to as *blocking filters* since they block all radiation beyond a certain cutoff or cuton wavelength.

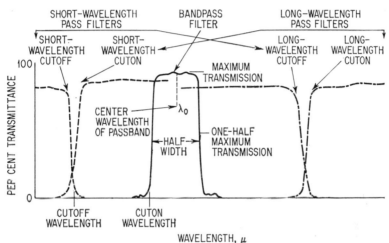

FIG. 6-18. Common forms of IR filter.

The *cutoff* or *cuton wavelengths* λ_c are those wavelengths at which transmittance is a certain low percentage, usually around 3 to 5 per cent of the maximum.   The slope measures the difference between λ_c and the wavelength at which transmittance is a high percentage, usually around 80 per cent of the maximum.   This wavelength difference is often expressed as a decimal fraction of λ_c.

Bandpass filters have high transmittance over a certain bandwidth determined by the cuton and cutoff wavelengths of the filter.   This passband may be very narrow or quite wide depending upon the characteristics of the filter.   Bandpass filters are generally of the interference or composite type.   The *center wavelength* λ_0 is the wavelength of the center of the passband.   The *half-width* is the width of the passband at 50 per cent of maximum transmittance, and is usually expressed as a decimal fraction of λ_0.   Thus if λ_0 occurs at 5 μ and the half-width is 0.50 λ_0, this means that the passband is 2.5 μ wide.

The various types of filters are illustrated in Fig. 6-19.   *Transmission* or *absorption-edge filters* have high transmission beyond or below a certain wavelength where high absorption produces a sharp wavelength cutoff or cuton.   They usually consist of a single filter coating deposited or evaporated in a vacuum on a substrate material.   *Composite filters* consist of two filter films of different materials evaporated or deposited on the opposite sides of a substrate.   *Interference filters* are composed of thin, multilayer films of various filter materials deposited on various substrates.   The employment of various filter and substrate materials with different absorption characteristics, and variation of the film thicknesses enable accurate control of λ_c and λ_0 to be exercised within a wide spectral range.

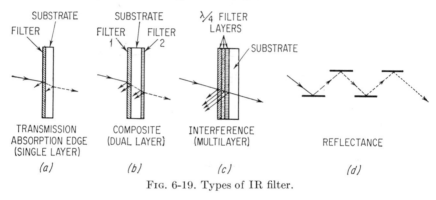

FIG. 6-19. Types of IR filter.

Reflectance filters have been used for many years for spectroscopic investigations at long wavelengths in the far IR.   The surface reflection from plates of several metallic salts, minerals, and other materials increases rapidly at a certain wavelength or within a narrow wavelength band.   The use of multiple plates enables incident IR energy to be selectively reflected at a sharp maximum or *restrahlen* wavelength.   In the case of cesium iodide, for example, reflected energy rises sharply between 120 and 170 μ, peaking at about 145 μ.

The selection of a suitable filter for a particular function involves the following considerations:

1. The optical efficiency of the filter, the sharpness of its cutoff, and its transmittance curve
2. The physical strength and surface hardness of the filter
3. Its stability under prolonged irradiation
4. Its cost and availability

Prior to World War II, a few optical filters or filtering techniques were available for use in the IR spectral region. The Christiansen filter[56] was being manufactured, but had only limited use for IR work. Early work on optical filters was carried out by Gorton,[57] who investigated short-wavelength scattering, Lecomte,[58] and Pfund,[59] who made a thorough study of the effect of particle size. However, many of the filters available at the time were either nonimage-forming, or were only useful in the visible region of the spectrum.

Since 1939 a large number of new optical filters has been developed for use in the IR spectral region. Some of the more commonly used filters are described in the following sections.

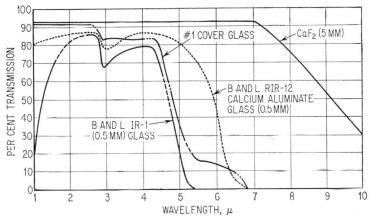

Fig. 6-20. Transmission of four commonly used substrates for near -IRfilters. (*Reference 60.*)

Near- and Middle-IR Filters. For the near- and middle-IR spectral regions, films of antimony on lithium fluoride, of bismuth and magnesium oxide on calcium fluoride, and of tellurium on silver chloride make effective filters. Figure 6-20 shows the transmission curves of four substrate materials, in common use for filters in these spectral regions, manufactured by the Bausch and Lomb Optical Company.[60] Substrates of other materials with high refractive indexes, such as silicon, germanium, and arsenic trisulfide glass, result in lower transmittances. Other substrate materials such as sapphire can only take satisfactory filter coatings within a limited wavelength range. In applications where a thick substrate is needed to meet strength requirements, fused quartz has excellent transmission characteristics out to about 3.4 μ.

The IR spectrum of cellophane has intense absorption bands at 3 and 7.5 μ, with many weak intervening bands. At 5 μ, transmittance is almost 70 per cent. By varying the thickness of cellophane film, or by coating it with various materials, several useful filters for the near- and middle-IR spectral regions can be made. Filters of cellophane coated with a film of magnesium oxide are practically opaque to radiation at 3.6 μ and have better than 50 per cent transmittance at 5 μ. The absorption bands of cellophane, various glasses, and other materials can be used for isolating spectral bands in the near- and middle-IR regions.

A great deal of the stray radiation in prism spectrometers occurs in the 1.5- to 3.5-μ region. A scattering filter consisting of a roughened mirror or plate of potassium bromide is useful in reducing stray radiation in this region. Also useful for this purpose is a transmission filter

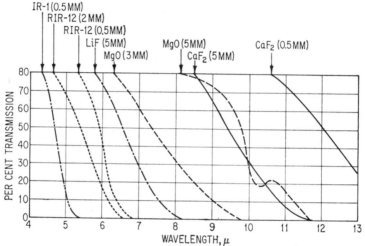

FIG. 6-21. Substrate transmission limits for long-wavelength cutoff control of long-wavelength-pass filters. (*Reference 60.*)

of silver chloride, coated with a film of silver sulfide. Diffraction gratings are widely used to reduce stray radiation in the short-wavelength region of the IR spectrum.

Long-wavelength-pass Filters. The transmission limits of several substrate materials used to control the long-wavelength cutoff in filters of this type are shown in Fig. 6-21.

Optically polished silver chloride is extremely transparent out to wavelengths of 27 μ. A series of silver chloride filters, coated with silver sulfide or polystyrene, are made by the Eastman Kodak Company.[61] The spectral transmittance is dependent on the nature of the coating, and how it is applied. Long-wave-pass filters of this type are available with a specified spectral transmittance for any of several equally spaced, short-wavelength cutoffs, ranging from 1 to 5 μ, and to within a tolerance of 0.2 μ. These far-infrared filters are made by depositing suitable coatings on both sides of a silver chloride blank, with a protective coating if required.[61] Their transmission characteristics are illustrated in Fig. 6-22.

In the longer-wavelength region from about 25 to 40 μ, reflection filters of calcium fluoride, lithium fluoride, and sodium fluoride are useful.

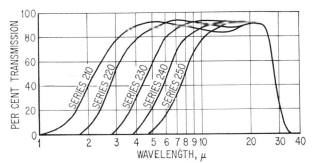

FIG. 6-22. Characteristics of Kodak far-IR filters. (*Courtesy Eastman Kodak Company, Rochester, N.Y.*)

Absorption filters with an absorption edge at about 3.9 μ formed by the deposition in a vacuum of evaporated layers of lead sulfide, lead selenide, or lead telluride on various substrate materials have been made.[62] With suitable low-reflection coatings, transmittances of over 80 per cent at wavelengths longer than 3.9 μ have been obtained.

6-7. REFLECTANCE AND LOW-REFLECTION COATINGS

Reflectance or reflection loss occurs when IR radiation is incident upon an air-material interface. For windows, lenses, prisms, and irdomes having a finite thickness, a second reflection loss occurs upon reemergence of the radiation from the material into air.

The surface-reflection loss for unpolarized, normally incident IR radiation passing from air into a medium of refractive index n is given by the Fresnel expression

$$\text{Reflectance} - \left[\frac{(n - 1)}{(n + 1)} \right]^2 \qquad (6\text{-}1)$$

This expression also holds to a good degree of approximation for angles of incidence up to 45°.

Reflection loss increases with increasing refractive index of the medium and is roughly doubled for reflection at two surfaces. The variation of percentage reflection loss with refractive index for various optical materials is shown in Fig. 6-23.

Reflection losses can be reduced for specific wavelength bands by coating both surfaces of a refractive material, or the single (front) surface of a mirror, with a quarter-wavelength-thick film of an appropriate antireflection material, such as magnesium oxide.   These coatings are usually evaporated on, since control of the thickness of the deposit is mandatory.   One-quarter-wavelength thickness of the deposit is required for the particular wavelength considered to ensure that radiation reflected from the front surface of the coating is exactly one-half wavelength out of phase with radiation reflected by the rear surface of the coating (surface of mirror or lens).   Radiation from single or multiple reflections is then reduced by destructive interference.   Several IR optical materials, particularly some of the semiconductor materials,

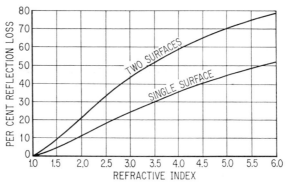

FIG. 6-23. Variation of reflection loss with refractive index.

have high refractive indexes.   Examples are silicon ($n = 3.5$) and germanium ($n = 4.0$), for which transmittance is reduced so much by high Fresnel reflection losses that antireflection coatings are required on both surfaces.   In the case of a single quarter-wavelength-thick dielectric coating, zero reflectance at that particular wavelength can be achieved if the refractive indexes of the antireflection coating and of the substrate are related by

$$n_c = \sqrt{n_s} \qquad (6\text{-}2)$$

where n_c = refractive index of antireflection coating material
       n_s = refractive index of substrate material
Thus for germanium ($n = 4$) a suitable coating material should have a refractive index of 2.   If two zero-reflectance minima are required, a double-layer coating is used.   For both layers of equal thickness

$$n_{c_1} n_{c_2} = n_s \qquad (6\text{-}3)$$

where n_{c_1} = refractive index of outer layer

n_{c_2} = refractive index of inner layer

n_s = refractive index of substrate and $n_{v_1} < n_{c_2} < n_s$

The characteristics[63] of four useful semiconductor IR optical and filter materials are listed in Table 6-3. The IR transmittance of high-purity samples of these materials is shown in Fig. 6-24. It will be seen that because of high Fresnel reflection losses, the average transmittance of these uncoated materials out to 15 μ is about 50 per cent. The effect of suitable antireflection coatings is to increase transmittance to a peak of better than 98 per cent at any desired wavelength up to about 15 μ.[63] Suitable coating materials are silicon monoxide (SiO, $n \approx 1.9$), zinc sulfide (ZnS, $n \approx 2.2$), cerium dioxide (CeO$_2$, $n \approx 2.2$),

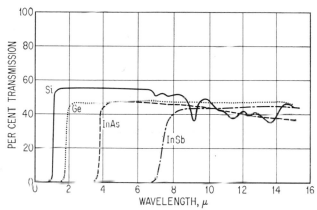

FIG. 6-24. Transmission of some high-purity semiconductor-type IR filters. (*After J. T. Cox and G. F. Jacobus.*[63])

and magnesium fluoride (MgF$_2$, $n \approx 1.35$). Films are deposited on the substrate material by evaporation in a vacuum at 1 to 5×10^{-5} mm of mercury, at a rate of from 10- to 50-A thickness/sec.[63]

These coatings are extremely hard and durable. Zinc sulfide coatings are most suitable for all four semiconductor materials in the 8- to 15-μ spectral region. The improvement in transmittance obtained with a single-layer zinc sulfide coating is shown in Fig. 6-25. Silicon monoxide coatings are excellent for silicon and germanium in the near-IR spectral region. Beyond 8 μ silicon monoxide becomes very strongly absorbing.[63]

The effect of double-layer coatings of these materials on the IR transmittance of silicon and germanium is shown in Fig. 6-26, which demonstrates the accomplishment of peak transmittance at two wavelengths.

A common reflecting surface used on mirrors consists of evaporated

Basic Principles of Infrared Radiation

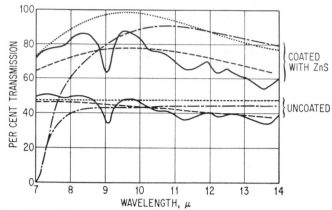

FIG. 6-25. Effect of ZnS coating on IR transmission of semiconductor-type filter materials.

——— Silicon plate.................. 1.5 mm thick
...... Germanium plate.............. 1.0 mm thick
- - - - Indium arsenide plate........... 0.125 mm thick
—·—·—·— Indium antimonide plate......... 0.08 mm thick
InSb coated with ZnS, $nt = \lambda/4$ at 10.8μ
Other materials coated with ZnS, $nt = \lambda/4$ at 9.8μ

All materials at room temperature.　(*After J. T. Cox and G. F. Jacobus.*[63])

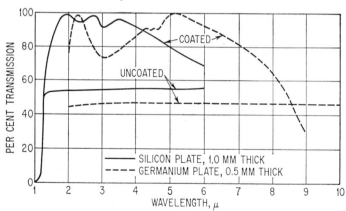

FIG. 6-26. Effect of double-layer antireflection coatings on IR transmission of silicon and germanium.

——— Silicon plate................ 1.0 mm thick
...... Germanium plate............. 0.5 mm thick
Si coated with $CeO_2 + MgF_2$, $nt = \lambda/4$ at 2.2μ
Ge coated with ZnS + SiO, $nt = \lambda/4$ at 3.3μ

All materials at room temperature.　(*After J. T. Cox and G. F. Jacobus.*[63])

aluminum, which requires a protective coating that is hard, durable, and does not affect the reflectivity of the surface. Thin, evaporated magnesium oxide (MgO) coatings are widely used for this purpose to provide the required abrasion, scratch, and corrosion resistance. Silicon monoxide and magnesium fluoride coatings are widely used to protect IR windows and irdomes.

REFERENCES

47. Gordon, J. M.: *J. Opt. Soc. Am.*, vol. 48, p. 583, August, 1958.
48. Plyler, E. K., and Acquista, N.: *J. Opt. Soc. Am.*, vol. 42, p. 286, 1952.
49. Plyler, E. K., and Acquista, N.: *J. Opt. Soc. Am.*, vol. 48, p. 668, September, 1958.
50. Runyan, W. R., Cole, R. L., Willmore, J. M., and Jones, L. E.: Growth Techniques and Mechanical Properties of Optical-quality Silicon, *Proc. IRIS*, vol. 3, no. 4, p. 49, December, 1958.
51. Buckley, H.: "Crystal Growth," John Wiley and Sons, New York, 1951.
52. Data for this section supplied by Dr. Richard W. Kebler of the Linde Co., Division of Union Carbide Corp., New York, March, 1959.
53. Ballard, S., and Wolfe, W.: Optical Materials in Equipment Design, a Critique, Office of Naval Research, *Proc. Infrared Inform. Symposia*, vol. 4, no. 1, p. 185, March, 1959. See also *Proc. IRE*, no. 9, pp. 1540–1546, September, 1959.
54. Data for this section supplied by Eastman Kodak Co, Rochester, N.Y.
55. *Infra-Red Progr. Rept.* 1, Bausch and Lomb Optical Company, Rochester, New York, April, 1958.
56. Christiansen, C.: *Ann. Physik u. Chemie*, vol. 23, p. 298, 1884; also vol. 24, p. 439, 1885.
57. Gorton, A. F.: *Phys. Rev.*, vol. 7, p. 66, 1916.
58. Lecomte, J.: "Le Spectre Infrarouge," Presses Universitaires de France, Paris, 1928.
59. Pfund, A. H.: *Phys. Rev.*, vol. 36, p. 71, 1930; and *J. Opt. Soc. Am.*, vol. 23, p. 375, 1933; vol. 14, p. 337, 1927.
60. *Infra-red Progr. Rept.* 3, Bausch and Lomb Optical Company, Rochester, N.Y., Sept. 8, 1958.
61. Data for this section supplied by Eastman Kodak Co., Rochester, N.Y.
62. Braithwaite, J. G. N.: Infrared Filters Using Evaporated Layers of Lead Sulphide, Lead Selenide, and Lead Telluride, *J. Sci. Instr.*, vol. 32, January, 1955.
63. Cox, J. T., and Jacobus, G. F.: Antireflection Coatings for Infrared Filters of Semiconducting Materials, *Proc. IRIS*, vol. 4, no. 1, p. 108, March, 1959.

7

Infrared Detectors

The various types of IR detectors are described. Comparison criteria, operating conditions, production methods, and the uses of these detectors are discussed.

7-1. CLASSIFICATION OF IR DETECTOR TYPES AND THEIR APPLICATIONS

The first detectors employed for investigations in the IR spectral region were thermal detectors: thermocouples, thermopiles, and various types of bolometers. These have been used in science and industry for many years, principally in the longer-wavelength regions of the IR spectrum.

The extensive development efforts in the 1930s and 1940s produced new and improved types of thermal detectors, and introduced the photoconductive, photoemissive, and thalofide cells, new phosphors, and photographic detectors to the IR field. Much of this work was pioneered in Germany, England, and the United States. During the postwar years, the increasing importance of solid-state physics and semiconductor research and the rapid growth of scientific, industrial, and military applications of IR have resulted in the development and production of an increasingly wide variety of sensitive detectors.

These detectors have different properties and uses, and may be classified in various ways. Jones[64] has used detectivity as a basis for classification. Since in this book we shall discuss many applications of IR in various fields, we shall use a broader classification system. IR detectors are classified into three main groups, according to the wavelength regions of the IR spectrum in which they have the best responsivity and the most applications (Fig. 7-1).

Group I consists of photoemissive and thalofide cells, photodiodes, photographic plates, and some phosphors, used for detection purposes

142

in the near-IR region of the spectrum. Group II includes photoconductive cells primarily used in the intermediate-IR spectral region. Group III includes thermal detectors which arc generally used for applications in the far-IR spectral region. This is a broad and somewhat loose classification. Many detectors in group I have applications extending into the intermediate-IR region. At the present time, group II detectors are primarily confined to the intermediate-IR region, but some of the newer cells in this group extend their useful range into the far IR, while several thermal detectors in group III are useful in parts of the intermediate-IR region. However, in discussing the many types

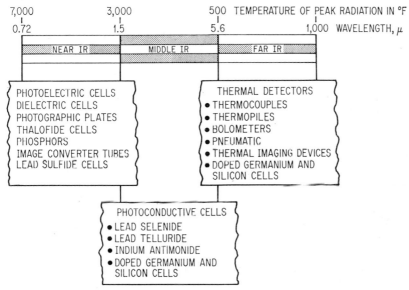

FIG. 7-1. Useful spectral regions of IR detectors.

of IR detector described, the reader will find it helpful to think of a particular detector primarily as a near-, intermediate-, or far-IR detector, or in borderline cases, as, say, an intermediate-far IR detector.

While the majority of detectors sensitive to near-IR radiation are operated at room temperature, many of the photoconductive detectors and the newer, doped-silicon and -germanium semiconductor alloys have to be cooled in order to achieve their maximum detectivity. The operating temperatures required for optimum operation of the different types of detector are illustrated in Fig. 7-2. These are sometimes used as another broad basis of classification; detectors are referred to as room-temperature, liquid-nitrogen, or lower-temperature-operated

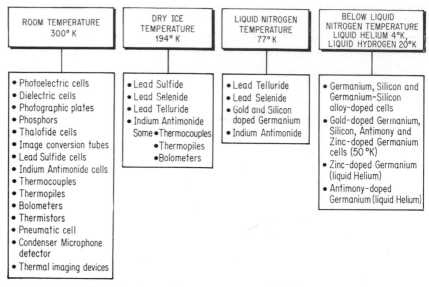

Fig. 7-2. Operating temperatures of IR detectors.

TABLE 7-1. ADVANTAGES OF IR DETECTOR TYPES

Detector type	Advantages
I. Photoelectric cells, including photoemissive, some photoconductive, photovoltaic cells; dielectric cells, thalofide cells; photographic plates; phosphors and phosphor cells. Image-conversion tubes	Superior responsivity in the visible and near-IR spectral regions; large signal amplification possible in photomultiplier cells
II Photoconductive cells	More responsive to lower-temperature sources; superior detectivity in intermediate-IR spectral region; faster time constants; faster recovery from transients; may be directly coupled to preamplifiers
III. Thermal detectors	More responsive to low-temperature sources; responsive over wide wavelength bands, in the far-IR spectral region detect greater fraction of the total IR radiation than photocells; mechanical chopping often not required; cooling of detector to low temperatures generally not required

TABLE 7-2. SOME APPLICATIONS OF VARIOUS IR DETECTORS

Detector type	Applications
I. Photoelectric cells, dielectric cells; thalofide cells, photographic plates, phosphors, phosphor cells, image-conversion tubes	Near-IR spectral region; spectroscopy; IR photography, thermoradiography, display devices; IR television
II. Photoconductive cells	Primarily intermediate, extending into far-IR spectral regions; IR search and tracking devices; IR communications; IR telescopes, microscopes; IR target detectors; IR ranging devices; pyrometers; radiometers; process-stream analyzers
III. Thermal detectors	Far-IR spectral region; pyrometers; radiometers; IR cameras; process-stream analyzers; automatic-control devices; IR surveillance

detectors. Table 7-1 lists the advantages of these three main groups of detectors. A breakdown of their more common applications is given in Table 7-2.

Before describing the various types of detectors and their properties it is necessary to discuss the methods and criteria used in judging cell performance.

7-2. CRITERIA USED IN COMPARISON OF DETECTORS

The performance of a detector cell depends upon many factors. The characteristics of the incident radiation, the spectral response characteristics of the sensitive surface of the cell, and the conditions under which the detector cell is operated, must all be considered. The criteria that have been established for comparing the performance of different detectors under these conditions are largely products of the work of Jones[68] and are described briefly in the following paragraphs.

Detector Time Constant (τ). Many radiation detectors have a responsivity versus frequency curve that is an approximation to the form $R(f) = R_0/[1 + (2\pi f \tau)^2]^{\frac{1}{2}}$. When this is true, the shape of the responsivity versus frequency curve is compactly described by giving the value of the time constant τ. But when the shape of the curve departs widely from the above equation there is no generally accepted way to define a time constant. The majority of detectors have a single time constant. Some detectors, such as bolometers, lead telluride, and lead selenide, may possess more than one physical time constant. Lead telluride and lead selenide detectors, for example, have two time constants, thereby exhibiting both fast and slow decay.   In some detectors the time constant is wavelength-dependent. In others, such as germanium, the time constant is affected by the temperature. τ is expressed in microseconds (μsec), milliseconds (msec), or in seconds, depending upon the particular detector being considered.   The frequency response of a detector is therefore dependent upon its time-constant characteristics and determines the chopping speed or modulation frequency of the incident radiation required to produce optimum signal response from a given detector.   Frequency-response measurements are made, of course, in that wavelength band within which the detector exhibits its maximum responsivity.

Responsivity (R_v).   For   detectors   with   an   electrical   output, responsivity is defined as

$$R_v = \frac{\text{rms output voltage}}{\text{rms power incident upon the detector}} \qquad (7\text{-}1)$$

R_v is measured in rms volts per rms watt. R_v is a function of the modulation frequency of the incident radiation.   The type of signal, such as steady, isolated-pulse, square-wave, or sinusoidally modulated, for which R_v is measured should be specified.   Also, the circuit impedance should be specified, especially when the detector is a bolometer.

Relative Spectral Response (R_λ).   The responsivity of photoconductive cells, and in fact, most types of detectors, varies with the wavelength λ of the incident radiation.   The relative spectral response R_λ of   a   detector   normalizes   the   detector   responsivity   at   a   particular wavelength, against the peak responsivity.   It is defined

$$R_\lambda = \frac{\text{detector responsivity at any wavelength}}{\text{detector responsivity at wavelength of peak responsivity}} \qquad (7\text{-}2)$$

R_λ also varies with the temperature of the detector.
In testing the spectral response characteristics of a detector, a monochromator is used to determine its response to radiation of a particular wavelength.

Efficiency to Black-body Radiation (ξ).   In testing detector characteristics, a 500°K black-body reference source is usually employed. The efficiency of a detector to this radiation depends upon the relative spectral response R_λ of the detector and is also a function of the absolute temperature T of the source.   It is defined

$$\xi = \frac{\int_0^\infty W_\lambda R_\lambda \, d\lambda}{\int_0^\infty W_\lambda \, d\lambda} = \frac{\int_0^\infty W_\lambda R_\lambda \, d\lambda}{\sigma T^4} \qquad (7\text{-}3)$$

where W_λ = function of T; black-body spectral radiant emittance

ξ = function of T, measured in effective watts per total watts incident upon the detector

σ — Stefan's constant

R_λ = corresponding ordinates of the relative spectral response curve of the detector cell

Normally the limits of integration are dependent upon the wavelength-cutoff limits of the optical system, determined by the windows, lenses, and filters employed.

Noise Equivalent Input (NEI). This is defined as the minimum radiation input that will produce an rms signal-to-noise ratio of unity. It is also called the *noise equivalent power* (NEP) when the input is measured in total incident power (in watts), or the *noise equivalent flux density* (NEFD) when the input is measured in flux density (in watts/cm^2).

Thus

$$\text{NEP/NEFD} = A \qquad \text{cm}^2 \text{ (the cell area)} \qquad (7\text{-}4)$$

In measuring these quantities, the signal-to-noise ratio of the detector is maximized by choosing an appropriate cell-bias voltage.

Detectivity (D). This is defined, in general, as

$$D = \frac{R_v}{\text{rms noise-voltage output of cell}} \qquad (7\text{-}5)$$

D is the reciprocal of the *NEP*.

The detectivity D^* is a very special kind of detectivity. D^* is the detectivity D reduced to unit bandwidth of the noise and unit area of the detector. D^* is defined as

$$D^* = (A \ \Delta f)^{\frac{1}{2}} D \qquad (7\text{-}6)$$

where D is the detectivity measured with a noise-equivalent bandwidth Δf and A is the area of the detector. D^* is measured in cm(cps)$^{\frac{1}{2}}$ watt^{-1}. The detectivity D^* is a way of describing the detectivity so that the actual area of the detector and the bandwidth used in measuring the detectivity do not affect the result. It is a useful method of intercomparing the performance of detectors that have different areas.

The detectivities of various cooled and uncooled photoconductive IR detectors are shown in Figs. 7-26, 7-27, and 7-28.

Jones "S" (S_j). In order to perform an accurate comparison of different detectors it is necessary to normalize the different variables. This is a difficult task since the nature of many of these variables is imperfectly understood. In an attempt to simplify this problem, Jones proposed that the measured NEP be defined for specific reference conditions. These are a cell area of 1 cm², a bandwidth $\Delta f = (f_2 - f_1)$ specified by $f_2/f_1 = e = 2.718$, and a chopping frequency low enough to give maximum cell response. This value of the NEP, normalized in this manner for the chopping frequency, the detector area, and the amplifier bandwidth, is known as the Jones "S" (S_j). For a photoconductive cell that is current-noise limited

$$S_j = \frac{\text{NEP}}{\sqrt{A(\Delta f/f)}} = \frac{\text{NEP}}{\sqrt{A \log_e (f_2/f_1)}} \tag{7-7}$$

where A = sensitive area of detector cell

      f = chopping frequency

      f_2 = upper frequency limit of amplifier

      f_1 = lower frequency limit of amplifier

      Δf = amplifier bandwidth used in measuring NEP, small compared with f

For the reference conditions specified above, $S_j = \text{NEP}$ in rms watts. In much of the older literature on detectors, the concept of Jones "S" is used, and it is included for this reason. The concept of Jones "S" is now obsolete, and it has been replaced by D^*.

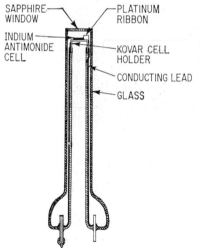

SAPPHIRE WINDOW

INDIUM ANTIMONIDE CELL

PLATINUM RIBBON

KOVAR CELL HOLDER

CONDUCTING LEAD

GLASS

Fig. 7-3. Philco Type 1SC-350 indium antimonide detector enclosed in Dewar flask. (*Courtesy Philco Corporation Research Division, Philadelphia, Pa.*)

Effects of Detector Operating Conditions. *Effect of Cooling the Detector.* A change in cell temperature may be caused by environmental conditions or by the absorption of incident radiation. For photoconductive detector cells, a rise in cell temperature decreases cell resistance, and, therefore, increases its conductivity and increases noise. It may be necessary to cool the detector by artificial means.

Certain detectors perform best at the temperature of dry ice. The photoelectromagnetic type of indium antimonide cell is an example. Many of the longer-wavelength-sensitive photoconductive detectors, however, require cooling to the temperature of liquid nitrogen, 77°K (Fig. 7-27). Some of the doped silicon and germanium detectors achieve their optimum detectivity at even lower temperatures (Fig. 7-28), and require cooling by liquid helium.

For this purpose, miniature cooling units or *minicoolers* are used. These may be of two types: nonregenerative or regenerative. In each case the back of the detector cell must be enclosed in a small, double-walled Dewar vacuum flask in order to maintain the low temperature (Fig. 7-3).

The *nonregenerative* type of minicooler employs a replaceable or refillable bottle of liquid nitrogen under pressure. Liquid nitrogen droplets

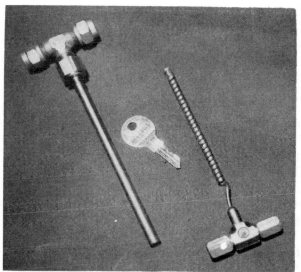

Fig. 7-4. Miniature cryostat developed by ITT Laboratories, Fort Wayne, Ind. (*Courtesy International Telephone and Telegraph Corporation.*)

or nitrogen gas is then piped through an insulated tube to the back surfaces of the sensitive area of the detector.

The *regenerative* or closed-circuit cooling system uses extremely pure, dry nitrogen gas which is circulated under pressure by means of a small compressor and expanded through a small orifice in a miniature cryostat surrounded by the Dewar flask. Repeated expansion in the cryostat causes successive lowering of the gas temperature (the Joule-Thompson effect), until a supply of liquid-nitrogen droplets is fed to the back of the detector cell. A miniature cryostat, manufactured by the ITT Laboratories, Fort Wayne, Indiana, a division of the International Telephone and Telegraph Corporation, is illustrated in Fig. 7-4.

Small fluctuations in the minicooler temperature may introduce noise in doped crystal detectors sensitive to wavelengths beyond 9 μ, if the thermal capacity of the cell elements is too small.

Cell cooling improves the detectivity and long-wavelength response of lead-salt detectors. The long-wavelength response of lead sulfide cells, for example, is increased to an ultimate of nearly 6 μ by cooling to the temperature of liquid nitrogen, with a sharp drop in response occurring at about 4 μ (Fig. 7-26). Generally the effect of cooling a photoconductive type of detector is to increase its responsivity at longer wavelengths, its detectivity, and its cell resistance. A disadvantage of cell cooling, particularly in IR systems requiring a fast response time, is that the time constant of the cell is increased.

Effect of D-C Bias Voltage. An increase in the d-c bias voltage across a photoconductive cell increases the current and hence the noise. For a given signal, the d-c bias voltage is usually adjusted in practice to give a maximum signal-to-noise ratio. Depending upon the cell resistance and the chopping frequency, if the lowest bias rate that achieves this is chosen, then maximum stability of operation is obtained.

Effect of Cell Area. The effective area (A) of the detector is that portion of its surface which is sensitive to irradiation. In the case of thermocouples, A may be the area of a single junction; for thermopiles it may include all the hot and cold junctions, or the hot junctions only. For a bolometer, A may be the area of one or both strips, depending upon whether one is shielded or not. It is therefore necessary to specify clearly exactly what A is for a particular detector.

For lead sulfide cells, the signal-to-noise ratio is inversely proportional to the square root of A for constant radiant flux. Generally, for photoconductive-type detectors, the smaller the area of the sensitive surface, the higher is the S/N ratio. In many detectors, the smallest usable cell area is limited only by manufacturing techniques and the size of the blur circle of the focused optical image.

Effect of Background Noise. This and other types of noise affecting detector performance are discussed more fully in Sec. 7-6. The effect of various cell and operating parameters on detector noise is discussed for lead sulfide cells in the following paragraphs. The noise limitations of the various types of detector are listed in Table 7-4.

7-3. NEAR-IR DETECTORS

In this spectral region (0.72 to 1.5 μ) many different types of detector cells have been developed during the last three decades. These include the following types of detectors.

IR Photoelectric Cells. There are three basic types of photoelectric cell, all of which find application in the near-IR spectrum.

1. *Photoemissive Cells.* These operate on the principle that IR radiation incident on the sensitive surface of the cell causes the photoemission of electrons. In the photomultiplier tube the electron stream from the cathode is amplified by employing the principle of secondary emission from multiple dynodes.

2. *Photoconductive Cells.* These depend for their operation on the change in the originally high resistance of semiconductor materials when they are illuminated by IR radiation.

3. *Photovoltaic Cells.* These are also known as barrier photocells. In this type of cell, a photosensitive barrier of high resistance, deposited between two layers of conducting material, builds up a potential difference between these two layers when exposed to IR radiation.

Specific examples of cells of these different types are described in the following paragraphs.

IR Photoemissive Cells. Pioneering investigations in this field were carried out by Carl Bosch and the *Reichsposforschung Institut* in Germany during the war years.[3] The detector cells developed were limited to high-temperature (400°C and above) source detection, with peak detectivities in the neighborhood of 1.3 μ. The cells developed by Bosch used cesium cathodes sensitized with dicyanide. The photosensitive surface was deposited on a spongy colloidal support. The spectral response was extended to a maximum of about 2.4 μ.

The *Bildwandler* image-conversion tube for use in the near-IR spectral region was developed by the Institut. It is discussed more fully in Sec. 5-13.

The principle of photoemission has been applied in the multiplier phototube to produce a detector with very high detectivity and rapid response in the visible red and the near-IR spectral regions. A widely used tube of this kind is the type 7102 multiplier phototube, developed and manufactured by the Radio Corporation of America.[65] It is illustrated in schematic form in Fig. 7-5. Incident IR radiation causes electron emission at the photosensitive cathode. The electrons emitted are accelerated through the grill and strike the No. 1 dynode. Amplification of the signal is achieved by electrical focusing of the electron streams through ten dynode stages, at each of which secondary emission increases the electron output. Electrons emitted by the No. 10 dynode are collected by the anode and form the highly amplified output current. This tube is capable of detecting input pulses having a duration of 0.01μ sec, and with an S-1 response covers a spectral range of 0.42 to 1.1 μ. Peak detectivity is in the neighborhood of 0.8 μ.

Near-IR applications of photoemissive detectors include IR ranging, communications, optical pyrometry, astronomical measurements, and IR spectrometry.   Photoemissive detectors with a sensitive surface of silver-oxygen-cesium have been in use for many years.   The RCA type 6929 image-conversion tube, sensitive in the near-IR spectral region, has already been described in Sec. 5-13.

Photoconductive Cells.   The discovery that lead sulfide ores were photosensitive was made in 1930 by Kutzscher of ELAC in Germany, and independently by Gudden in Prague.   Commercial lead sulfide detector cells, responsive in the near-IR spectral region, were manufactured in the late 1930s and early 1940s by the Zeiss-Ikon, ELAC, and AEG Companies in Germany and were used extensively in both military and scientific applications.[3]

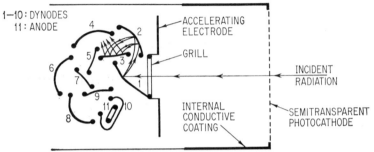

Fig. 7-5. Schematic arrangement of RCA Type 7102 photo-multiplier tube. (*Reference 65.   Courtesy Electron Tube Division, Radio Corporation of America, Harrison, N.J.*)

The thallium sulfide cell, employing a sensitive surface of thallium oxysulfide, was first reported in 1920 by Case.   Investigation of its properties was carried out at the National Bureau of Standards in the United States by Coblentz.   This type of detector cell was further developed for commercial applications by Cashman at Northwestern University in the United States[66] and by Gudden at Prague.[3]   The cell has a spectral response through the visible region out to about 1.45 μ, with peak responsivity at a wavelength of approximately 1 μ.

Germanium photodiodes are also used in the near-IR spectral region. A more complete discussion of the photoconductive cells is given later in Sec. 7-4.

Photodielectric Cells.   The photodielectric effect, or D-K effect, whereby the effective dielectric constants of some materials change when irradiated by light of different wavelengths, was first observed by Lenard, and later investigated fully by Pohl and Wesch.   This phenomenon has been extensively studied by Wesch in Germany since

1933.   He also investigated the preparation and properties of zinc sulfide, cadmium sulfide, cadmium selenide, cadmium telluride, zinc telluride, lead sulfide, lead selenide, and their combinations.[3]   By con-
trolling the annealing process and temperature, as well as the amount
of activator, cells were prepared with sharply peaking responsivities
at various wavelengths.   The types of D-K cell[3] developed by Wesch
are illustrated in Fig. 7-6.   The cell illustrated in Fig. 7-6b is constructed by evaporating a layer of gold on a quartz or glass cover plate.
The gold layer is then grooved with a fine dividing machine which cuts
into the layer down to the surface of the cover plate.   The photosensitive material is then spread over the grooved surface, its thickness
determining the depth of penetration of IR radiation, which may fall
on the cell from either side.   Cells of this type were made with an
NEFD as high as 1.5×10^{-10} watt/cm².

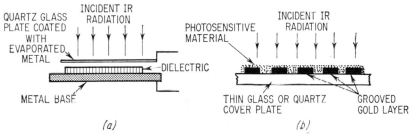

Fig. 7-6. Wesch D-K photodielectric cells.   (After T. M. Odarenko.[3])

Phosphor Cells.   In this field, fundamental development work was
carried out in Germany, primarily with regard to applications in image-
converter tubes.

Becker, of the Philip Lenard Institut, Heidelberg, worked on the
development of photoquench phosphors.   The fluorescence of a screen
of zinc sulfide, zinc tetrasulfide, or copper, activated by ultraviolet
light or by α particles from a radioactive source, decreases when an
IR image is projected on it.   The decrease is approximately proportional to the intensity of the incident IR radiation.   Screens were
developed with a response extending to about 2.8 μ.[3]

Siemens of Halske developed a screen of rare-earth materials which
was capable of storing an IR image for periods up to 1 day.[3]   Lodz of
Siemens-Werke developed two types of phosphor.   One type, composed of zinc sulfide, zinc selenide, and fluorescent zinc oxide, after
suitable activation emitted visible light which was inhibited by IR.
In the second type, incident IR radiation caused an increased emission
of visible light after activation.   A red phosphor was developed which,
when activated by daylight, emitted red light when exposed to IR radi-

ation.   A much more sensitive green phosphor, when activated by a mercury-vapor lamp, emitted a green glow when under the influence of IR radiation.   These phosphors were composed of europium oxide and samarium nitrate combined with calcium fluoride.   They were used over the 0.7- to 1.5-μ spectral band, with peak response near 1 μ.[3]

Photosensitive phosphors were also used for coating telescope lenses and field glasses.   Katze employed a fluorescent screen of red or green phosphor material in combination with a convex glass lens and an IR optical filter for the detection of enemy IR searchlights.[3]

The luminescent efficiency of some phosphors is dependent upon temperature.   Such phosphors are applied in thermoradiography. The majority of these phosphors, however, are suitable for the intermediate- and far-IR spectral regions and will be discussed in succeeding sections of this chapter.

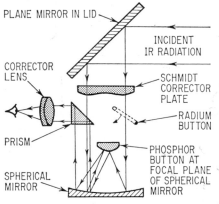

FIG. 7-7. Schematic of type 'F' metascope. (*After A. H. Canada.*[45])

The Type 'F' Metascope.   Photoquench phosphors such as lead-activated zinc sulfide and some rare-earth phosphors were used in the United States to develop the metascope.[45]   This is a visual image-forming IR detector which, unlike the electron image-converter devices described in this chapter and in Chap. 5, does not require a power supply.   Similar devices were also developed in Britain and in Germany for military applications.

In photoquench phosphors, upon activation by exposure to ultraviolet light or to radium emanation, electrons are raised to a higher energy level.   Some electrons drop back to their original energy levels during the activation process, releasing their surplus energy in the form of an afterglow.   Other electrons remain at the higher energy levels until the excitation is removed, when they then release their surplus energy as an afterglow.   Some electrons, however, remain at their higher energy levels until the phosphor is illuminated with near-IR radiation up to about 1.2 μ, when their energy is then released as visible light.

The metascope utilizes this phenomenon.   The principle of its operation is illustrated schematically in Fig. 7-7.   Incident near-IR radiation is reflected by a plane mirror enclosed in the collapsible lid of this small portable device, through a Schmidt corrector plate, and focused by a spherical mirror on a curved phosphor button located at the focal plane of the optical system.   The phosphor button has been previously charged by emanations from a radium button which is pivoted out of the way when no longer required.   Visible light released by the phosphor button is reflected from the spherical mirror, through a prism and a corrector lens to the eye of the viewer.   The advantages of this device are its small size, portability, and its operation without a power supply.

IR Photographic Emulsions.   It was realized in the late 1930s that the ability of a photographic emulsion to integrate the radiation from a weak or distant source over exposure times of seconds, or even minutes, had great potential value in military applications.   Consequently a great deal of research was performed in several countries on the development of stable and highly sensitive photographic emulsions suitable for use in the IR spectral region.   Halogen-silver-gelatin emulsions sensitive to the near-IR spectral region were developed during World War II, principally in the United States, Britain, and Germany. Emulsions which incorporated suitable IR-filter materials were produced; these were used with cameras equipped with telephoto lenses of very long focal length.   Cameras of this type, employing long exposure times, were used by the Germans to photograph ships, convoys, and coast installations at ranges up to 65 km.[3]

The majority of the emulsions developed were confined to operation in the near-IR spectral region.   They had limited use in adverse weather conditions because of water-vapor absorption and the scattering of IR radiation from the target, or against targets with relatively low temperatures.   The life span of these emulsions was generally quite short.

Modern developments in IR photography have made available stable photographic emulsions with a long shelf life.   Usefulness has been extended into the intermediate- and far-IR spectral regions.   Today, these emulsions are widely used in industrial, scientific, and military applications.

ITT Type 6411/IC-16-3 Infrared Image-converter Tube.*   This tube, developed by the ITT Laboratories, Fort Wayne, Indiana, employs a cathode with an S-1 response, operating in the near-IR portion of the spectrum, and a phosphor screen active in the visible portion of the spectrum, to convert an IR image into a visual image.

Its many uses include the determination of temperature distribution in heated objects, the inspection of photographic film, medical and bio-

---

* Data for this section by courtesy of ITT Laboratories, Fort Wayne, Ind., a division of International Telephone and Telegraph Corporation.

logical research, criminal investigations, high-speed photography, and other applications.

The tube is illustrated in Fig. 7-8. For the majority of viewing applications a filtered tungsten lamp is used for irradiating the object

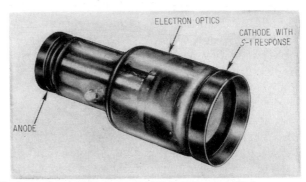

FIG. 7-8. Photograph of ITT type 6411/1C-16-3 near-IR image-converter tube. (*Courtesy ITT Laboratories, Fort Wayne, Ind., a division of International Telephone and Telegraph Corporation.*)

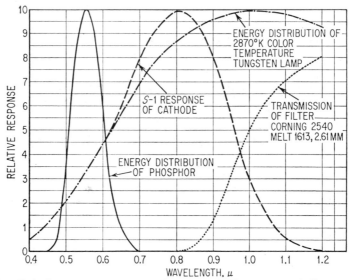

FIG. 7-9. Relative response vs. wavelength of ITT type 6411/1C-16-3 near-IR image-converter tube. (*Courtesy ITT Laboratories, Fort Wayne, Ind., a division of International Telephone and Telegraph Corporation.*)

under investigation, the visible component of the lamp's radiation being suppressed by a suitable filter such as the Corning 2540 or Wratten 87C or 88A. The relative spectral responses of the phosphor screen, cathode, tungsten lamp, and the Corning filter are shown in Fig. 7-9.

The tube is normally used in conjunction with an objective lens and magnifying eyepiece. The inverted image formed on the cathode is reinverted by the electron optics of the tube so that the image appearing on the screen or seen through the eyepiece is erect. Either a refractive or reflective (Schmidt) objective may be used, and should be designed with proper consideration given to the spherical cathode surface. Usually a field-flattener lens is used in conjunction with the objective. A good quality achromat eyepiece with a field slightly in excess of the useful phosphor-screen area (0.750-in. diameter), such as a 7-power Hastings triplet, is satisfactory for most purposes.

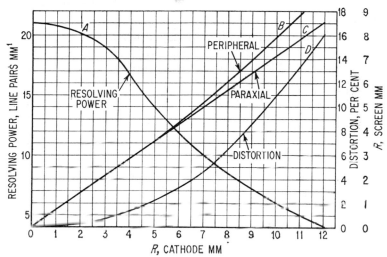

Fig. 7-10. Characteristic curves of ITT type 6411/1C-16-3 near-IR image-converter tube. (*Courtesy ITT Laboratories, Fort Wayne, Ind., a division of International Telephone and Telegraph Corporation.*)

The resolving power is shown in curve A, Fig. 7-10. This is the number of equally spaced, parallel, opaque lines per unit length (with spacing equal to the width of the lines) at the cathode which may be observed in the resulting screen image. The distortion is shown in curve D, Fig. 7-10. The magnification at points on curves B and C for peripheral and paraxial rays is given by the slope of the curve at that point (Fig. 7-10).

7-4. INTERMEDIATE-IR DETECTORS

Photoconductive Detectors. Photoconductive detectors, as distinct from other types of IR detectors, are constructed from semiconductor materials. Their widest applications are in the intermediate-IR spectral region, with continued development and research extending their spectral response to the longer-wavelength, far-IR spectral region. The long-wavelength limit of the majority of these types of detectors available in production quantities is in the neighborhood of 7 to 8 μ. Detectors of zinc-doped germanium, sensitive out to 40 μ, are also now available.

The earliest photoconductive detectors were the lead sulfide cells developed in Germany and in England prior to the outbreak of World War II in 1939. Work was also started on the development of lead selenide and lead telluride cells.

Postwar research and development, principally in the United States, England, Germany, France, and Russia, have led to the commercial production of lead sulfide, lead selenide, lead telluride, and, more recently, of indium antimonide and doped germanium detector cells.

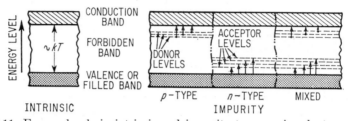

FIG. 7-11. Energy levels in intrinsic and impurity-type semiconductors. (*After Arthur R. von Hippel, "Dielectrics and Waves," p. 246, John Wiley & Sons, Inc., New York, 1954.*)

The detectivities of these cells approach those of lead sulfide cells, and the entire intermediate-IR and part of the far-IR spectral regions have been opened up for use by their development.

Intrinsic and Impurity-type Photoconductive Cells. Photoconductive detectors made of semiconductor crystals change their electrical conductivity when exposed to IR radiation. In order to understand this phenomenon of photoconduction (hence, the name *photoconductive cell*), let us consider a chemically pure semiconductor crystal. The molecules of the crystal contain electrons with different energy levels, as illustrated in Fig. 7-11.

Under normal conditions, electrons within the crystal are tightly bound to the atoms and occupy various energy levels in the *valence* or *filled band*. Radiation of the correct wavelength incident on the crystal excites some of the electrons sufficiently to raise their energy to a higher level.

In an intrinsic photoconductive material, there is a *forbidden band* within which no energy levels can be occupied by electrons. The energy absorbed by the electrons from incident IR radiation must be sufficient to excite them to energy levels in the *conduction band*. When this occurs, the electrical conductivity of the crystal increases and is dependent upon the wavelength of the incident radiation and the energy absorbed.

Impurity photoconductive materials are made by introducing small amounts of a chemical impurity during the crystal-growing process. The crystals are said to be *doped*. These materials contain energy levels in the forbidden band. The *n-type semiconductor* materials contain only *acceptor levels* in the forbidden band. Electrical conductivity of the crystal increases when incident radiation excites an electron sufficiently to raise its energy from a level in the valence band to an acceptor level, or to a higher energy level in the conduction band. The *p-type semiconductor* materials contain only *donor levels*. Electrical conductivity of the crystal is increased when incident radiation excites an electron from the valence band or from a donor level in the forbidden band to the conduction band. A *mixed-type semiconductor* may contain both acceptor and donor energy levels.

In all cases, electrons freed by incident IR radiation in this manner can be drawn through the crystal by application of a potential difference, thus forming a photoconductive current. The energy-level difference between the valence and conduction bands, or band separation, is given approximately by kT, where k = Boltzmann or molecular gas constant = 1.38×10^{-23} joule/deg and T = absolute temperature.

In a chemically pure semiconductor crystal, the energy required to excite an electron to a higher energy level determines its spectral response characteristics. The long-wavelength cutoff λ of the photoconductor is determined by

$$E = \frac{hc}{\lambda} = h\upsilon \qquad (7\text{-}8)$$

where h = Planck's constant = 6.623×10^{-34} joule sec

c = velocity of light = 3×10^{10} cm/sec

υ = frequency of exciting radiation

λ = wavelength of exciting radiation

E = energy required to activate an electron, electron volts (ev)

From this equation, the activation energy E (in electron volts) required for a semiconductor to be responsive to incident radiation of wavelength λ is plotted against λ in Fig. 7-12.

In addition to excitation of electrons by incident radiation, the thermal energy of the crystal lattice may produce excitation of the carrier electrons. This results in a *dark current* which adds to the photoconductor-current noise. In impurity-type photoconductors it reduces the number of carrier electrons available for excitation by incident radiation. It is important, therefore, when selecting a photoconductor for a particular IR application to choose one with an activation energy E greater than the minimum energy required for a desired long-wavelength cutoff. Thus, for use in the 2.0- to 4.0-μ region, an activation energy greater than 0.3 ev is required.

Impurity-type semiconductors contain controlled amounts of impurity in the crystal. This makes it possible to select a particular impurity level, donor or acceptor, as the active energy level. At room temperatures, impurity levels are almost completely excited. At the temperature of liquid nitrogen (77°K) this thermal excitation effect is greatly reduced, and the crystal becomes a more efficient semiconductor. For this reason many semiconductor-type photoconductive detectors require cooling to achieve their maximum detectivity.

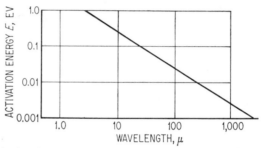

Fig. 7-12. Activation energy vs. wavelength response in semiconductors.

In a mixed semiconductor, impurities are added during the crystal-growth process to adjust the activation-energy level, in order to produce a desired spectral response. Examples of this are gold, indium, or zinc doping of mixed germanium-silicon semiconductors. In the case of pure germanium with indium impurity added, the activation energy of indium is 0.01 ev. In pure silicon, the activation energy of indium is 0.16 ev. In a silicon-germanium mixture with added indium impurity, the activation-energy level can, therefore, be varied within these limits.

Examples of intrinsic semiconductors are gray tin and indium antimonide. Examples of impurity semiconductors are indium, gold, or zinc in silicon or in germanium, or in a silicon-germanium mixture; and arsenic in germanium.

The band separations at 27°C for the semiconductor materials commonly used in IR detectors at the present time are shown in Fig. 7-13.

Preparation of Photoconductive Detectors. From the point of view of production, photoconductive detectors may be broadly classified into two main groups:

In group I are the lead sulfide, lead selenide, lead telluride, and photoconductive indium antimonide detectors. These are prepared by chemical deposition or by evaporation in a vacuum of the lead or indium salt on a small cell blank. A method for the preparation of evaporated-surface lead telluride cells is described in Reference 67.

In group II are the intermetallic semiconductor crystals such as indium phosphide, indium arsenide, indium antimonide (photoelectromagnetic and photovoltaic types), and the germanium, silicon, and doped germanium-silicon mixtures. These detectors are prepared by the Czochralski crystal-growth process. In doped crystals, the impurities are added to the pure zone-refined crystal in controlled amounts during growth. The indium antimonide (InSb) photovoltaic detector is either a grown junction type of semiconductor crystal with its sensitive region at the junction, or a diffused or alloy type of crystal with

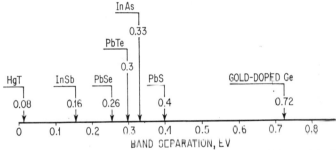

FIG. 7-13. Band separations of various semiconductor materials used in IR detectors (at room temperature 27°C).

the sensitive region at one of the free surfaces. These indium antimonide p-n junction detectors are difficult to make in production quantities with controlled characteristics and are still in the experimental stage. A method of preparing this type of indium antimonide photovoltaic detector is described in Reference 69.

Photoconductive Detectors and Their Properties. Properties of photoconductive and other types of IR detectors are given in Table 7-3. The values used in this table are approximate in the sense that they are representative of average good-quality detectors.

In any batch of production detector cells, particularly in the case of some of the newer intermetallic semiconductors, some cells for reasons that are not fully understood are exceptionally responsive, while others are below average.

Lead-sulfide detector cells, although they have the highest detectivity at the present time, are limited in their spectral range. Their long-wavelength-cutoff limit can be extended somewhat by cooling at liquid-nitrogen temperatures, but even then the detector responsivity drops

TABLE 7-3. CHARACTERISTICS OF IR DETECTORS
(for average quality detectors)

Detector	Operating temperature, °C	IR response limits, μ	Usual long-λ cutoff, μ	Detectivity $D*$ cm(cps)$^{1/2}$/watt unless otherwise stated	Time constant, μsec	Resistance approx., megohms	Sensitive area	Limiting noise
PbS	Room (25)	0.72-4.7	2.5-3.0	1×10^{12}	5-1,000	1	0.0001-1 cm²	current
PbS	-78	0.72-5.5	3.0-3.5	2.5×10^{12}	1,000-3,000	20		current
PbS	-196	0.72-5.9	3.5-4.0	1.5×10^{13}	250-3,000	1-100		current
PbTe	-196	0.72-6.0	5.5	$5-8 \times 10^{9}$	<30	100	4 mm²	current
PbSe	-196	0.72-6.5	5.5	1.5×10^{9}	10-40	0.2-20	0.0005 cm²	current
InSb(PEM-type)	25	0.72-7.0	6.5	2×10^{9}	1-5	1×10^{-6}	2 mm²	Johnson
InSb(PEM-type)	-196	0.72-7.0	6.7	$7 \times 10^{9}-1.5 \times 10^{10}$	2-10	$2-7 \times 10^{-6}$	8 mm²	Johnson
InSb(n-type)	-196	0.72-7.0	6.7	3×10^{7}	2-5	5-6	12 mm²	current
InSb(p-type)	-196	0.72-7.0	6.7	$0.8-4 \times 10^{9}$	2-5	0.2-.5	4 mm²	current
InSb(diffused junction)	-196	0.72-7.0	5.5	2×10^{10}	1-2	9×10^{-3}		current
Ge: Au	-196	0.72-11	9.5	2×10^{10}				current
Ge: Au, Sb	-196	0.72-6	4.0	2×10^{10}				current
Ge: Au, Zn	-223	0.72-45	40	4×10^{9}	<0.01	0.3	4 mm²	current
Thermistor bolometer	25	0.72-25		2×10^{8}	5,000			Johnson
Thermistor superconducting		0.72-35		4×10^{9}	20-100			Johnson
Golay detector		0.72-1,000		2×10^{10}	20,000			temperature
Evaporograph		0.72-18		to 0.1°C	$4 \times 10^{5}-1.2 \times 10^{7}$			

rapidly beyond about 4 μ. Due to their high internal resistance, lead sulfide cells require a well-regulated and filtered bias voltage. Cooling the cell, while increasing the longer-wavelength spectral response, also increases the time constant.

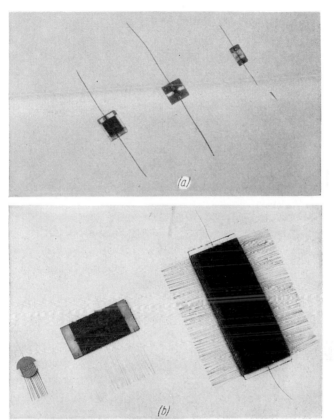

FIG. 7-14. Photographs of (a) flat-plate single lead sulfide cells; (b) lead sulfide mosaic cells. (*Courtesy Infrared Industries, Inc., Waltham, Mass.*)

Of all the photoconductive cells, lead sulfide, because of its high detectivity, excellent performance characteristics, amenability to quality control, and high production rates, has reached the highest state of development. Lead sulfide films can be applied on quartz substrates in single-cell form, in mosaic form consisting of several hundred separate cell elements (Fig. 7-14a and b), or on curved surfaces. Where wide angular coverage or high optical gain is a requirement, the principle of immersion optics is used by depositing the lead sulfide film on optical elements of sapphire or strontium titanate[70] (Fig. 7-15).

Fig. 7-15. Photograph of lead sulfide detectors deposited on immersed optics. (*Courtesy Infrared Industries, Inc., Waltham, Mass.*)

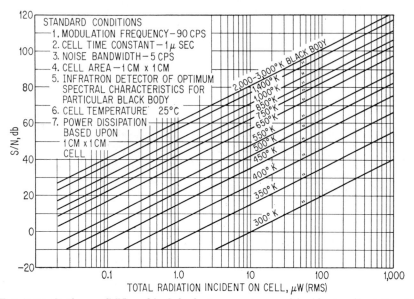

Fig. 7-16. Optimum S/N vs. black-body temperature and incident radiant flux for Infratron lead sulfide detectors. (*Courtesy Infrared Industries, Inc., Waltham, Mass.*)

Figures 7-16 through 7-21 facilitate the determination of the optimum S/N ratio or NEP, for given operating conditions of the Infratron series of lead sulfide cells manufactured by Infrared Industries, Inc., Waltham, Mass.[70] If the operating conditions differ from the standard conditions listed in Fig. 7-16, the db corrections indicated in Figs.

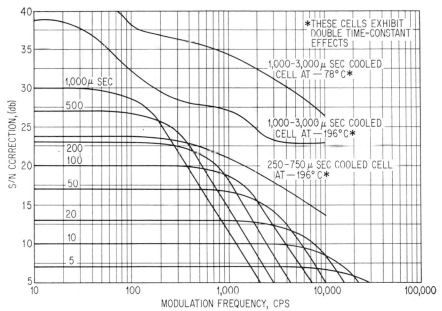

FIG. 7-17. Correction to S/N for time-constant and frequency— Infratron lead sulfide detectors. (*Courtesy Infrared Industries, Inc., Waltham, Mass.*)

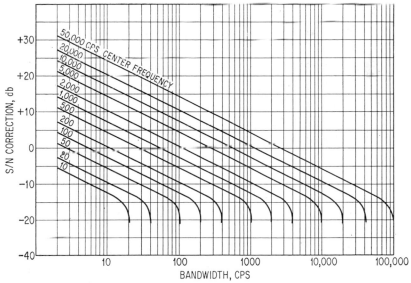

FIG. 7-18. Correction to S/N for bandwidth—Infratron lead sulfide detectors. (*Courtesy Infrared Industries, Inc., Waltham, Mass.*)

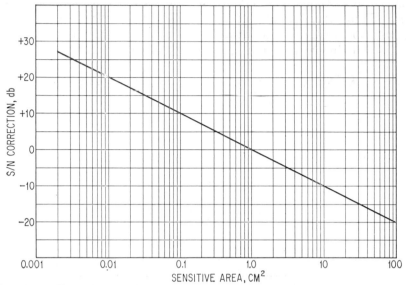

FIG. 7-19. Correction to S/N for cell area—Infratron lead sulfide detectors. (*Courtesy Infrared Industries, Inc., Waltham, Mass.*)

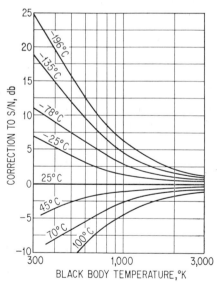

FIG. 7-20. Correction to S/N for cell temperature with varying black-body temperature—Infratron lead sulfide detectors. (*Courtesy Infrared Industries, Inc., Waltham, Mass.*)

7-17 through 7-20 should be added or subtracted from the S/N reading obtained from Fig. 7-16. These curves also illustrate the dependence of the S/N ratio on incident radiant flux, time constant, bandwidth, cell area, cell temperature, source temperature, and modulation frequency. The double time constant effect at low temperatures is clearly shown in Fig. 7-17.

To avoid the effects of bright-sky backgrounds and to detect cooler targets in IR systems such as air-borne search and tracking devices, a short-wavelength cut-off of 3 to 4 μ is required, and a detector cell responsive in the 3- to 6- or 7-μ region of the spectrum must be used. Here the designer has a choice of several of the newer *long-wavelength-type* detectors. These detectors have not had the extensive development time devoted to the earlier lead sulfide cells, and the best of them have at the present time a detectivity at least one order of magnitude smaller

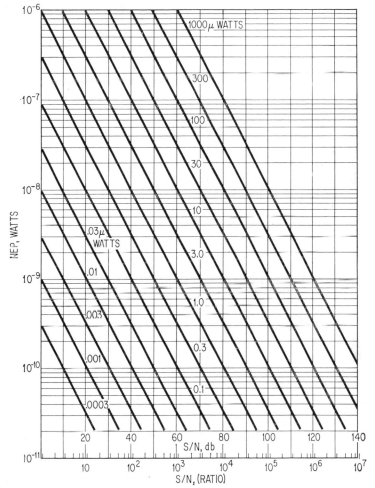

FIG. 7-21. Conversion of S/N to NEP for various incident radiant flux—Infratron lead sulfide detectors. (*Courtesy Infrared Industries, Inc., Waltham, Mass.*)

than a good lead sulfide cell, as shown in Table 7-3. Some of these detectors are in production; others are still in the experimental stage.

Lead Telluride Detectors. In these detectors the sensitive lead salt film is deposited on a suitable substrate material either in the form of a single cell of controlled thickness and dimensions, or as multiple cells forming a mosaic (Fig. 7-22). Detectors of both types are available in production quantities. One of the pioneer developers and manufacturers of these detectors in the United States is ITT Laboratories of the International Telephone and Telegraph Corporation, Fort Wayne, Indiana.

Since these cells require cooling at the temperature of liquid nitrogen, they are enclosed in a miniature Dewar flask, usually with a sapphire window. With a long-wavelength cutoff at about 5.5 μ and an NEP of less than 4×10^{-10} watt at the optimum bias voltage, these detectors are widely employed for applications in the intermediate-IR spectral region. The absolute spectral responses of an average lead telluride detector, when operated uncooled and at liquid nitrogen temperatures, are shown in Figs. 7-26 and 7-27. Detector characteristics for an average production cell are listed in Table 7-3.

FIG. 7-22. Photograph of lead telluride mosaic detector. (*Courtesy ITT Laboratories, Fort Wayne, Ind., a division of International Telephone and Telegraph Corporation.*)

Lead Selenide Detectors. These detectors, like lead telluride, are deposited or evaporated on a suitable substrate, or on the end of the inner Dewar flask. For optimum detectivity lead selenide detectors require cooling with liquid nitrogen to $-196°C$. Their absolute spectral response, cooled or uncooled, is superior to that of lead telluride (Figs. 7-26 and 7-27), and is dependent upon the film thickness and the sensitization process employed.

Advantages of lead selenide detectors are their high detectivity and excellent spectral response, the cooled cell having a long-wavelength cutoff at about 5.4 μ. They are extensively used in IR applications in the intermediate spectral region, and cells of uniform quality and various sizes, down to extremely small strip detectors suitable for IR search and tracking systems, are in production. The characteristics of an average production type lead selenide detector cell are listed in Table 7-3.

Indium Antimonide Detectors. More recently photovoltaic, photoelectromagnetic, and photoconductive types of indium antimonide cells have become available, with detectivities comparable to good lead selenide or lead telluride detector cells. These detector cells have decided advantages and will be used in IR devices to an increasing extent as their performance and their availability improve. They have a fairly flat spectral-response curve out to 6 μ. The *photoelectromagnetic* (PEM) *type cells* operate at room or dry-ice temperatures. These cells have low internal resistance which reduces microphonics. No regulated bias supply is required. They have excellent stability and reliability and can withstand exposure to very high IR flux levels without damage to the cell. Time constants of a few microseconds result in fast response and the ability to take advantage of high chopping frequencies.

The PEM-type cell depends upon the Hall effect for its operation. This is illustrated in Fig. 7-23. IR radiation is concentrated on one side of a single crystal situated in a strong magnetic field. Electron-hole pairs are created at the irradiated surface, and flow away as a diffusion

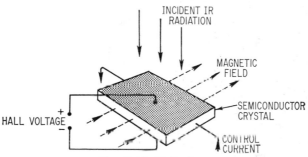

INCIDENT IR RADIATION

MAGNETIC FIELD

SEMICONDUCTOR CRYSTAL

HALL VOLTAGE

CONTROL CURRENT

FIG. 7-23. Hall effect.

current. The magnetic field separates the electrons from the holes and causes a potential difference to be developed across the ends of the crystal, proportional to the magnetic field strength. This PEM effect is linear up to magnetic field strengths of about 8,000 gauss at room temperature, and 4,000 gauss at liquid-nitrogen temperatures. PEM-type detectors have an NEP of about 1×10^{-9} watt, and a long-wavelength cutoff of about 6.7 μ. Characteristics of this type of detector are very low resistance and low noise. They are Johnson-noise limited, a factor which prevents their full utilization, since it is extremely difficult to build a preamplifier with a sufficiently low noise level to take advantage of the ultimate detectivity of the cell.

The photoconductive cells, of both intrinsic and impurity types, operate on the principles described earlier in this section. They are somewhat more responsive than the PEM-type detectors, and require liquid-nitrogen cooling.

The photovoltaic cells, or diffused junction-type detectors, depend upon the *photodiffusion effect* for their operation. Incident IR radiation produces electron-hole pairs in the detector material by the difference in the diffusion coefficients for electrons and holes. The long-wavelength cutoff of this type of detector occurs at about 5.5 μ. The absolute spectral-response curves peak at about 4 μ when the detectivity $D^*(500°,90,1)$ may reach about 2×10^6 cm(cps)$^{1/2}$/watt.

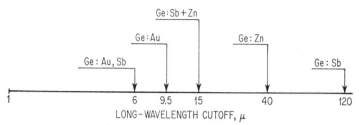

Fig. 7-24. Wavelength cutoffs of doped germanium detectors.

Spectral-response curves for average detectors of these types are given in Figs. 7-26 and 7-27. Detector characteristics are listed in Table 7-3 where the figures given are approximate for average production cells.

Germanium and Silicon Detectors. Still largely in the development stage, intrinsic and impurity-type photoconductive detectors of germanium, silicon, and alloys of these materials have detectivities comparable to those of the lead telluride, lead selenide, and indium antimonide detectors. Doping of silicon, germanium, and their alloys with various metallic impurities increases their long-wavelength response out into the far-IR region. Figure 7-24 shows the long-wavelength cutoffs of germanium detectors doped with controlled amounts of various impurities during the crystal-growing process. Gold- and antimony-doped germanium detectors are in limited production. Zinc-doped germanium detectors with a long-

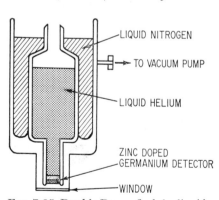

Fig. 7-25. Double Dewar flask for liquid–helium–cooled zinc-doped germanium detector. (*Courtesy Perkin-Elmer Corporation, Norwalk, Conn.*)

wavelength cutoff near 40 μ are in production at the Perkin-Elmer Corporation. Liquid-helium cooled, a detectivity $D^*(500°,800,1)$ of 4×10^9 cm(cps)$^{1/2}$/watt is obtained. Cooling to liquid-helium temperature requires the use of a double Dewar flask containing liquid helium in the inner flask and surrounded by liquid nitrogen in the outer flask, as illustrated in Fig. 7.25.

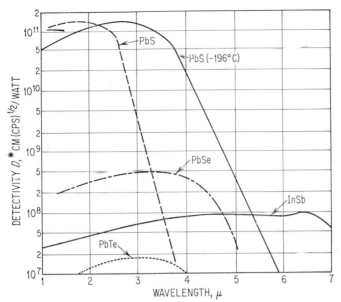

FIG. 7-26. Comparison of absolute spectral response of typical detectors at room temperature. D^* is monochromatic detectivity at 900-cps chopping frequency and 1-cps bandwidth. (*After W. Beyen, P. Bratt, W. Engeler, L. Johnson, H. Levinstein, and A. MacRae, Infrared Detectors Today and Tomorrow, Proc. IRIS, vol. 4, no. 1, March, 1959.*)

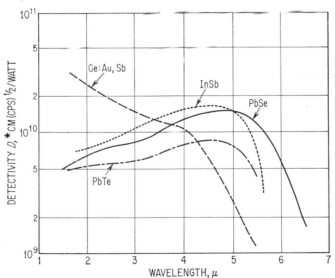

FIG. 7-27. Absolute spectral response of typical detectors cooled to liquid-nitrogen temperatures. D^* is monochromatic detectivity at 900-cps chopping frequency and 1-cps bandwidth. (*After W. Beyen, P. Bratt, W. Engeler, L. Johnson, H. Levinstein, and A. MacRae, Infrared Detectors Today and Tomorrow, Proc. IRIS, vol. 4, no. 1, March, 1959.*)

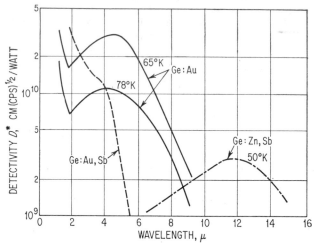

FIG. 7-28. Absolute spectral response of doped germanium crystal-detectors. D^* is monochromatic detectivity at 900-cps chopping frequency and 1-cps bandwidth. (*After W. Beyen, P. Bratt, W. Engeler, L. Johnson, H. Levinstein, and A. MacRae, Infrared Detectors Today and Tomorrow, Proc. IRIS, vol. 4, no. 1, March, 1959.*)

7-5. FAR-IR THERMAL DETECTORS

This group of detectors measures incident IR radiation by a change in some physical property caused by an increase in the temperature of their sensitive surfaces. (Table 7-4).

TABLE 7-4. PHYSICAL PROPERTY VARIATIONS USED IN THERMAL DETECTORS

Thermal detector	Physical property variation
Thermocouples; thermopiles	Resistance of junction
Thermistors	Resistance of heat-sensitive semiconductor
Bolometers	Resistance of metal ribbon or sensitive strip
Golay pneumatic detector; condenser microphone	Expansion of gas causing movement of membrane or diaphragm
Nonlinear phosphors	Change in luminescent efficiency
Thermal imaging devices	Change in vapor pressure, in physical dimensions, in wavelength of optical absorbing edge, in dielectric constant

Thermal detectors differ from those in the previous two groups considered, in that their response curves are generally flat, with fairly uniform responsivity throughout the entire optical and most of the IR spectrum. Detectivities are lower than those for photoconductive cells. Time constants are longer, and vary from a few tenths of a second to a few milliseconds.

Thermal detectors are used extensively in IR spectroscopy and in the far-IR spectral region where the more sensitive detectors of the types described in Secs. 7-3 and 7-5 are not suitable.

Thermocouples and Thermopiles. A thermocouple consists of a pair of thermoelectric junctions of dissimilar metals. One junction is blackened to receive IR radiation; the change in temperature which results produces an output voltage. The other junction is shielded from the incident IR radiation and forms part of a balanced bridge circuit to counteract the effects of changes in environmental conditions.

A thermopile is a number of thermocouples connected in series. These detectors are generally low-impedance elements with a maximum resistance of a few hundred ohms, and time constants on the order of a few milliseconds.

Thermocouples and thermopiles of various types and constructions are widely used in IR work. A brief description of several contemporary types of these detectors and their applications follows.

Silver-Palladium Thermocouples.[71] The junctions are formed of palladium wire electrically annealed at 1400°C and silver wire annealed at 700°C. The silver wire is fused to the palladium wire to form a hot junction. Junctions are mounted in a flat, twin-bore silica tube. These thermocouples have an accuracy of ±0.1°C, maintainable over considerable periods of time. They require careful handling, however, and are therefore used in the laboratory for high-accuracy measurements in the temperature range from 200 to 600°C. They have been used for several years at the National Physical Laboratory as secondary standards for the calibration of base-metal thermocouples in this temperature range.

Weyrich Vacuum Thermocouple. This thermocouple consists of two junctions of two different antimony-bismuth alloys, both junctions being designed for use as radiation receivers. The thermocouple may be enclosed in a vacuum or used at atmospheric pressure. It has been used in IR spectroscopy for many years.

The Harris Thermocouples.[87] Two thermocouples, each having a hot-junction area of 1.2 mm^2, were constructed, evacuated, and backed with cellulose film. One was a bismuth-tellurium thermocouple with a time constant of 212 msec. The other was a bismuth-antimony thermocouple with a time constant of 90 msec.

The Harris and Scholp thermocouples are bismuth-antimony and bismuth-tellurium thermocouples constructed by the sputtering process.[87]

A High-temperature Thermocouple. This thermocouple, developed by the Thermo-Electric Co., Saddle Brook, New Jersey, in the United States,[72] is designed specifically for use in high-velocity gas streams such as jet-engine afterburners, ramjets, and rocket plumes. The thermocouple junction is constructed of platinum—6 per cent rhodium and platinum—30 per cent rhodium alloys for gas-stream temperatures up to 3000°F, and of iridium and iridium-rhodium alloy for temperatures up to 3600°F. The support tube and radiation shield are constructed of a *cermet* or ceramic-metal combination. This eliminates the requirement for water- or air-cooling and the conduction errors caused by cooling. Radiation losses to the duct walls are reduced about 60 per cent with this type of construction. This thermocouple has been tested without failure for up to 1½ hr in a Mach 1 gas stream at a temperature of 3000°F.

Thermopiles. These consist of a number of thermocouples arranged in series in a convenient mounting. Typical of the many types of thermopile in use are such examples as the Hornig and O'Keefe thermopiles,[73] consisting of wire thermocouples employing bismuth-antimony and bismuth-tin alloy junctions. The sensitive area of a thermopile may vary considerably, depending upon the type and number of thermocouples employed. Thus, the Schwartz thermopiles,[64] manufactured by Adam Hilger, London, consist of two hot and two cold receivers, each of 2 mm² area, in a pin-type mounting. The Eppley-Emerson thermopiles[64] consist of 12 hot junctions, arranged to cover an area of ½ in. by ¼ in., and 12 cold junctions covering a similar area.

Bolometers. *Metal Bolometers.* These consist of blackened strips or ribbons of metal backed with glass or film to reduce the time constant. Incident IR radiation increases the temperature of the ribbon or strip. The resulting change in resistance causes a potential drop across the bolometer which is measured in a balanced bridge circuit. For high responsivity, materials with a low heat capacity and a high temperature coefficient of resistance are chosen.

The detectivity of metal bolometers is limited by their Johnson noise. When cooled to temperatures near absolute zero, superconductivity occurs, that is, the electrical resistance approaches zero. Many of the newer types of bolometers are based upon this principle.

Polaroid Bolometers. Developed by Billings at the Polaroid Corporation, United States,[64] these bolometers consist of a cruciform shape of four sensitive strips. They are prepared by evaporating nickel on to an 800-A thick nitrocellulose film.

The Strong Bolometers. Developed by Strong at Harvard University, United States, these bolometers consist of six unbacked nickel strips operating in a hydrogen atmosphere at a pressure of 1 mm of mercury.

Columbium Nitride Bolometer. Developed by Andrews at Johns Hopkins University, United States, this bolometer consists of a small, blackened, columbium nitride strip which is mounted on a block of solid copper cooled by a liquid-nitrogen cryostat. Columbium nitride becomes superconducting at the triple point of hydrogen. Over a very narrow range in this temperature region, the resistance changes very rapidly with temperature. This bolometer has a time constant of approximately 0.5 msec for a 63 per cent response, and is far superior to the average d-c thermocouple.

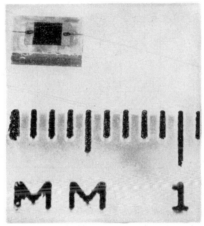

FIG. 7-29. Photograph of thermistor flake. (*Courtesy Barnes Engineering Company, Stamford, Conn.*)

Evaporated-gold Bolometer. This bolometer[91] consists of a 2.6- by 0.6-mm strip of evaporated gold on a thin, plastic-film backing, enclosed in an evacuated chamber. With a resistance of 15 megohms, and a time constant of 7 msec, its noise level is approximately equal to the Johnson noise. This bolometer is used in radiometers and in IR spectroscopy for long-wavelength IR work.

Thermistor Bolometers. Thermistors (abbreviation of *thermally sensitive resistors*) are constructed of extremely thin flakes, about 10 μ thick, of electronic semiconductor material with a high temperature coefficient of resistance. The active element is a square or rectangular flake with linear dimensions varying from 0.1 to 10 mm (Fig. 7-29). It is blackened to achieve absorption of 80 per cent (or better) of the incident IR radiation. The active flake, together with a matched compensating flake which is shielded from incident radiation, is firmly attached to a heat sink, to improve detectivity and speed of response, and sealed in a compact housing (Fig. 7-30). These two matched flakes form a bridge circuit which compensates for changes in environmental conditions (Fig. 7-31). Positive and negative bias voltages are applied to the active and compensating flakes, respectively. Their

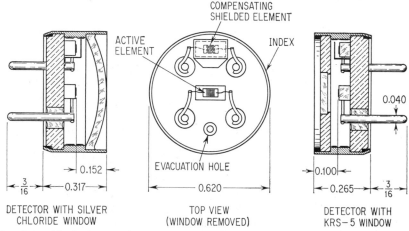

DETECTOR WITH SILVER   TOP VIEW   DETECTOR WITH
CHLORIDE WINDOW   (WINDOW REMOVED)   KRS-5 WINDOW

FIG. 7-30. Typical thermistor detector. (*Courtesy Barnes Engineering Company, Stamford, Conn.*)

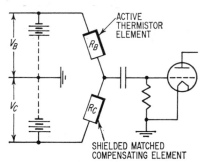

FIG. 7-31. Thermistor bolometer circuit. (*Courtesy Barnes Engineering Company, Stamford, Conn.*)

common junction, the signal lead, is at ground potential. IR radiation, modulated by a chopper, incident on the active flake causes a corresponding change in resistance, and produces an a-c voltage at the signal lead.

Commercially produced thermistors vary in resistance from about 1 to 10 megohms, permitting convenient a-c amplification of the output signal. Various semiconductor materials are used. They may consist of small flakes of heat-treated mixtures of the oxides of cobalt, nickel, or manganese. Commercially produced thermistors such as the *Optitherm* types manufactured by the Barnes Engineering Company, Stamford, Connecticut, or the *Servotherm*® types manufactured by the Servo Corporation of America, Hicksville, New York, have resistances of 2 to 3 megohms, time constants of a few milliseconds, and an NEP of the order of 1×10^{-8} watt. These units are free from microphonics. Bolometer noise is approximately equal to the Johnson noise of the equivalent resistance. These detectors are available with windows of

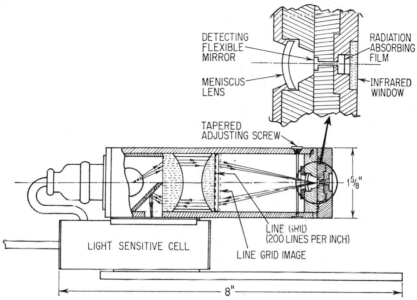

FIG. 7-32. Golay pneumatic detector. (*Courtesy The Eppley Laboratory, Inc., Newport, R.I.*)

glass, sapphire, silver chloride, arsenic trisulfide, and other optical materials, permitting detection of radiation over a wide IR-spectral region. They are also made in the form of multielement mosaics (Fig. 5-27).

Modern thermistors are used extensively in radiometers, pyrometers, and other IR instruments with wide applications in industry, especially in spectroscopy, automatic product analysis, and the automatic control of manufacturing operations.

The Golay Pneumatic Detector. Developed by Golay,[75] this detector is comparable in detectivity to photoconductive detector cells.

The detector consists of a small cell containing a radiation absorbing film of low heat capacity, evacuated and filled with xenon gas, and closed by an IR window (Fig. 7-32). IR radiation incident on the film heats the gas, which expands and flexes a flexible mirror, consisting of a collodion membrane of about $\frac{1}{16}$ in. diameter, mirror finished by evaporation of antimony.   An optical system containing a source, grid, and photocell is arranged so that flexure of the mirror window causes modulation of light reaching the photocell.   For spectrometric applications the incident IR radiation is usually chopped at 10 cps, and the photocell signals are amplified, rectified, and recorded.

This detector is noise-limited by the temperature noise due to thermal coupling between the gas and the cell walls.   The Golay detector is useful throughout the IR spectral region, into the microwave region. Because of its high responsivity to long-wavelength IR radiation, this cell is used widely in IR spectroscopy.

IR Condenser Microphone Detector.   Based upon a somewhat similar operating principle, this detector makes use of the expansion of an irradiated gas to alter the capacitance of a parallel-plate condenser.

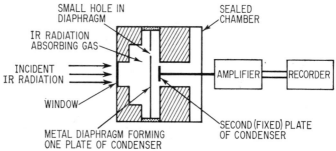

FIG. 7-33. Schematic of IR condenser-microphone-detector. (*After A. H. Canada.*[45])

IR radiation, incident on the IR-transmitting window of a small, sealed chamber containing a radiation-absorbing gas, causes a slight movement of a thin metal diaphragm.   This diaphragm has a small hole drilled in it to slowly equalize the gas pressure on either side and forms one plate of a parallel-plate condenser (Fig. 7-33).   Movement of the diaphragm changes the capacitance of the condenser.   This change is amplified in a suitable electronic circuit, and recorded.   Various window materials are available to ensure wide coverage of the IR spectrum.

Far-IR-sensitive Phosphors.   The luminescent intensity of zinc sulfide, zinc-cadmium sulfide, and zinc-cadmium-selenide phosphors is strongly temperature-dependent.[76]   It was found by Hemmendinger in the course of research on phosphors during World War II that the sensitivity of these phosphors to temperature changes can be greatly increased.   This was achieved by poisoning the phosphors with certain impurities, called activators, and exposing them to strong excitation by ultraviolet light. Some phosphors which exhibit this property are shown in Fig. 7-34, which illustrates the temperature dependence of their luminescent intensity.

CURVE	PHOSPHOR	CRYSTALLIZATION TEMPERATURE,°C	EXCITATION, Å
①	ZnS (48%), CdS (52%): 0.01% Ag	940	3,650
②	ZnS (60%), ZnSe (40%)	730	3,650
③	ZnS (60%), ZnSe (40%):0.005% Ag	730	3,650
④	ZnS (60%) ZnSe (40%):0.005% Cu	730	3,650
⑤	ZnS (88%), CdS (12%):0.008% Cu	1230	3,650
⑥	B"−ZnS, 0.01% Ag: 0.005% Cu	1260	3,650

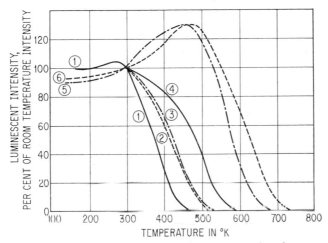

FIG. 7-34. Dependence of luminescent intensity of some phosphors upon temperature. (*After H. W. Leverenz.*[76])

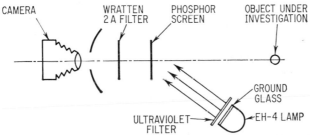

FIG. 7-35. Use of thermoluminescent phosphors for thermoradiography. (*After F. Urbach et al.*[77])

This phenomenon may be exploited to measure and record the distribution of IR radiation from an object, at wavelengths extending into the far-IR spectral region. A precision method for measuring slight changes in temperature or in temperature distribution,[77] used in thermoradiography, is illustrated in Fig. 7-35.

IR radiation from the object under investigation is incident upon a screen of the selected phosphor mixture. This screen is excited by an intense source of ultraviolet light. A two-dimensional image of the distribution of radiation from the object is displayed on the screen, and may be observed visually or photographed through a suitable filter. The sensitivity of this device is between one hundredth and one thousandth of that of a Golay cell or a good thermistor. The minimum detectable energy is about 500 μw/cm^2.

Some of these IR phosphors, after excitation by ultraviolet light or by exposure to a radioactive substance, are capable of retaining over half of their stored light for periods up to 1 week when kept in the dark at room temperature. When exposed to IR radiation of a suitable wavelength and intensity, they release their stored light in the visible region in a very short time.

Thermal-imaging Devices. A great deal of work is being done in the development of new phosphorescent materials for use in various types of thermal-imaging devices. Mention has been made in Chaps. 1 and 5 of German and Allied applications in this field, developed during the war years. Devices such as the sniperscope (Chap. 11) and metascope (Sec. 7-3), the *Bildwandler* tube, and more recently the 6926 image converter (Chap. 5), operate in the near-IR and intermediate-IR spectral regions and all employ phosphorescent screens to produce visible images of an IR target.

In the far-IR spectral region, several thermal-imaging devices have been produced and others are under development at the present time. Many of these devices are of a proprietary nature or are still classified, and therefore cannot be described here. Others are in commercial use. A brief description of the method of operation of two interesting devices of this type will illustrate the general physical principles involved.

The Electron-mirror Image-conversion Tube.[3] This device was developed in Germany during the war for target-detection purposes in the intermediate-IR and far-IR spectral regions. As illustrated in Fig. 7-36, an evacuated glass bell, coated with an aquadag layer on its inside surface, has several pockets. Situated in pocket 1 is an electron gun (A), with a barium-activated equipotential cathode. A beam formed by a diaphragm system, upon leaving pocket 1, is accelerated by a potential difference of 4,000 volts applied to the aquadag layer, and directed by a magnetic field generated by two coils perpendicular to the plane of the figure, into pocket 2. Situated here is an electro-optical system composed of two concentric metal cylinders (B), with a variable positive potential with respect to the cathode of the electron gun. This accelerates and focuses the electron beam upon the electrode (C). This electrode, at a slightly negative potential relative to the cathode of (A), is coated with an IR-sensitive material. The electron beam reflected from (C) is therefore modulated by the IR image formed on (C) by radiation incident upon IR windows in either pocket 2 or pocket 3. This IR-modulated electron beam is then reaccelerated in (B) and redirected by the magnetic field to a phosphorescent screen (D) situated in pocket 4, where a visual image is formed.

The final visual image is thus formed by electrons which are first generated in the gun (A), then modulated by the photoeffect of the IR-sensitive material on (C). This device is capable of detecting IR radiation out to 7 μ from sources at temperatures of approximately 150°C.

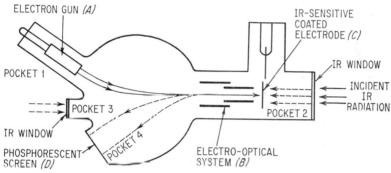

FIG. 7-36. Schematic of electron-mirror image-converter tube. (*After T. M. Odarenko.*[3])

The Czerny Evaporograph. This device, used for detecting long-wavelength IR radiation from relatively low-temperature sources, was developed originally by Czerny and his associates at the University of Frankfurt before the war.[78,79] As in long-wavelength IR photography, incident IR radiation energy is integrated over a period of several seconds by this device.

One side of a nitrocellulose membrane less than 0.1 μ thick is coated with a thin layer of blackened aluminum, zinc, or bismuth, with a high absorption efficiency to incident IR radiation. The other side is coated with a very thin layer of paraffin oil or some other substance that easily volatilizes when irradiated by IR (Fig. 7-37). When evaporated on to the membrane in a layer a few tenths of a micron thick, this oil assumes a vivid interference color which changes noticeably on exposure to IR radiation. This change may be observed visually or recorded photographically.[45] The volatilization rate is regulated by air pressure. The rapid evaporation of oil at near-vacuum pressures is halted by admitting air.

Detectivity is good, noticeable effects being produced by changes of 0.01 μ. The screen must be used intermittently, however, and operation is slow. Human beings were observed in 8 to 10 sec operating time at ranges of about 100 m. Objects with temperatures of 15 to 20°C above ambient were successfully recorded. An improved, more sensitive and versatile evaporograph is under development in the United States.

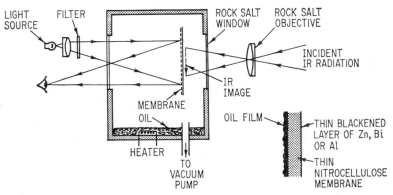

FIG. 7-37. Schematic of Czerny evaporograph. (*After Reference 45.*)

An IR detector based upon the principle that some semiconductor materials exhibit a steep absorption edge at a certain wavelength, which shifts with a change in temperature, has been developed in the United Kingdom. This device, known as the edgegraph, has a high response speed.

7-6. BACKGROUND NOISE IN DETECTORS

The effective detectivity of a detector is a measure of its over-all signal-to-noise response to incident IR radiation of given spectral characteristics. Extremely high detectivities would be possible if the interfering and limiting effects of noise could be eliminated. Some forms of noise can be largely reduced; others, however, cannot be reduced to the same extent.

Noise may be broadly defined as anything that interferes with efficient detection. No matter what kind of detector is being employed in an IR device, its detectivity is limited by noise of one kind or another. A photographic plate, for example, is limited in detectivity by grain size in the emulsion, and by diffraction, aberration, and transmission loss in the optical system of the camera. Background noise in an IR system may be broadly classified into three groups, as follows.

1. Signal Background Noise.   The IR-radiation source frequently undergoes statistical fluctuations in signal intensity.   The magnitude of these fluctuations will determine the smallest change that can be detected in a *steady* signal.   In addition, the radiation source often operates against a nonuniform background.   An example of this is the sky background with its varying spatial emissivity and thermal gradients due to scattered sunlight, reflected sunlight from clouds, and so on, against which a target such as an aircraft or celestial body has to be detected.   This type of noise, as we have seen, can be greatly reduced by efficient filtering techniques.

2. Environmental Background Noise.   The temperature of the detector itself and that of its immediate environment are sources of black-body radiation that interfere with incident IR radiation in the system.   This type of noise, known as photon noise, can be reduced in many instances by cooling the detector and its housing.   Environmental background noise is particularly important in the case of the longer-wavelength detectors operating against relatively cool target sources.

3. Internal Background Noise.   Various kinds of background noise are introduced by the detector itself, and by the associated circuitry.   Examples of this are density fluctuations in the emulsion of a photographic plate, *shot noise*, and *flicker noise* caused by random thermionic emission in photoelectric cells and photomultiplier tubes.   *Johnson noise, current noise,* and semiconductor noise occur in photoconductive cells and bolometers.   Johnson and current noise occur in thermocouples and thermopiles.   Current, Johnson, and *microphonics noise* occur in electronic circuits.   These types of background noise are difficult to reduce, and form an inherent limitation in the effectiveness of most IR detectors.   The causes and effects of these various types of noise[68] are discussed in more detail in the following paragraphs.

Photon Noise.   This is sometimes called *radiation noise* and gives rise to a flat noise spectrum.   Photon noise is caused by fluctuations in the rate at which photons of incident IR radiation arrive at the sensitive surface of the detector.   Consequently the power spectrum of photon noise has approximately the same shape as the response curve of the detector, and is frequency-dependent.

Temperature Noise.   This occurs in all detectors which operate on the principle of changes in a physical constant with temperature.   Thermal detectors fall into this category.   Fluctuations in the interchange of heat energy between the cell's sensitive surface and its immediate environment cause temperature noise.   The noise spectrum is essentially flat, that is, independent of frequency.

Shot Noise. This type is an electrical noise, present in amplifier tubes, electronic circuits, photoconductors, photoelectric cells, and photomultiplier tubes where random emission of electrons can occur. The power spectrum of shot noise is frequency-dependent, and is proportional to the responsivity of the detector.

Flicker Noise. This occurs in vacuum tubes at low frequencies. It also is an electrical noise, caused by fluctuations in the state of the hot cathode surface. Depending upon the nature of the cathode, flicker noise is either inversely proportional to the frequency or to the square of the frequency.

Johnson Noise. This is also known as *Nyquist noise* or *thermal noise,* occurs in resistors, and is caused by thermal fluctuations in the electrons themselves. The noise spectrum is independent of frequency and therefore flat, up to very high frequencies. The noise power spectrum, which describes the frequency distribution of the detector's mean square voltage fluctuation per unit frequency bandwidth, is proportional to the resistive component of the detector's impedance.

Current Noise. This noise is caused by the current flowing through a resistor, and produces a voltage fluctuation across the resistor. Not yet completely understood, it may be partly caused by contact noise. At present, current noise in semiconductors and its frequency dependence are being extensively studied.

Microphonics Noise. This noise is present in electronic circuits where vibration occurs.

Signal-to-Noise Ratio. IR detectors should be operated under such conditions that their performance is limited by detector noise rather than by IR system noise, in order to achieve the maximum possible detectivity.

In photoconductive-type detectors, this involves operating the detector at the optimum bias current, such that any further increase in bias current begins to reduce the detectivity.

In all types of detectors detectivity is dependent upon the frequency of the received signal, and, as we have seen, the chopping rate is adjusted to an optimum rate for the time constant of the particular detector employed. Detectors with time constants of a few microseconds, such as the indium antimonide and doped germanium cells, require higher chopping rates than lead sulfide or some of the thermal detectors, for the highest detectivity, in their sensitive spectral regions. Time constants may also be wavelength- and temperature-dependent for some detectors.

The dependence of detectivity on frequency for a detector is measured in the laboratory by observing the effect on detector signal by incident monochromatic radiation chopped at different frequencies. Detectivity dependence on wavelength is observed by varying the wavelength of monochromatic radiation.

REFERENCES

3. Odarenko, T. M.: "German Wartime Developments in Infrared," *Office of Technical Services, Department of Commerce, Rept.* PB 95308, March, 1948.
45. Canada, A. H.: Infrared Military and Peacetime Uses, *General Electric Company Data Folder* no. 87516, 8th printing, December, 1947.
64. Jones, R. Clark: *J. Opt. Soc. Am.*, vol. 39, p. 335, 1949.
65. *RCA Electron Tube Division Bull.* 7102, p. 4, December, 1957.
66. Cashman, R. J.: New Photoconductive Cells, *J. Opt. Soc. Am.*, vol. 36, p. 356, 1946.
67. Young, A. S.: Photoconductive Detectors for Infra-red Spectroscopy, *J. Sci. Instr.*, vol. 34, p. 142, 1957.
68. Jones, R. Clark: "Performance of Detectors for Visible and Infrared Radiation," Advances in Electronics Series, vol. 5, pp. 1–96, Academic Press, Inc., New York, 1953.
69. Avery, D. G., Goodwin, D. W., and Rennie, A. E.: New Infra-red Detectors Using Indium Antimonide, *J. Sci. Instr.*, vol. 34, p. 394, October, 1957.
70. Infratron Lead Sulphide Photoconductors, a State of the Art Report, *Tech. Bull.* 2, Infrared Industries, Inc., Waltham, Mass.
71. Barber, C. R., and Pemberton, L. H.: Silver-Palladium Thermocouples, *J. Sci. Instr.*, vol. 32, no. 12, December, 1955.
72. *Aviation Age*, January, 1958, p. 175.
73. Hornig, D. F., and O'Keefe, B. J.: *Rev. Sci. Instr.*, vol. 18, p. 474, 1947.
74. Archbold, E.: *J. Sci. Instr.*, vol. 34, no. 6, June, 1957.
75. Golay, M. J. E.: A Pneumatic Infrared Detector, *Rev. Sci. Instr.*, vol. 18, p. 357, 1947, and vol. 20, p. 816, 1949.
76. Leverenz, H. W.: *RCA Rev.*, vol. 7, p. 238, 1947.
77. Urbach, F., Nail, N. R., Perlman, D., *J. Opt. Soc. Am.*, vol. 36, p. 372, 1946.
78. Czerny, M.: Veber Photographie im Ultraroten, *Z. Physik*, vol. 1, p. 53, 1929.
79. Czerny, M., and Mollet, P.: Neue Versuche Zur Photographie im Ultraroten, *Z. Physik*, vol. 85, p. 108, 1938.

ADDITIONAL BIBLIOGRAPHY

Becker, J. A.: "Development of Thermistor Bolometers," Bell Telephone Laboratories, Inc., New York, June, 1948.
Billings, B. H.: "Research Techniques Leading to the Development of a Long Wavelength Infrared Viewer Evaporograph," Baird Associates Inc., Cambridge, Mass., June, 1951.

Burstein, E., et al.: Infrared Photoconductivity Due to Neutral Impurities in Germanium, *Phys. Rev.*, vol. 93, p. 65, 1954.

Clark, M. A., and Cashman, R. J.: Transmission and Spectral Response of PbS and PbTe, *Phys. Rev.*, vol. 85, p. 1043, March 15, 1952.

Daunt, J. G.: "Thermocouple Design," Oxford University, Clarendon Lab., June, 1946.

Davydov, B. I., and Gurevich, B.: Voltage Fluctuations in Semiconductors, *J. Phys.* (USSR), 7, 138, 1943.

Ellickson, R. T.: Light Storage in Infrared Sensitive Phosphors, *J. Opt. Soc. Am.*, vol. 36, p. 501, 1946.

Fonda, G. R., and Seitz, F.: "Solid Luminescent Materials," John Wiley & Sons, Inc., New York, 1948.

Frederickse, H. P. K., and Blunt, R. F.: Photoeffects in Intermetallic Compounds, *Proc. IRE*, vol. 43, no. 12, p. 1828, December, 1955.

Garlick, G. F. J.: Infrared Sensitive Phosphors, Telecommunications Research Establishment (Great Britain), November, 1947.

Gebbie, H. A., and Starkiewicz, J.: Lead Selenide Photoconductive Cells, *Services Electronics Research Lab. (Great Britain) Quart. Rept.* 21, January, 1957.

Hayes, H. V.: A New Receiver of Radiant Energy, *Rev. Sci. Instr.*, 7, 202 (1936).

Hewlett, et al.: Thallous Sulphide Photoconductive Cell, General Electric Co., West Lynn, Mass. (February, 1945).

Hickman, R. W.: "High Speed Thermistors," Harvard University Press, Cambridge, Mass., June, 1941.

Hickman, R. W.: The Development of Fast Thermopiles, Massachusetts Institute of Technology, Cambridge, Mass., December, 1946.

Jones, R. Clark: A New Classification System for Radiation Detectors, *J. Opt. Soc. Am.*, vol. 39, p. 327, 1949.

Jones, R. Clark: Factors of Merit for Radiation Detectors, *J. Opt. Soc. Am.*, vol. 39, p. 344, 1949.

Jones, R. Clark: On the Relation Between the Speed of Response and the Detectivity of Lead Sulphide Photoconductive Cells, *J. Opt. Soc. Am.*, vol. 43, p. 1008, 1953.

Jones, R. Clark: A Method of Describing the Detectivity of Photoconductive Cells, *Rev. Sci. Instr.*, vol. 24, p. 1035, 1953.

Jones, R. Clark: On the Minimum Energy Detectable by Photographic Negatives, *Phot. Sci. Tech.*, vol. 2, p. 56, 1955.

Kurnick, W. W., and Zitter, K. N.: Photoconductive and Photoelectromagnetic Effects in Indium Antimonide, *J. Appl. Phys.*, vol. 27, no. 3, p. 278, March, 1956.

Langton, W. G., and Barr, E. E.: "Development of High Speed Bolometers," Baird Associates, Inc., Cambridge, Mass., June, 1950.

Liang, T., et al.: "Research Investigation into Factors Affecting Long-range Photography," Cornell University Press, Ithaca, N.Y., November, 1952.

Moss, T. S.: The Ultimate Limits of Sensitivity of PbS and PbTe Photoconductive Detectors, *J. Opt. Soc. Am.*, vol. 40, p. 606, 1950.

Moss, T. S.: "Photoconductivity in the Elements," Academic Press, Inc., New York, 1952.

Moss, T. S.: Lead Salt Photoconductors, *Proc. IRE*, vol. 43, no. 12, p. 1869, December, 1955.

Mott, N. F., and Gurney, R. W.: "Electronic Processes in Ionic Crystals," Oxford University Press, London, 1950.

O'Brien, B. J.: Development of Infrared Sensitive Phosphors, *J. Opt. Soc. Am.*, vol. 36, p. 369, 1946.

Rose, A.: Performance of Photoconductors, *Proc. IRE*, vol. 43, pp. 1850–69, 1955.

Schaffernicht, W.: Summary of Recent Developments on Image Converters, *OKH* (trans. from German by AMC Report F-7S-2743-RE), May, 1949.

Schultze, M. L., and Morton, G. A.: Photoconduction in Germanium and Silicon, *Proc. IRE*, vol. 43, no. 12, p. 1819, December, 1955.

Simon, E.: "Photovoltaic Cells," Purdue University Research Foundation, Lafayette, Ind., December, 1952.

Smith, R. A., Jones, F. E., and Chasmar, R. P.: "Detection and Measurement of Infrared Radiation," Oxford University Press, London, 1957.

Suits, G., et al.: Excess Noise in Indium Antimonide, *J. Appl. Phys.*, vol. 27, p. 1385, 1956.

Vis, V. A.: A Method of Obtaining Uniform Evaporated Layers, *J. Opt. Soc. Am.*, vol. 45, p. 906, 1956.

Wesch, Ludwig: "Phosphors, Centimeter Waves, etc.," trans. from German. Report PB 14529, Dept. of Commerce, Washington, D.C., 1945.

Wilson, A. H.: "The Theory of Metals," Cambridge University Press, New York, 1953.

Wolfe, Bertram: On the Specific Noise of Lead Sulphide Photoconductors, *Rev. Sci. Instr.*, vol. 27, p. 60, 1956.

Zworykin, V. K., and Morton, G. A.: Applied Electron Optics, *J. Opt. Soc. Am.*, vol. 26, p. 181, 1936.

8

Infrared System Design Considerations

Preliminary design considerations influencing the choice of materials and the design of IR optical-detector systems for different purposes are discussed. The effects of target, background, atmospheric, optical, scanning, detector, and other parameters on system design are discussed.

8-1. PRELIMINARY DESIGN CONSIDERATIONS

Design Objectives. It has been emphasized that every IR system is designed to fulfill a specific purpose. Whether it be a pyrometer, a spectrophotometer, a camera, a telescope, a communications system, or an air-borne search and tracking system, the factors and parameters described in Chap. 2 must be considered, both in relation to the over-all efficiency of the IR system, and in relation to each other. A successful IR-system design, like a successful marriage, involves a great deal of compromise!

The design objective is to produce an optimum IR system for its particular application, within the cost budget, that will stand up to the environmental conditions encountered.

Although the materials available are somewhat limited, particularly in the longer-wavelength region, there are so many interdependent parameters involved that an orderly plan of attack on the design problem is essential. Let us now consider how these parameters influence design, and how the design problem can be tackled.

Before embarking upon any specific design, the following performance requirements of the IR system must be established.

1. What is the basic function of the proposed system?
2. What are the wavelength-cutoff limits of the system?
3. What order of system sensitivity is required?

In keeping with the tenor of this book and in view of the wide variety

188

Infrared System Design Considerations 189

of optical systems in use, these considerations will be examined from an over-all or generalized viewpoint; there will be no attempt at giving a detailed design analysis of one particular IR system.

System Function. Consideration of this will indicate the following design requirements:

1. Instantaneous and over-all field of view. Narrow and fixed, or wide angle? Is it required that the instantaneous field of view be mechanically scanned over a large total field of search?

2. Wavelength requirements. Is it required that IR radiation be detected over a relatively broad waveband? If so, what are the wavelength-cutoff limits required? Or is it necessary to detect monochromatic IR radiation at a single wavelength or in a very narrow band, or to select monochromatic radiation within a wide spectral range?

These considerations will indicate the type of optical system required, whether it should have a long or short focal length, and whether a mechanical scanning system is required as in a search-track system, or precision monochromatic coverage by a grating or prism is required as in a spectrometer. An indication will also be given as to whether reflective or refractive optics are more suitable, or a combination of both.

The optical-detector system required may range from a very simple system to a highly complicated, precise system. For example, an IR pyrometer may require a simple, rugged system. Either reflective or refractive optics may be employed and chromatic aberration can be tolerated. A relatively narrow, fixed field of view, with or without image chopping, may be used. A simple pyrometer may consist merely of an IR window, condensing and imaging lenses, and a detector.

On the other hand, an astronomical telescope similar to that illustrated in Fig. 9-17 may require a highly complicated and precise design. The telescope itself cannot tolerate aberrations. Reflective optics are desirable. Correction for earth rotation is required. A telescope of long focal length, with an extremely narrow instantaneous field of view, is desirable. It should be capable of being directed anywhere within a wide search field. The associated monochromator and spectrometer require a high-quality prism and a precision grating, in addition to a chopping device and first-class reflective optics.

System Wavelength Limits. Consideration of the nature and temperature of the source or target, its background, and the distance which source radiation is required to penetrate through an atmospheric or other type of environment to reach the detector will indicate the wavelength limits between which optimum system detectivity can be achieved.

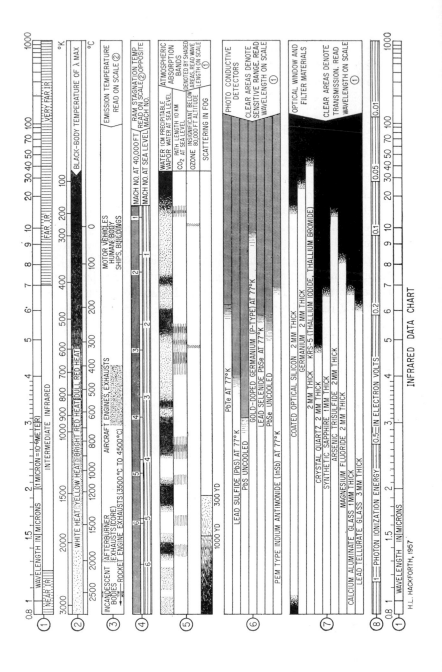

INFRARED DATA CHART

H.L. HACKFORTH, 1957

190

This chart is designed as a ready reference of approximate values and of conversions for common parameters used in infrared work.

Scale ② is related to scale ① by Wien's Law, λ max T = constant. λ max is the wavelength of maximum intensity for a radiating black body at T degrees absolute temperature. Scales ③ and ④ are referenced to scale ②. Scales ⑤, ⑥, ⑦, and ⑧ are referenced to scale ①.

Example of Use: IR search system is required for detection of a 600°C source.

1. Scale ② indicates detection is required in neighborhood of 3.2 μ. Lay slider across scales ① at this figure.

2. Scale ⑤ indicates a water-vapor absorption band from 2.5 to 3 μ and atmosphere "windows" of good transmission from 2 to 2.5 and 3 to 5 μ.

3. Scale ⑥ shows that a liquid-nitrogen-cooled PbS, PbTe, or PbSe detector is required to take advantage of the atmosphere windows indicated in 2 above. Scale ⑤ shows that radiation cutoff below 2 μ is desirable for suppression of scattered sunlight. This can be effected by a germanium filter, scale ⑦, which also indicates suitable optical material.

4. Scale ⑧ shows that if a semiconductor-type photoconductive detector is used, a photon-ionization energy of about 0.5 ev is required.

5. Scale ③ indicates types of sources radiating at this temperature. Scale ④ shows that the nose of an aircraft flying at Mach 3.25 at sea level or Mach 3.9 at 40,000 ft altitude would achieve a ram-stagnation temperature of this value.

FIG. 8-1. IR data chart for preliminary design considerations.

191

Once these limits have been established the designer can list the available detector types, and the window, irdome, filter, and optical materials to be considered.

The nature of IR radiation emitted from various sources, and the relationship between source temperature and the spectral distribution of radiation have been discussed in Chaps. 2 and 3. The effect of atmospheric attenuation for various path lengths, altitudes, and constituents can be computed from the data presented in Chap. 4. Using

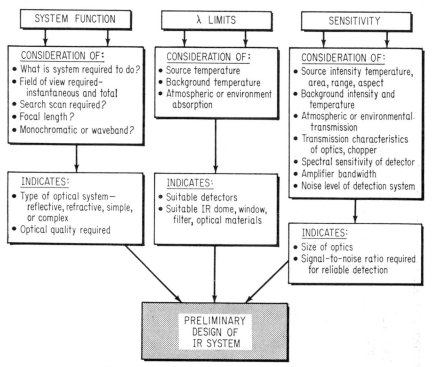

FIG. 8-2. Preliminary design considerations.

the principles described in Chap. 6, a choice of the most suitable optical materials for the IR system can be made.

A useful aid to the IR-system designer in making a preliminary appraisal of this nature is the Infrared Data Chart presented in Fig. 8-1. A typical example of its operation is described.

System Sensitivity. A similar consideration of the source radiation intensity and distribution, the interference and attenuation effects produced by the background and atmosphere, enables the designer to compute the minimum irradiation arriving at the aperture of the optical system.

Examination of the IR-transmission properties, the optical and physical properties of the various optical materials available, is required. Consideration of the spectral-response curves and noise properties of the various detectors available is also necessary. The designer is then able to make a final choice of a detector and optical materials that will give optimum system detectivity and performance.

Consideration of various optical designs, the suitability of refractive or reflective optics, whether a chopper is required and if so, what type, then follows. Filtering and electronic techniques are reviewed. From a preliminary analysis of this type the designer is able to outline the IR-system design. Figure 8-2 summarizes the preliminary design considerations required.

The next step consists of a more detailed analysis of the effects of these parameters on the efficiency of the optical-detection system, leading to a final design of the IR system.

8-2. FACTORS DETERMINING RECEIVED SIGNAL

We will now consider in greater detail the factors determining the received signal from a given source. The input signal, determined by the total effective irradiance or signal flux at the surface of the window, entrance slit, or irdome, depends upon the following parameters:

The spectral irradiance $I(\lambda)$ at the objective of the optical system, at a given wavelength λ, is a function of the following factors:

The radiant emittance of the Source $J(\lambda)$ at a given wavelength λ. This is dependent upon (1) the temperature, size, and emissivity of the source, which determine its radiant-intensity spectrum; and (2) the distance of the source from the detector, and the aspect angle of the source.

$J(\lambda)$ is a function of wavelength. For given conditions Chap. 2 describes how $J(\lambda)$ may be computed. It is measured in watts per steradian per micron for a particular source.

The objective aperture of the optical-detector system may subtend a small part of one steradian of solid angle at the source, depending upon the distance between the source and the detector. It may be convenient to express $J(\lambda)$ for a given source in terms of watts per square centimeter of objective aperture per micron.

The effect of background radiation superimposed upon the source radiation is the introduction of unwanted noise into the detection system (Chap. 3). In order to minimize this, the instantaneous field of view of the optical system may have to be reduced, and spectral, space, or electronic filtering techniques may have to be incorporated in the detector system.

Consider the example of the IR astronomical telescope in Fig. 9-17. Here a long focal length is required to produce an extremely narrow field of view, of the order of a few minutes of arc, to reduce background effects. In addition, spectral filtering by optical IR filters, space filtering to discriminate between the target and bright background areas,

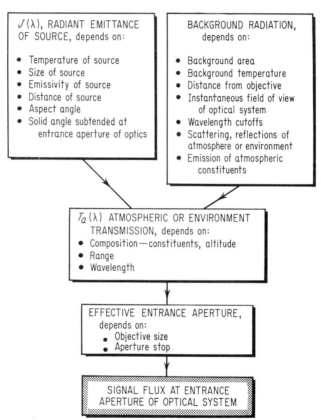

FIG. 8-3. Factors determining signal flux at entrance aperture of optical system.

modulation of the received radiation, and electronic filtering and processing of the detector output signal are required.

The effect of atmospheric attenuation of the source radiation depends upon the range and path orientation between the source and the detector, and upon the composition and spectral-transmission characteristics of the intervening atmosphere. The atmospheric transmission factor, $T_a(\lambda)$, as a function of range, wavelength, altitude, and atmospheric constituents, can be computed as shown in Chap. 4.

At the entrance aperture of the detection system, the irradiance $I(\lambda)$ at a particular wavelength λ can be expressed as

$$I(\lambda) = \frac{J(\lambda)T_a(\lambda)}{r^2} \qquad \text{watts}/(\text{cm}^2)(\mu) \qquad (8\text{-}1)$$

where $I(\lambda)$ = spectral irradiance of source at entrance aperture of optics (generally normalized to unity at its peak value)

$J(\lambda)$ = spectral radiant emittance of source, watts/$(\mu)(\text{cm}^2)$ of aperture

$T_a(\lambda)$ = atmospheric transmission factor at wavelength λ for path length r

r = path length between source and entrance aperture of optical system

These factors are summarized in Fig. 8-3.

8-3. EFFECTS OF THE OPTICAL SYSTEM

The optical system includes all windows, irdomes, mirrors, lenses, filters, prisms, or gratings used in the IR-detection system. It may be very simple in the case of a pyrometer, or very complex, as in the case of a spectrophotometer or a solar telescope. In addition to spectral filtering the optical system may also incorporate some form of space filtering, by means of stops, by a very narrow instantaneous field of view being scanned over wide look angles, by means of a rotating reticle, or a mosaic detector.

Detailed optical design is based upon the preliminary design considerations (Fig. 8-2) within the limitations imposed by the size, weight, and system function required and the environmental operating conditions. This requires a more detailed analysis of the effects and parameters listed in Fig. 8-4, and described in previous chapters. Here much compromise is necessary. The trade-off effects and advantages of different optical elements and optical and mechanical system designs must be carefully weighed. Thus, in IR systems employing telescopes, the optimum f value of the telescope consistent with size, field of view, and angular-accuracy limitations; the degree of correction required for aberrations; the type of scanning system employed and how it is mechanized; whether electrical or hydraulic drives are used for moving parts; these and other pertinent design factors must be considered.

The ultimate objective of the final optical and mechanical design is to obtain the maximum optical gain, detectivity, and spectral response for the IR system within the limitations imposed.

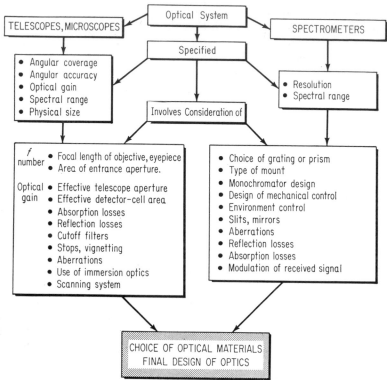

Fig. 8-4. Optical design considerations.

The over-all effect of the optical system on the signal flux reaching the detector may be expressed as a spectral transmission factor, $T_o(\lambda)$, which is a function of wavelength. For a given wavelength λ this is

$$T_o(\lambda) = A_o t_o(\lambda) E_s \qquad (8\text{-}2)$$

where $T_o(\lambda)$ varies between zero and 1.0

A_o = effective aperture area of optical system, cm²

$t_o(\lambda)$ = combined transmission function of all optical elements in the optical system, including optical filters and chopper or reticle if employed; $t_o(\lambda)$ is a function of wavelength λ and may vary between zero and 1.0.

E_s = efficiency of scanning pattern, if the instantaneous field of view of the optical system is scanned mechanically over a larger search volume

The effects of modulating the received signal by a reticle or chopper and the effects of scanning are discussed more fully in Secs. 8-5 and 8-6.

8-4. DETECTOR CONSIDERATIONS

Preliminary design considerations having established the spectral response and approximate detectivity required of the system, the designer will have a good idea of the type of detector cell that is most suitable.   For example, for operation in the 3- to 4-μ region, he may have decided to use a liquid-nitrogen-cooled photoconductive detector. Here he has a choice of several types of detector; lead sulfide, lead selenide, lead telluride, indium antimonide, and some of the germanium or

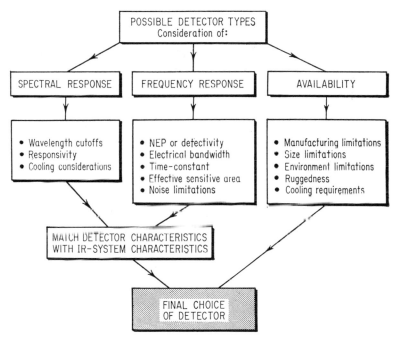

Fig. 8-5. Detector considerations.

silicon intrinsic and impurity-type detectors.   Further consideration of the characteristics of the available types of detector that will best match the characteristics of the IR system is necessary in order to make a final choice of detector.   The detector characteristics that require evaluation are summarized in Fig. 8-5.   Here again, compromise is necessary.   As an example, an indium antimonide detector may be the most suitable choice as far as spectral- and frequency-response characteristics are concerned, but may not be available with a sufficiently small sensitive area either to exploit the maximum optical gain of the system or to match the blur circle of the optical system for background discrimination purposes. At the same time, the detector noise may be so low that the system is limited by the preamplifier noise and thus is unable to use to advantage the ultimate detectivity of the detector cell. The spectral response of the detector is expressed as a relative spectral response, $R(\lambda)$, which is normalized to unity at the peak response. $R(\lambda)$ varies between zero and 1.0. It is wavelength-dependent and is given for the effective detector sensitive area A_d.

From Eqs. (8-1) and (8-2), the total effective radiant flux or irradiance at the detector is:

$$I_{\text{eff}} = \int_{\lambda_1}^{\lambda_2} I(\lambda) T_o(\lambda) R(\lambda) \, d\lambda \qquad \text{watts} \qquad (8\text{-}3)$$

where λ_1 and λ_2 are the lower and upper wavelength cutoff limits respectively, as determined by the optical-detector system.

Cooling the detector cell increases its detectivity, but at the expense of increasing its time constant.

The signal-to-noise ratio R can be obtained by dividing I_{eff} by the experimentally observed value of the NEP of the detector.

$$R = \frac{I_{\text{eff}}}{\text{NEP}_{\text{obs}}} \qquad (8\text{-}4)$$

In the case of photoconductive detectors, we have seen that

$$\text{NEP} = \frac{(A_d \, \Delta f)^{1/2}}{D^*} \qquad (8\text{-}5)$$

where A_d = effective sensitive area of detector cell
Δf = noise equivalent bandwidth used in measuring detectivity D (see Sec. 7-2)
D^* = Detectivity D reduced to the value that would be obtained with unit bandwidth of the noise and unit area of the detector. D^* is measured in $\text{cm}(\text{cps})^{1/2}/\text{watt}$.
NEP = noise equivalent power, watts

It can be seen from Eq. (8-5) that by reducing the effective sensitive area of the detector, the NEP is also reduced, that is, the detectivity is increased. A further advantage of a small A_d is an improved background discrimination capability. Equation (8-5) also demonstrates that an increase in detectivity can be gained by narrowing the bandwidth Δf.

The effective sensitive area A_d of the detector functions as an optical stop in its effect on the instantaneous field of view of the IR system. If

F = effective focal length of optical system as determined by the f number and aperture A_o of the optics

ϕ_A = azimuth angular instantaneous field of view

ϕ_E = elevation angular instantaneous field of view

then

$$A_d = F\phi_A F\phi_E = F^2 \phi_A \phi_E \qquad (8\text{-}6)$$

which shows that reducing A_d also reduces the instantaneous field of view.

We have already seen (Sec. 5-12) that the optical gain of the IR system can be defined

$$\text{Optical gain} = A_o/A_d \qquad (8\text{-}7)$$

where A_o = effective aperture of optical system, corrected for transmission losses incurred in the optical system

A_d = effective sensitive area of detector cell

Equation (8-7) demonstrates that optical gain is improved by reducing A_d.

When the radiation incident on the sensitive surfaces of the detector is frequency modulated, either at the source as in the case of an IR voice-communication system, or at the receiving end as in the case of a large number of IR systems, the effects of detector time constant τ and of the fundamental modulation frequency f on the responsivity of the detector must also be considered. We have seen from Eq. (7-2) that many radiation detectors have a responsivity curve that is an approximation to the form

$$R_V = R_o \left[1 + (2\pi f \tau_D)^2\right]^{-\frac{1}{2}} \qquad (8\text{-}8)$$

where f = modulation frequency, cps

τ = detector cell single time constant, sec

The effects of operating conditions on detector performance have been discussed in Chap. 7. It is important, in choosing the detector for a particular IR system to employ those operating conditions that ensure the system is detector-noise limited rather than system-noise limited, in order to achieve optimum performance. This involves consideration of the frequency dependence of the noise power spectrum, and of the single or multiple time constants of the detectors being considered for the IR system.

8-5. DETECTION RANGE

A minimum S/N ratio for the satisfactory operation of an IR system under given conditions is established during the preliminary design analysis.   In IR search systems a minimum detection range on a certain type of target for given operating conditions is generally a design requirement.   The system must be designed to achieve a minimum signal-to-noise ratio under these conditions.

It follows from Eqs. (8-1), (8-3), and (8-4), since $I(\lambda)$ is dependent upon $T_a(\lambda)$, the atmospheric transmission factor, which is itself dependent upon the range r, that the signal-to-noise ratio R in Eq. (8-4) cannot be solved directly for the maximum detection range. This is true at altitudes where $T_a(\lambda)$ is a function of path length r.   The maximum detection range possible with a given IR system is, therefore, obtained by plotting R as a function of r, and reading off $r_{\max}$ at the maximum value of R.

At higher altitudes, where $T_a(\lambda)$ can be considered independent of r, with little error, we have, from Eqs. (8-1), (8-3), and (8-4)

$$R = \frac{k}{r^2 \text{NEP}} \int_{\lambda_1}^{\lambda_2} J(\lambda) T_a(\lambda) T_o(\lambda) R(\lambda) \, d\lambda \qquad (8\text{-}9)$$

where k is a constant.

The range for a given signal-to-noise ratio is then obtained directly from

$$r = \left[\frac{k \int_{\lambda_1}^{\lambda_2} J(\lambda) T_a(\lambda) T_o(\lambda) R(\lambda) \, d\lambda}{R(\text{NEP})} \right]^{1/2} \qquad (8\text{-}10)$$

PART II

APPLICATIONS OF
INFRARED RADIATION

9

Infrared Instruments

Application of the basic concepts developed in the previous chapters to the design of infrared instruments widely used in the scientific and industrial fields is described. The principles of design and method of operation of typical examples of these infrared instruments are discussed.

9-1. IR RADIOMETERS AND PYROMETERS

The amount of radiation from an object depends, as we have seen in Chap. 2, upon its temperature and the emissivity of its surface. Radiometers and pyrometers measure radiation. In order to determine the temperatures corresponding to their readings, they must be calibrated against a standard black-body source at a known temperature.

Radiometers and pyrometers are used widely in many fields of science and industry. There are several excellent commercial models available, which use various types of detectors and optical systems in their construction. Two examples of typical commercial products are given, one employing a refractive lens system, the other a reflective optical system.

The Servotherm® 1372 Radiation Pyrometer. Manufactured by the Servo Corporation of America, this pyrometer is extensively used throughout industry for automatic measurement and control purposes. The pyrometer head contains two detector cells. IR radiation from the source being monitored is focused on one cell by a Servofrax meniscus lens. This lens, of arsenic trisulfide glass, covers a field of view 1 deg² and may be focused from a range of 2 ft to infinity. Its IR-transmission range is from 1 to 12 μ.

Radiation from an internal reference heat source, which may be adjusted by an amplifier reference dial, falls on the other cell. The two cells form a bridge which may be balanced by adjusting the internal heat source until its radiation output is equal to that of the external source. The calibration reading is given on a reference dial.

This procedure may be repeated at the tolerance levels required for manual control of the manufacturing process being monitored. This, for example, may be the measurement and control of a heat-cured assembly line product such as for an armature. Alternatively the pyrometer may be preset at an optimum reading. The differential

TYPICAL CONTROL ARRANGEMENT

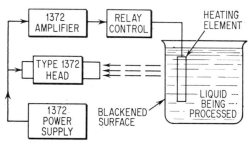

FIG. 9-1. Servotherm® Model 1372 radiation pyrometer. (*Courtesy Servo Corporation of America, Hicksville, N.Y.*)

between the source monitored and the internal reference source is then amplified to drive an automatic control to balance the incoming radiation against the preset internal reference source.

The pyrometer and a typical industrial control arrangement are shown in Fig. 9-1.

Modifications are available to adapt the pyrometer to particular needs. A wide range of detectors and optical windows covering various spectral wavelength regions and special optics for very small fields of view are available. Special choppers are available to solve the prob-

lem of background transmission.   Internally cooled reference sources
are available for monitoring processes with temperature changes below
ambient.   This pyrometer is sensitive enough to detect the heat from
a man's finger at a range of 200 yd.

Barnes Optitherm Model R4D1 Industrial Radiometer.   Manufactured by the Barnes Engineering Company, Stamford, Connecticut,
this radiometer has a high-gain reflective optical system, Fig. 9-2.   IR
radiation from the target source being monitored is collected and
focused on the detector by a pseudo-Cassegrainian optical system consisting of a primary mirror with a clear center area and a secondary
mirror.   A chopper, placed in front of the detector and electrically
driven, modulates the incident radiation.   Radiation from an internal

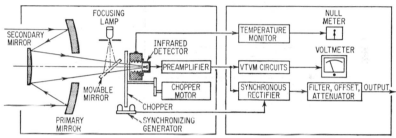

FIG. 9-2. Model R4D1 system block diagram. (*Courtesy Barnes Engineering Company, Stamford, Conn.*)

reference black-body source with variable temperature control is
focused by the auxiliary mirror, which has a clear center area, on to
the chopper, whose opaque sectors are silvered on the inside surface.
The reference-source radiation is then reflected onto the detector
surface.

The detector, therefore, receives target-source radiation transmitted
through the clear sectors of the chopper, and reference-source radiation
reflected by the opaque sectors of the chopper, thus modulating both
sources in an identical fashion.   Calibration is achieved by adjusting
the reference-source temperature to null the incoming radiation.

This radiometer is used extensively in far-IR photography and
thermography.   As with the Servotherm® 1372 pyrometer, a variety of
windows and detectors are available.

9-2.   INFRARED CAMERAS

Several types of infrared cameras operating over various spectral
ranges for air-borne, terrestrial, industrial, and scientific uses have
been designed and built.   These cameras employ a variety of detectors

and optical systems, designed for a specific application, and generally employ some kind of scanning mechanism to scan the relatively narrow field of view of the optical system over a wider area.

A typical example of such a camera, designed for use in industry in the far-IR region, is described in the following paragraphs.

Barnes Far-IR Camera.   This camera,[80] widely used in industry, is an ingenious application of the principles described in previous chapters.   It consists of a standard Barnes 8-in. Optitherm radiometer with a flake thermistor detector, a scanning attachment, and a small camera using standard photographic film (Fig. 9-3).   A Polaroid Land camera

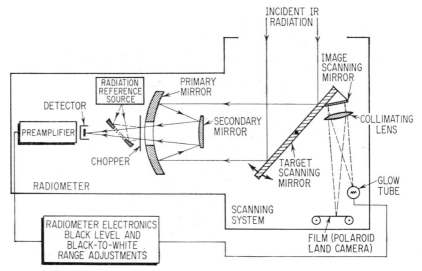

Fig. 9-3. Schematic of Barnes IR camera.   (*Courtesy Barnes Engineering Company, Stamford, Conn.*)

is usually employed to give rapid results (Fig. 9-4).   The scan mirror consists of a large plane mirror actuated by a conventional gear cam system in order to scan over the object plane the small area subtended by the IR detector.   The detector output is amplified and used to modulate the intensity of a glow tube.   Light from the glow tube, focused by a collimating lens, is reflected by a small recorder mirror rigidly attached to the back of the scan mirror and moving synchronously with it, across the photographic film.   The scanning mirror covers the object plane in a rapid horizontal scan, with a small vertical step deflection after each horizontal sweep.   A blanking circuit cuts off the glow-tube output during each rapid horizontal return to avoid retrace lines on the film.

A calibrated gray scale is automatically superimposed on the film by the camera mechanism. Calibration for a given target is achieved by adjusting the electronic gain so that the black area in the scale corresponds to a reference source at a known temperature, and the black-to-white range in the scale corresponds to a known temperature difference. For fast visual analysis of a thermal photograph the gray scale is divided into eight black-to-white sections, each section representing a precisely known temperature area. Thus, the temperature variations in the object under investigation can be determined directly from the photograph.

FIG. 9-4. Photograph of Barnes far-IR camera. (*Courtesy Barnes Engineering Company, Stamford, Conn.*)

This camera can detect a temperature differential of 0.02°C in the range −170 to 500°F. A thermistor bolometer detector provides sensitivity out to wavelengths exceeding 25 μ. The optical gain is 20,000, and a field of scan of 20° horizontal by 10° vertical containing 30,000 resolution elements is achieved. Scanning time varies from approximately 2 to 15 min depending upon the size of the scanned field and resolution desired.

Applications of this and other IR cameras are discussed in Chap. 11.

9-3. IR MONOCHROMATORS

Monochromators are used in IR work and in spectroscopy to provide single-wavelength or very narrow waveband radiation of high spectral purity. This is achieved by the use of either a diffraction grating or a prism to provide wide dispersion of the IR radiation and high resolution.

The Single-pass Monochromator. A simple single-pass prism monochromator[81] is illustrated schematically in Fig. 9-5.

IR radiation from the object under investigation passes through the entrance slit to an off-axis paraboloid mirror which sends a collimated beam to the prism. The beam is dispersed by the prism, reflected by the plane mirror back to the prism where a second dispersion occurs, and focused by the paraboloid on the exit slit. The exit and entrance slits are placed as close together as possible for minimum aberration. The narrow exit slit permits the passage of a narrow wavelength band of radiation from the dispersed beam to the detector. By rotating the prism the entire spectral region under investigation may be scanned.

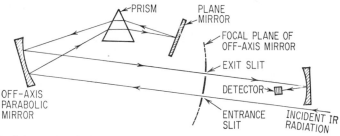

Fig. 9-5. Schematic of single-pass prism monochromator. (*After Reference 81.*)

This type of monochromator has a limited resolution, determined by the finite size and quality of the prism employed. Radiation scattered by the various optical components causes an impure spectrum.

Great improvement in both resolution and purity of spectrum can be achieved by either using a double monochromator or converting the single-pass instrument to a double-pass monochromator.

The Double-pass Monochromator. A typical example of this type of instrument is the Perkin-Elmer Model 99 double-pass monochromator illustrated in Fig. 9-6.

Incident IR radiation passing through the entrance slit is collimated by the off-axis paraboloid mirror on a prism where refraction occurs. The beam is reflected by a Littrow mirror back to the prism where further dispersion occurs, and is focused by the paraboloid on the corner mirror. The corner mirror slightly displaces the beam and returns it through a chopper back through the system for further dispersion in the prism. The emerging beam, now highly dispersed, is focused by the paraboloid on a narrow exit slit through which it passes to the detector. The signals of first-pass radiation of wavelength λ and second-pass radiation of wavelength $\lambda + \Delta\lambda$ emerging through the exit slit are separated by the chopper. The bilateral entrance and exit slits are controlled equally and simultaneously by a micrometer screw graduated in microns. The angle setting of the Littrow mirror is also controlled by a micrometer.

To ensure wavelength stability, the monochromator is maintained at a constant temperature by strip heaters, and bimetallic temperature-compensating strips are attached to the Littrow mirror. Mirrors are used for high reflection efficiency and low radiation absorption. Better resolution and higher energy for a given slit width are obtained in this

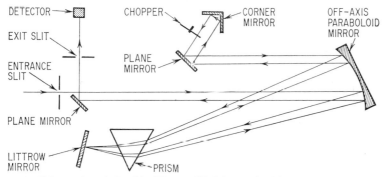

FIG. 9-6. Schematic of Perkin-Elmer Model 99 double-pass monochromator. (*Courtesy Perkin-Elmer Corporation, Norwalk, Conn.*)

type of monochromator. Greater purity of the spectrum due to the suppression of scattered radiation is achieved by means of the longer path length traversed by the radiation and the improved dispersion obtained in this instrument.

9-4. IR GRATING SPECTROGRAPHS

IR grating spectrographs are used for spectroscopic studies of molecular structure, where rapid automatic recording and extremely high resolution are required. When used with multiple reflection cells, long path-length studies in gases and liquids can be made. Fast recording is achieved by using highly sensitive lead sulfide, lead telluride, lead selenide, or indium antimonide detector-cells with rapid response times. The many applications of grating spectrographs are discussed more fully in Chap. 10.

There are two main types of grating spectrographs. The off-axis type is simpler in design. Mirrors of high quality are used to obtain good images and high resolving power. A typical example of this type is described in this section.

The Pfund type, employing on-axis paraboloid mirrors and plane mirrors with a hole in the center, produces superior images and higher resolving power. A typical example of this type is described in this section.

The majority of modern spectrographs are either evacuated or sealed to prevent unwanted absorption bands due to atmospheric gases. All controls to mirrors, slits, and prisms are operated through vacuum seals.

The accuracy of wavelength determination required decides the geometry of the optics required, and the number of lines per inch ruled on the grating. It also determines the angular displacement required of the grating arc. This may be a fraction of a second of arc for wavelength measurements required to an accuracy of a few hundredths of an angstrom.

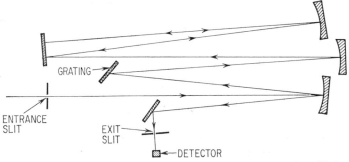

Fig. 9-7. Schematic of double-pass off-axis grating spectrograph. (*Reference 2.*)

A wide range of grating driving speeds and extremely uniform motion are required. Friction must be reduced to a minimum. Vibration and heating are minimized by mounting the drive motor outside the spectrograph and transmitting motion through selsyns. Gear reductions of the order of 100,000:1 between the drive motors and the grating table are used to minimize irregularities during slow-speed motion. Motion is transmitted to the grating table by a very accurate tangent screw operating against a rigid arm.[82]

An off-axis-type double-pass IR grating spectrograph designed and built by D. H. Rank at Pennsylvania State University is illustrated schematically in Fig. 9-7.

This grating spectrograph[2] has a focal length of 10 m, achieved by mounting the grating in Littrow fashion to ensure double passage of the radiation beam through the optical system. Using a grating of great perfection, a resolving power of 120,000 to 140,000 lines per inch in the 1.3- to 1.7-μ region, with an increase in resolving power of about one order of magnitude at longer wavelengths, has been obtained.

A typical on-axis Pfund-type direct-recording spectrograph[2] is illustrated schematically in Fig. 9-8. Incident IR radiation focused by a collimating lens on the entrance slit and modulated by a chopper, passes through the central hole of a plane mirror M_1. Reflected by the paraboloidal mirror P_1, it emerges as a parallel beam of radiation which is reflected by the mirror M_1 to the grating. The diffracted

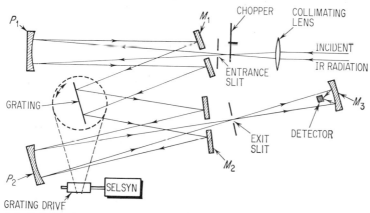

FIG. 9-8. Schematic of Pfund-type grating spectrograph. (*After Reference 2.*)

beam, reflected by M_2, is focused by a second paraboloid P_2 through the central hole of M_2 to the exit slit, emerging to the ellipsoidal mirror M_3 which focuses the beam on the detector. This type of on-axis system produces a better spectral image and superior resolution.

9-5. IR SPECTROMETERS

Modern IR spectrometers and spectrophotometers are widely used in industry for the rapid analysis of complex organic compounds and the routine analysis of gaseous, liquid, or solid samples. By automatically recording absorption spectra, the rapid identification, or "fingerprinting," of complex structures which would require many hours of routine chemical analysis is achieved. The widespread uses of these instruments are described in Chaps. 10 and 11.

Some typical examples of a few of the many commercial instruments available are described.

Perkin–Elmer Model 137 Infracord Spectrophotometer. Figure 9-9 is an optical schematic of this spectrophotometer, manufactured by the Perkin-Elmer Corporation, Norwalk, Connecticut. The plane mirror M_1 and two toroid mirrors M_{T_1} and M_{T_2} split radiant energy from a

1200°C heated ceramic-tube source producing IR energy in the 2.5-
to 15-μ region into sample and reference beams.   Toroid mirror M_{T_1}
focuses the sample beam through the sampling area onto the 100 per
cent comb.   Toroid mirror M_{T_2} focuses the reference beam onto a high-
accuracy optical wedge or attenuator.   After passing through the sampling area, sample and reference beams are directed by plane mirrors
M_2, M_3, and M_4 onto a semicircular-sector mirror M_5, rotating at 13
revolutions per second. M_5 alternately reflects the reference beam and
transmits the sample beam through an aperture stop.   This ensures

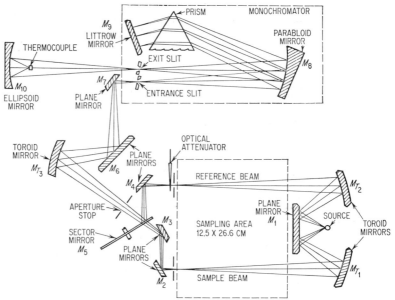

FIG. 9-9. Optical schematic of Perkin-Elmer Model 137 spectrophotometer.
(*Courtesy Perkin-Elmer Corporation, Norwalk, Conn.*)

that both reference and sample beams are the same size and follow
identical paths through the remainder of the optical system.

The signal beam leaving the sector mirror consists therefore of alter-
nate pulses of sample and reference radiation, chopped 180 degrees out
of phase for comparison purposes.   The signal beam is now focused by
toroid mirror M_{T_3} and reflected by plane mirrors M_6 and M_7 through
the entrance window of the monochromator onto its entrance slit,
which is situated at the focal point of the toroid mirror.

The beam now diverges to an off-axis paraboloid mirror M_8, which
reflects it as a collimated beam (parallel rays) onto a rock salt prism
with a 70° apex angle.   This prism has a serrated base, forming light

traps to reduce scattered light. The 70° apex angle gives high dispersion and about 50 per cent more energy than conventional 60° prisms. The prism disperses the component wavelengths into IR wavelengths which are then reflected by the Littrow mirror M_9 back into the prism for further dispersion.

The dispersed radiation is then focused by the paraboloid mirror M_8 on the exit slit as a band of individual wavelengths falling across the slit. The rotational position of the Littrow mirror determines the particular wavelength which emerges from the exit slit, and is then focused by an ellipsoid mirror M_{10}, on the thermocouple detector. The Littrow mirror is mechanically linked, with no lag or backlash, with the recorder-drum shaft so that the wavelength scale on the drum exactly corresponds to the reflected wavelength. True correlation between the drum-wavelength scale and the transmitted wavelength, despite temperature variations, is automatically maintained by a bimetallic strip on the Littrow mount. The monochromator is sealed and dessicated to protect the prism from moisture and dust.

The high-speed, high-sensitivity thermocouple is enclosed in a steel casing to eliminate pickup, and evacuated to increase its signal-to-noise ratio. It is sealed by a potassium bromide IR window.

When the energy in both sample and reference beams is equal, the thermocouple produces a d-c voltage which is not amplified by the a-c amplifier of the instrument. When radiation at characteristic wavelengths is absorbed by the sample, the intensity of the sample beam is reduced. An unequal signal is then produced at the detector by the pulses of energy from the sample and reference beams; this signal is converted to an alternating voltage and amplified by the 13-cycle amplifier. This amplified signal is then employed to drive a servo motor which moves the optical wedge in or out of the reference beam to equalize or null the beam intensities. The wedge is mechanically coupled to the recorder pen with no backlash. Attenuation of the optical wedge is linear, so that the recorder pen reads directly in transmittance.

This recording spectrophotometer is used extensively in scientific and industrial laboratories for both quantitative and qualitative measurements in the fundamental infrared region.

Unicam IR Spectrometer with Prism-grating Double Monochromator.* This high resolution instrument, manufactured by Unicam Instruments, Ltd., Cambridge, England, is designed to cover the

---

* Courtesy of Unicam Instruments, Ltd., Cambridge, England. A more complete description of this instrument will be found in C. S. C. Tarbet and E. F. Daly, *J. Opt. Soc. Am.*, vol. 49, no. 6, pp. 603–608, June, 1959.

widest possible spectral range without breaks for optical changes or adjustments.

The prism monochromator which has four interchangeable prisms is ganged with the grating monochromator having two interchangeable gratings, by cams linear in wave number, driven by a common shaft. The instrument may be used either as a prism-grating double monochromator, or as a prism spectrometer by blanking the grating monochromator. Gratings, prisms, and cams may be automatically interchanged by means of push buttons.

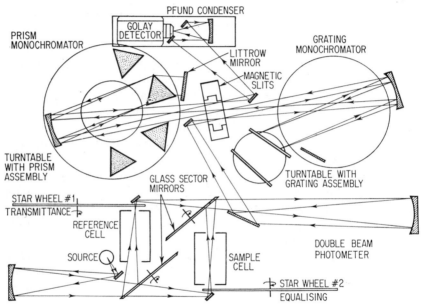

FIG. 9-10. Schematic of Unicam multiple-prism spectrometer. (*Courtesy Unicam Instruments, Ltd., Cambridge, England.*)

Figure 9-10 shows the optical layout. Magnetically operated slits, programmed by a tapped potentiometer, provide a constant energy background. A Starwheel time-sharing beam attenuator is used in the double beam photometer.

Flame-temperature Spectrometer. A typical example of the adaptation of these techniques to the measurement of large-area flame temperatures is described. Thermocouples and pyrometers require either the introduction of a probe into the flame, or a knowledge of the emissivity of the object to be measured.

With the advent of turbojets, ramjets, afterburners, and rockets, a method is required for measuring the temperature of flames up to 5 ft in diameter at temperatures of several thousands of degrees centigrade, moving at supersonic speeds. A design by Tandler, developed by the Industrial Scientific Company, New York, that is rapid, accurate, and requires no calibration or attenuation of the gas stream uses an IR spectrometer (Fig. 9-11). IR radiant energy from a source of known emission passes through the hot gas stream where absorption bands occur due to the water vapor and carbon dioxide present in the gas stream as products of combustion. The IR beam is focused on the

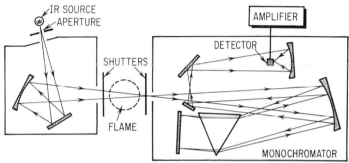

FIG. 9-11. Schematic of IR flame-temperature spectrometer. (*Courtesy Perkin-Elmer Corporation, Norwalk, Conn.*)

entrance slit of a Perkin-Elmer Model 83 monochromator. At a given wavelength, with the shutter out of the beam, the radiant energy E_1 is measured.

$$E_1 = E_S\alpha + E_T(1 - \alpha) \qquad (9\text{-}1)$$

where E_S = known energy from the source
E_T = energy from black-body source at gas temperature T
α = unknown per cent transmission of carbon dioxide and water vapor in gas stream

With the shutter in the beam, the energy E_2 is measured, where

$$E_2 = E_T(1 - \alpha) \qquad (9\text{-}2)$$

Equations (9-1) and (9-2) are then solved for α and E_T, from which the gas-stream temperature is obtained.

Beckman Model IR-4 IR Spectrophotometer. This versatile IR spectrophotometer combines in a single instrument the advantages of single-beam and double-beam systems, together with the advantages of double-beam monochromator design. A schematic of this instrument is shown in Fig. 9-12. The photograph of this spectrophotometer, Fig. 9-13, clearly shows the recording chart and control panel.

For double-beam operation, radiation from a Nernst glower N passes through the half mirror C_1 rotating at 11 cps, and through the sample during one-half revolution of the mirror, where it is recombined by the

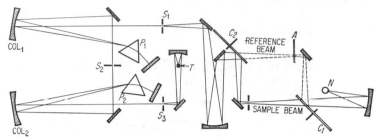

Fig. 9-12. Schematic of Beckman Model IR-4 spectrophotometer. (*Courtesy Beckman Instruments, Inc., Fullerton, Calif.*)

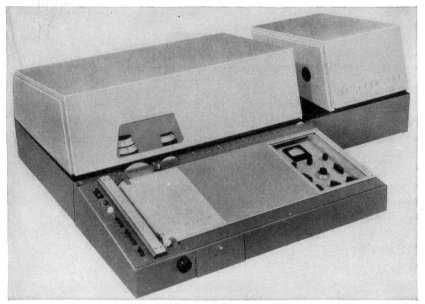

Fig. 9-13. Photograph of Beckman Model IR-4 spectrophotometer. (*Courtesy Beckman Instruments, Inc., Fullerton, Calif.*)

synchronously rotating half mirror C_2. During the other half revolution of the mirror the beam is deflected through the reference. Mirror C_1 chops the radiation beam at 11 cps and directs it alternately through the sample and through the reference.

The recombined beam is then directed through the entrance slit S_1 of controllable width, into the first of two monochromators. In the first monochromator the beam is transmitted by a collimator Col_1 through prism P_1 and associated Littrow mirrors for initial dispersion. This dispersed beam then enters via a fixed-width slit S_2 into the second monochromator. Here collimator Col_2 transmits it through prism P_2 and Littrow mirrors for further dispersion. These elements of the double monochromator are illustrated in Fig. 9-14.

FIG. 9-14. Photograph of double-beam monochromator in Beckman Model IR-4 spectrophotometer. (*Courtesy Beckman Instruments, Inc., Fullerton, Calif.*)

The now widely dispersed beam passes through the controllable exit slit S_3 and is focused on a thermocouple T. The signal from the thermocouple is amplified and used to position an optical attenuator A in the beam path, so that the radiation transmitted by sample and reference are equal in intensity. The position of A determines the position of the recorder pen, producing linear wavelength records.

For single-beam operation, the reference beam is blocked. The thermocouple receives only energy from the sample beam, chopped at 11 cps. The amplified thermocouple output is recorded directly by the pen.

This spectrophotometer, manufactured by Beckman Instruments Inc., Fullerton, California, is widely used by industrial and research organizations. An expanded scale is provided for high-resolution recordings. A typical high-resolution recording of the fine structure of an ammonia-vapor doublet obtained by this spectrophotometer is shown in Fig. 9-15.

9-6. IR MICROSCOPE

For the application of IR spectrometry to minute, nonhomogeneous samples, an IR microscope is

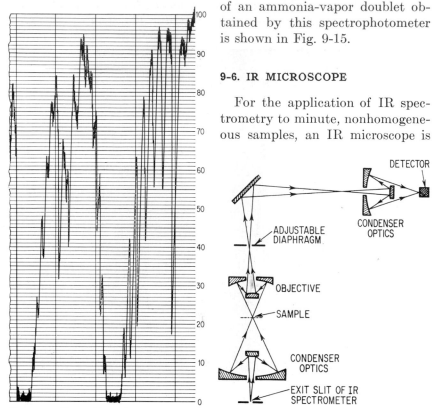

FIG. 9-15. Recording of ammonia sample at high-resolution run on Beckman IR-4 spectrophotometer. (*Courtesy Beckman Instruments, Inc., Fullerton, Calif.*)

FIG. 9-16. Elements of IR microscope. (*After Reference 84.*)

employed. This consists of an optical system designed to concentrate IR energy from the entire useful exit slit length of the monochromator of an IR spectrometer on a microsample, magnify the sample image, and focus it on a detector (Fig. 9-16). Magnifications on the order of 200× of a microsample a few microns thick are obtained. Reflective optics are used throughout to avoid chromatic aberration. Pfund-type on-axis optics are used to minimize distortion.

9-7. IR TELESCOPES

The different types of IR telescope optics have been discussed in Chap. 5. Applications to IR instruments are numerous and highly specialized in nature. The optical system of an IR telescope is always specifically designed for a particular purpose. The telescope itself is used with various types of detector, chopping and scanning mechanisms.

As an example, a telescope designed for use with a Pfund-type grating spectrometer and a cooled lead sulfide detector is described. This instrument[85] was designed at the McMath-Hulbert Observatory, Ann Arbor, Michigan, for investigation of the IR solar spectrum in the 1- to

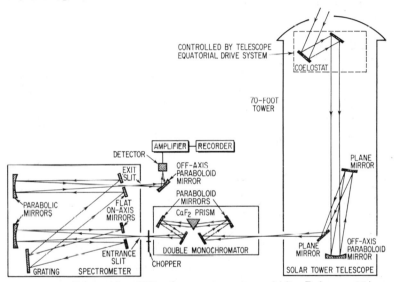

Fig. 9-17. Schematic of IR solar spectrometer. (*After Reference 85.*)

3.6-μ region, using the McGregor solar-tower telescope with an equatorial drive, and is illustrated schematically in Fig. 9-17.

A parallel beam of solar radiation is maintained in the field of view by a coelostat controlled by an equatorial-drive system which compensates for the earth's motion. The long-focal-length solar telescope employs reflective optics throughout to eliminate chromatic aberration. Radiation emerging from the telescope is focused on the entrance slit of a double monochromator, which also employs reflective optics throughout, with the exception of a calcium fluoride prism which has high transmission and dispersion in this spectral region. Radiation leaving the double monochromator, chopped at 1,080 cps by a sectored disk driven by a synchronous motor, is focused on the entrance slit of a long-focus all-reflecting Pfund-type spectrometer employing a plane reflection grating.   A grating with 600 lines per millimeter is used for the 1- to 2.5-μ band, a similar reflection grating with 200 lines per millimeter being employed for the 2.5- to 3.6-μ band.

Radiation emerging from the exit slit of the spectrometer is focused by an off-axis paraboloid mirror on a lead sulfide detector cell cooled with solid carbon dioxide and acetone.   The cell output signal, modulated at 1,080 cps by the chopper, is amplified in a variable bandpass amplifier designed to operate at this frequency and match the cell characteristics and recorded on a Leeds and Northrup Speedomax Recorder.   The over-all time constant of the system is 2 sec.

9-8. IR CONTINUOUS-PROCESS ANALYZERS

IR process-stream analyzers are used widely in industry and science for the continuous measurement and analysis of gaseous and liquid process streams.   These analyzers operate on the principle that the presence of particular chemical substances or compounds in the process stream are detected by their absorption of IR radiation at wavelengths corresponding to the characteristic frequencies of vibration of their molecules.

Industrial IR analyzers[86] at present operate in the spectral region between 2 and 15 μ approximately.   In this wavelength region a great many chemical compounds have strong absorption bands and can, therefore, be detected in complicated mixtures.   The wavelength region mentioned is limited only by the optical windows, materials, and detectors available.   It is being extended by the development of new materials and detectors with improved responsivity at longer wavelengths.

Chemical compounds exhibit one or many relatively narrow absorption bands.   (Typical IR spectra have been shown in Fig. 4-1 for gaseous atmospheric constituents.)   These absorption bands are unique for a particular substance.

Detectors used in commercial analyzers may be *nonselective* or wideband detectors such as thermocouples and thermopiles, or *wavelength-selective* such as the condenser-microphone detector filled with a specific IR-absorbing gas (see Chap. 7).

There are two basic types of analyzers, distinguished by the method they employ for wavelength selection.   *Nondispersive analyzers* use an optical filtering method.   Actually, they are self-filtering, since commercial analyzers of this type use as a filter a sealed container filled with a gaseous or liquid sample of the component to be detected.   Non-dispersive analyzers may employ either nonselective or selective detectors.   They are simple in construction, are stable over long periods and are relatively cheap in price.   *Dispersive* analyzers select the desired wavelengths by means of a dispersive element such as a grating or prism.   Movement of a narrow slit-shaped aperture in the IR spectrum isolates the particular wavelength desired.   These analyzers have superior sensitivity and background-elimination qualities.   However, they are more difficult to stabilize in industrial environments and are far more costly than the nondispersive analyzers.   A commercially available example of each type will be described.

The M-S-A Model 200 IR Analyzer.   An excellent example of a nondispersive IR analyzer, widely used in industrial plants, is the M-S-A Model 200 IR gas and liquid analyzer manufactured by the

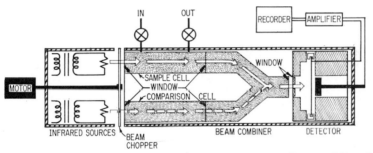

FIG. 9-18.   Schematic of M-S-A Model 200 IR analyzer.   (*Courtesy Mine Safety Appliances Company, Pittsburgh, Pa.*)

Mine Safety Appliances Company of Pittsburgh, Pennsylvania.   This analyzer is employed in the fields of process measurement and control, quality control, and the measurement of toxic and combustible gases or vapors.   It can accomplish, in the industrial plant, almost any gas or liquid analysis which can be made by laboratory IR spectrometers.

The principle of operation is shown in the schematic diagram, Fig. 9-18.   Beams of radiation from two similar sources of IR radiation in the form of Nichrome filaments travel through stainless steel cells. One beam traverses the sample cell; the other beam traverses the comparison cell.   Radiation emergent from the two cells converges in the beam combiner into a single condenser microphone detector.   Radiation is absorbed in the detector, increasing the temperature and pressure of its gas, causing a movement of the membrane.   This movement is converted and electrically amplified to produce an output signal.

Between the sources and the cells, a metal slide alternately blocks the radiation to the sample cell and that to the comparison cell.   The amplifier is tuned to produce an output signal only when a variation in light intensity occurs at the alternating frequency.   When the beams are equal in intensity, an equal amount of radiation enters the detector from each beam and the output is zero.

Upon the introduction into the sample cell of the gas or liquid to be analyzed, radiation reaching the detector from the sample beam is reduced by absorption.   The beams now become unequal, and the radiation entering the detector flickers as the beams are alternated, causing a corresponding expansion or contraction of the detector gas. The resulting movement of the membrane varies the capacity of the condenser microphone, which thus generates an electrical signal which is proportional to the difference between the two radiation beams. This signal is then amplified and fed to a recorder or indicating meter.

A Dispersive IR Analyzer.   The Model 93 Bichromator analyzer manufactured by the Perkin-Elmer Corporation, Norwalk, Connecticut, employs an optical null principle to measure continuously the ratio

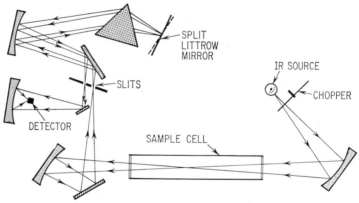

FIG. 9-19. Schematic of a dispersive IR analyzer.   (*Courtesy Perkin-Elmer Corporation, Norwalk, Conn.*)

of radiant power at two different wavelengths.   This has the advantage of largely eliminating the effects of changes in sample-cell transmission and changes in source temperature.

IR radiation from a source is chopped, and directed through the sample cell into a monochromator, where any two preselected wavelengths are isolated by a split Littrow mirror (Fig. 9-19).   The two preselected wavelengths are chosen so that one is at a strong absorption band of the material under investigation, and the other is not absorbed at all, or only slightly.   The source and monochromator are separately enclosed and pressurized.   This type of dispersive analyzer, unlike the nondispersive type described, does not have to store a gaseous sample of the material to be detected in the detector compartment. It can, therefore, analyze nonvolatile and unstable materials.

9-9. EMISSIVITY-MEASURING INSTRUMENT

This is an IR instrument developed and produced by the Barnes Engineering Company, Stamford, Connecticut.[87] It is used for the rapid and accurate measurement of the emissivity of various materials which may be in liquid, paste, powder, or solid form.

A schematic diagram of this instrument is presented in Fig. 9-20. It consists of a standard Barnes 8-in. Optitherm radiometer shown in

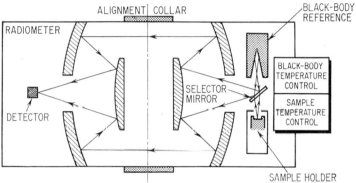

FIG. 9-20. Schematic of Barnes emissivity-measuring device. (*Courtesy Barnes Engineering Company, Stamford, Conn.*)

the left half of the diagram. The emissivity-measuring device shown in the right half of the diagram is coupled to the radiometer by an alignment collar. A collimating optical system, consisting of primary and secondary front-surfaced mirrors forming a Cassegrainian telescope similar to that used in the radiometer, collects the IR energy reflected from a selector mirror placed near the focal point and directs it into the radiometer.

In one position the selector mirror directs IR radiation from a black-body standard-radiation source through the optical system to the detector. In its other position the selector mirror directs IR radiation from the sample to the detector. The temperatures of both the standard source and the sample are independently and accurately regulated by means of temperature controllers.

In use, the two temperature controllers are set at a desired temperature T_1. Indicator lights show when both the sample and the black body have reached this temperature. The selector mirror is then set to reflect radiation from the sample. A constant voltage output V_{ST_1} from the radiometer indicates that the sample temperature has stabilized. The selector mirror is then set to its other position. Radiation from the standard black body at the same temperature T_1 is measured as a constant voltage output V_{BT_1}. The ratio of these two measurements gives the emissivity ϵ.

To eliminate inaccuracies due to stray radiation and temperature-gradient effects, these measurements are repeated for another temperature T_2, close to T_1. Then emissivity ϵ is given by

$$\epsilon = \frac{V_{ST_1} + V_{ST_2}}{V_{BT_1} - V_{BT_2}} \tag{9-3}$$

REFERENCES

2. Nielsen, A. H.: Recent Advances in Infrared Spectroscopy, *Office of Ordnance Research Tech. Memo.* 53-2, December, 1953.
80. *Barnes Engineering Co. Tech.*, Barnes Engineering Company, Stamford, Conn., Fall, 1957.
81. Walsh, A.: *J. Opt. Soc. Am.*, vol. 42, p. 95, 1952.
82. Nelson, B. C.: *J. Opt. Soc. Am.*, vol. 39, p. 68, 1949.
83. Courtesy of Perkin-Elmer Corporation, *Model* 137 *Bull.*, Norwalk, Conn., June, 1958.
84. *Perkin-Elmer Instr. News Sci. Ind.*, vol. 4, no. 4, Summer, 1953.
85. McMath, R. R., and Mohler, D. C.: *J. Opt. Soc. Am.*, vol. 39, p. 903, 1949.
86. Troy, Daniel H.: Infrared Process-Stream Analyzers, *Control Engineering*, November, 1957, p. 116.
87. Instrument for Measuring Emissivity, *Barnes Engineering Co. Tech.*, no. 8, Winter, 1957.

ADDITIONAL BIBLIOGRAPHY

Badger, R. M., and Newman, R.: A Microilluminator for the Study of the Infrared Spectra of Small Samples at Low Temperatures, *Rev. Sci. Instr.*, vol. 22, p. 935, December, 1951.
Fastie, D., and Pfund, A.: Selective Infrared Gas Analyzers, *J. Opt. Soc. Am.*, vol. 37, p. 762, 1947.
Oetjen, R. A., et al.: An IR Spectrograph for Use in the 40-150 Micron Spectral Region. *J. Opt. Soc. Am.*, vol. 42, p. 559, August, 1952.
Silverman, S.: Determination of Flame Temperatures by Infrared Radiation, *J. Opt. Soc. Am.*, vol. 39, p. 275, April, 1949.

$$10$$

IR Applications in the Sciences

Following a brief history of the growth of IR spectroscopy, the principles involved and methods employed in this important branch of spectroscopy are discussed. Applications of IR techniques in the pure sciences are described.

10-1. IR SPECTROSCOPY

Introduction. In the last 25 years, IR spectroscopy has literally grown from an academic laboratory aid to a highly accurate and indispensable technique which today is extensively used in modern science and industry. IR spectroscopy is, in fact, the most important and widely used branch of IR technology.

Following the early discoveries of the existence of radiation at wavelengths beyond the limits of the visible spectrum (Chap. 1), the unique value of IR for investigating this longer-wavelength portion of the spectrum gradually became evident. The growth of the science of nuclear physics and the realization of its far-reaching potential for military and peaceful applications also stressed the importance of IR as a new tool for the study of atomic and molecular structure.

Molecules are composed of a geometrical framework of atoms and groups of atoms held together by binding forces characteristic of the electronic structure of these atoms. A molecule may be regarded as a framework of x atomic particles, with $3x$ degrees of freedom, which permit the vibrational, rotational, and translational motion of individual particles. The motions of translation and rotation account for 6 degrees of freedom. The remaining $3x - 6$ (or $3x - 5$ in the case of a linear framework) degrees of freedom describe the vibrational motions, and are distributed in the IR spectrum out to approximately 50 μ.[2]

Because of this, a particular molecule has a unique IR absorption spectrum consisting of many individual absorption lines. Each absorption line corresponds to a particular vibration-rotation resonance frequency. It has also been found that in the case of complicated multicompound molecules such as those occurring in complex organic compounds, the complete IR spectrum is nearly equivalent to the sum of the spectra of the individual compounds. This means that the IR spectra of individual pure compounds can be recorded and catalogued for reference purposes, and used in the IR spectroscopic analysis of complex organic substances. In effect, a substance can be uniquely identified or "fingerprinted" by its IR spectrum. By this means, compounds which would ordinarily require many hours of tedious analysis by conventional chemical methods can be rapidly identified and analyzed.

IR spectroscopy is also invaluable as a fundamental tool for the study of molecular structure. The effects of vibration-rotation interaction, resonance interaction, coriolis-type coupling of vibration-rotation motions, and the intermolecular distances of atoms in molecular structures can be studied from the observation of IR spectral-line separations and their changes.

In complex molecules, the IR absorption spectrum may consist of hundreds of individual spectral lines, often with very little wavelength separation (fine structure). A typical example, showing the transmission of polystyrene film between 1 and 15 μ, is illustrated in Fig. 10-1.

Instruments used in IR spectroscopic analysis must, therefore, possess the following qualities to a high degree:

1. Sensitivity
2. High resolution
3. Rapid and preferably automatic recording of spectra
4. Wide waveband coverage

The IR spectrum of polystyrene, illustrated in Fig. 10-1, required 10 min of recording time on a Beckman Model IR-5 direct-ratio recording spectrophotometer.[112]

In order to see how these desirable features have been developed in modern IR spectroscopic instruments, a brief history of the development of IR spectroscopy is given.

Historical Background. Some of the earliest applications of IR spectroscopy employed reflection methods to investigate minerals and liquid solutions. IR radiation focused on a mineral surface was found to undergo successive reflections from the crystalline surfaces, producing maxima in the selectively reflected rays. The refractive index was abnormally decreased on the shorter-wavelength side and abnormally increased on the longer-wavelength side of an absorption band.   The increase in refractive index resulted in increased reflecting power and produced the maxima.   This *restrahlen* technique was employed by Rubens and Nichols[89-91] in 1897.   They employed a wire grating to extend their observations out to a wavelength of 60 μ.   The same technique was also used by Porter[92] to investigate a series of compounds in the IR spectral region out to 10 μ.

In the early days, few prism materials were available for use in the IR spectral regions.   Those generally employed were rock salt, useful out to about 15 μ, and sylvine (potassium chloride) crystals, useful out to 20 μ.   Aschkinass in 1900 used a rock salt prism to compare the IR reflecting power of minerals with that of silver.

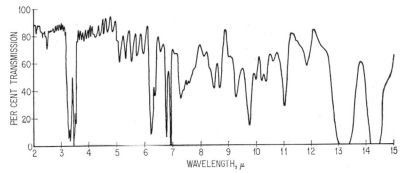

FIG. 10-1. IR spectrograph of polystyrene film.   (*Courtesy Beckman Instruments, Inc., Fullerton, Calif.*)

For many years suitable optical materials were very limited.   The principal detectors used were thermopiles and bolometers with slow response times on the order of 1 to 3 sec.[2]   IR spectra were manually recorded, a point at a time, using a galvanometer.   This was a time-consuming process involving frequent setting of the grating circle. Observation of the individual lines in a single absorption band was very inaccurate due to the instability of the instrument caused by variations in the environment.   Observations of this nature took many hours of tedious work.   Runs had to be repeated and averaged.   The observation of a spectral curve similar to that illustrated in Fig. 10-1 would take several weeks of work on a grating spectrograph.   Prism spectrographs, while not so tedious to operate, had similar drawbacks.

Military interest in the application of IR techniques for the ranging and locating of targets spurred an intensive development of new optical materials and new types of detectors.   Improved prisms of new crystalline materials and new glasses with superior IR transmittance in the longer-wavelength regions were developed.   New detectors with faster response times and higher detectivities became available. Thermo-couples, thermopiles, and bolometers with faster response times were developed, permitting chopping at higher frequencies.

Faster response times are important in IR spectroscopy since they permit increased recording speed with no loss in resolving power. The advent of photoconductive detector cells such as lead sulfide, lead selenide, and lead telluride with time constants of a few milliseconds or less, developed during the war, made possible chopping speeds as high as 1,000 cps.

These improved detectors and optical materials revolutionized the science of IR spectroscopy. In 1943, Baker and Robb attempted the presentation of spectral observations on an oscillograph screen. Daly and Sutherland used a fast bolometer to scan fairly rapid chemical changes. Silverman and Bullock used fast lead sulfide and lead telluride photoconductive detectors to present the spectra of combustion and explosions in gases on an oscillograph.[2]

In the postwar years, new prism materials such as cesium bromide, cesium iodide, lithium fluoride, and calcium fluoride have been developed; these have a high resolving power out to 50 μ. New types of detectors such as the indium antimonide cells with time constants of a few microseconds have further increased recording speeds. The Golay pneumatic detector, the condenser microphone detector, new thermopiles, and other developments have extended the useful range of IR spectroscopy out to longer wavelengths (see Chap. 7).

In the same period, new and improved types of IR sources have become commercially available. R. W. Wood in 1946 showed how to make excellent plastic replicas of original gratings. Today, large echelette gratings with 15,000 lines per inch or more are produced commercially on ruling machines. As a result of these developments, at the present time several thousand prism and grating spectrometers of high quality, capable of recording spectra, rapidly and automatically, on paper or on film are in use. Examples of typical commercial instruments are described in Chap. 9.

IR Prism Spectroscopy. The first commercial prism spectrometers employed a single beam of IR radiation. Two spectral records were made consecutively under identical conditions, the first with a sample in the beam, the second without a sample, for reference purposes. For rapid automatic recording of percentage absorption or optical-density measurements, two beams are more convenient, and are employed in most modern spectrometers.

Today, IR prism spectrometers are manufactured commercially by several companies throughout the world. Examples of contemporary commercial models are described in Chap. 9. Apart from minor differences, modern IR prism spectrometers have the following basic design principles in common.

Sources used vary according to the IR spectral region being investigated (see Chap. 3). IR radiation from the source enters the first part of the spectrometer where it is collimated by mirror optics into either a single beam or into twin beams, one of which is passed through the sample cell. In either case, the beams are modulated by a chopper before reaching the detector. The beam or beams are then combined if necessary by mirror optics and focused on the entrance slit of a monochromator, which forms the second part of the instrument. Here dispersion of the beam occurs in the prism. The various wavelengths are then directed through the exit slit of the monochromator on to the detector by either a slowly rotating Littrow mirror or by slowly rotating the prism. The modulated voltage output of the detector is amplified by a narrow-bandpass amplifier which is accurately tuned to the chopper frequency, and after rectification is recorded on a chart or film recorder.

IR Grating Spectroscopy. The dispersion obtainable with prisms is limited by the optical materials available with high transmission and high refractive index in the IR spectral region. For greater resolution of the fine line structure of absorption bands, much higher dispersion can be achieved with a grating.

Accurately ruled gratings with high dispersive power were not available commercially until after World War II. Wood (1910) constructed several fine echelette gratings by shaping the grooves of a Rowland grating, and in 1946 showed how to make excellent plastic replicas of original gratings.

Many improvements in the ruling process were made by Strong of Johns Hopkins University, who used optical flats of quartz or glass with a surface coating of evaporated aluminum, on which the gratings were ruled. This process ensures high reflectivity. A similar technique is now employed by optical companies for the commercial production by ruling machines of large echelette gratings.

Modern commercial gratings have extremely low ghost intensities, and are capable of resolving absorption-line spacings of a few thousandths of a centimeter. Improved gratings and recent improvements in detectors and in amplifier design have made possible the construction of grating spectrographs with resolving powers exceeding 150,000.

Optical systems employed in modern grating spectrographs are generally of the off-axis parabolic mirror type, or the on-axis Pfund type. Both types are discussed and illustrated in Chap. 9.

Far-IR Spectroscopy. As far back as 1897, Rubens studied the absorption and reflection spectra of mineral and liquid surfaces in the far-IR region using *reststrahlen* techniques.   Rubens and Woods (1910) developed focal isolation methods using potassium chloride prisms for IR studies out to 20 μ.[90,93] Total-reflection methods were employed by Jentzch and Laski[94] in the 1920 era.   The far-IR spectra of some inorganic and organic substances were studied beyond 20 μ by Strong,[95] who employed the method of residual rays and used the *reststrahlen* bands prepared by Schaefer and Matossi.[96]   More recent studies using a similar technique were made by O'Loane.[97]

Several long-wavelength spectra of various substances were obtained on apparatus developed first by Czerny, and later by Barnes, with wire gratings to study the IR spectral region from 20 to 135 μ.[2]

The first prisms of potassium bromide crystal, developed by Strong in 1930 and subsequently, extended prism spectroscopy out to about 30 μ.   Silver chloride, KRS-5 and KRS-6 prisms developed during World War II, extended the field out to about 40 μ.   More recently, cesium bromide and cesium iodide prisms were used by Plyler et al.[98] to extend prism spectroscopy to 54 μ.   The echelette gratings introduced by Wood in 1910 were used by Randall and coworkers in 1918 to build the first effective prism-grating spectrometer, employing the most sensitive thermopiles and amplifiers available at that time.[99]

Grating spectrometers for use even further into the far-IR spectral region have been built by many researchers.   These include instruments constructed by Randall et al.[100] for spectral studies between 25 and 200 μ, by Strong[101] for the 100- to 700-μ spectral region, and by Oetjen et al.[102] for studies from 25 to 400 μ, and several others.   These instruments were chiefly used for the spectral study of simple molecules, and for transmission studies of crystalline and filter materials.

Primary obstacles to be overcome, particularly in the design of fast, double-beam, double-pass IR spectrophotometers, are the low energies of radiation available, elimination of the effects of stray radiation and atmospheric absorption, and the requirement for a rapid-scanning instrument.   Because of these design difficulties, far-IR spectroscopy has only recently been widely used as an analytical tool.   Single-beam instruments with potassium bromide, cesium bromide, or KRS-5 optics are employed for the majority of measurements, still largely confined to studies of the more simple molecules.   Recent developments in double-beam spectrophotometers with interchangeable prisms of potassium bromide and cesium bromide, have made possible much higher scanning speeds, over a wider IR spectral region, and opened up new fields of research.   Modern recording spectrophotometers for far-IR studies are now commercially available from several manufacturing companies. A typical example is illustrated in Fig. 10-2, which shows a survey spectrum being recorded on a Perkin-Elmer Model 21 double-beam IR spectrophotometer.

Applications of IR Spectroscopy. Present-day applications of IR spectroscopy, and IR techniques in general, are so many and so varied that, in the pure sciences alone, a complete description of them all would fill several books. It is the purpose of the remainder of this

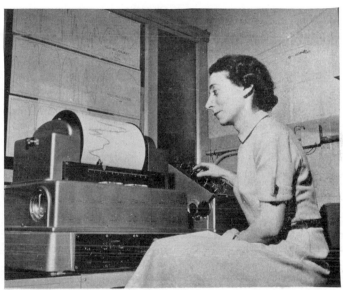

FIG. 10-2. Photograph of survey spectrum being run on Perkin-Elmer Model 21 IR spectrophotometer. Compared with known standard, curve quickly reveals presence or absence of impurities, hence its great value in product control. (*Courtesy Perkin-Elmer Corporation, Norwalk, Conn.*)

chapter to provide the reader with a brief summary of some of the more important applications in the pure sciences. A comprehensive bibliography, including several excellent books on applications of IR spectroscopy, is included for further reference.

Table 10-1 lists the more important applications of IR spectroscopy. Particularly in the far-IR spectral region, IR spectroscopy is a powerful research tool used in conjunction with Raman techniques to obtain essential information about molecular and atomic structure. Table 10-2 summarizes IR spectroscopic applications in this field. Further applications of IR techniques in other fields of pure science are described in the succeeding paragraphs.

TABLE 10-1. SOME APPLICATIONS OF IR SPECTROSCOPY

Field of application	Remarks
1. Investigation of molecular and atomic structure	Observation of vibration and rotation absorption bands under various conditions by near- middle- and far-IR spectroscopic methods
2. Low-temperature studies of gases, liquids, and solids	
3. Flame-emission and combustion studies	Investigation of high-speed, high-temperature jet, afterburner, and rocket-exhaust flames
4. Study of chemically unstable molecules	Discharge-tube studies
5. Transmission and optical-density measurements	Study of IR properties of optical materials, liquids, and gases
6. Studies of microscopic and nonhomogeneous samples	Qualitative and quantitative analyses, molecular structure studies
7. IR assaying....................	Identification and measurement of impurities in organic and inorganic compounds
8. Solid-state studies...............	Investigation of crystal structure, effect of lattice vibration, change of state
9. Rapid identification of unknown compounds	Molecular structure analysis using Bellamy and Colthup absorption-spectra reference charts
10. Environmental effects on molecular structure	Effect of temperature changes, irradiation, chemical reaction
11. Rapid analysis of highly complex materials	Plastics, rubbers, polymers, and complex organic compounds
12. Medical and biological studies.....	IR microscopic-spectroscopic investigation of tissues, cells, muscle fibers, blood, etc.
13. Astronomical and astrophysical studies	Investigation of solar spectrum, spectra of stars, planets, atmospheres of celestial bodies
14. Meteorological studies............	Laboratory investigation of absorption of IR by atmospheric gases in various path lengths. Studies of earth's atmosphere from balloons, planetary atmospheres from artificial satellites

10-2. IR APPLICATIONS IN PHYSICS AND CHEMISTRY

The majority of the lighter molecules exhibit a rotational fine structure coarse enough for adequate resolution by prism spectrometers. Where very closely overlapping spectral absorption bands are present, as in the case of the heavier molecules, higher resolving power is

TABLE 10-2. SPECTROSCOPIC INVESTIGATION OF MOLECULAR AND
ATOMIC STRUCTURE

Group	Spectral region	Information obtained
Electronic spectrum....	Ultraviolet, visible	Structural information on complex molecules
Vibrational spectrum..	Near- and middle-IR	Force constants and bonding forces between atoms in molecules; specific heats; thermodynamic data; molecular structure data
Rotational spectrum....	Far-IR, microwave	Far-IR gives information about low-lying vibrational absorption frequencies of organic molecules, pure rotation bands of light gases, fundamental vibrations in inorganic crystals[149] Moments of inertia, interatomic distances in molecules

required, and grating spectrometers are employed for spectroscopic analysis.

It has previously been stated that the IR spectrum of a multicomponent mixture is very nearly the composite of the individual spectra of its separate components. Large numbers of both inorganic and organic compounds contain functional groups whose IR absorption bands are well known. The American Petroleum Institute[103] has collected hundreds of spectra of extremely pure hydrocarbons, and developed qualitative analysis techniques employing IBM punched cards for the rapid isolation and identification of unknown compounds. Bellamy[104] and Colthup[105] have prepared charts of absorption spectra, correlating these with molecular structure to aid the chemist in performing IR spectroscopic qualitative analyses. A considerable amount of data on IR spectra is also available from other sources listed in the references at the end of this chapter.[106-109]

Using these reference spectra the chemist can quickly "fingerprint" or identify unknown materials by comparing the IR spectrum of an unknown sample with reference spectra of known materials. Thus, the presence of —OH, —CO, —CN, phenyl and other functional groups in an unknown sample can quickly be determined. For example, Fig. 10-3 shows the IR spectrum of an unknown drug sample. After grinding, mixing with potassium bromide, and pressing into pellet form, the sample was analyzed in a Beckman IR-5 double-beam IR spectrophotometer.   Absorption bands at 3.3, 6.7, 13, and 14 μ indicate the presence of a phenyl group.   Amine and carbonyl groups are indicated by bands at 3.0 and 5.7 μ.   The presence of these basic molecular groups indicated to the chemist that the sample was a barbital derivative.   By comparing this sample spectrum with reference spectra of similar pure materials until an exact match was obtained, the unknown drug was identified as Luminal.[112]

The near-IR spectrum is a region of overtones and combination bands.   These weak bands require long absorption path lengths, involving the use of multiple-reflection sample cells, for identification.   Sample cells of this type, with path lengths equivalent to 20 m at atmospheric pressure, have been designed by White for use with grating

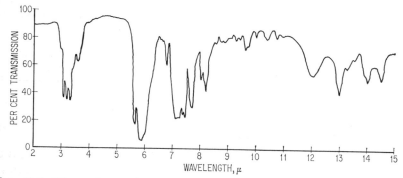

FIG. 10-3. IR spectrum of drug sample. (*After Beckman IR-5 spectrogram of Luminal; courtesy Beckman Instruments, Inc., Fullerton, Calif.*)

spectrographs.   The higher resolving powers obtainable with grating spectrographs have made possible the resolution of many new vibration-rotation bands for molecules like acetylene (C_2H_2), methane (CH_4), deuteromethane (CD_4), and others.[110]

Organic chemicals are primarily composed of combinations of atomic building blocks of the type —OH, —CN, —NH$_3$, —CH$_3$, —CO, —CS,

—COOH, etc., called functional groups.   These functional groups have characteristic IR absorption bands.   The presence of these characteristic absorption bands in an unknown sample indicates the presence of one or more of these functional groups and provides information on how they are assembled in the molecule.   The location of characteristic absorption bands in the most common functional groups is indicated in spectrum-correlation charts, and band assignments for thousands of organic compounds are listed in standard references.[110]

To the chemist, this greatly facilitates rapid qualitative analysis, since characteristic absorption bands in the IR spectrum of an unknown sample indicate its chemical nature. Figure 10-4 shows strong absorption bands in the IR spectrum of acrylonitrile, at those wavelengths where the frequencies of IR radiation correspond to the natural vibrational frequencies of the acrylonitrile molecule. The types of molecular vibration responsible for each major band are shown.[110]

Infrared spectroscopy is an extremely important aid in the quantitative analysis of chemical mixtures. The depth of an IR absorption band is proportional to the concentration of the component. Thus, by comparing a particular band with the depth of the same band in a known concentration of the material, the amount of material present in a sample can be found.[110] Known concentrations of a compound are

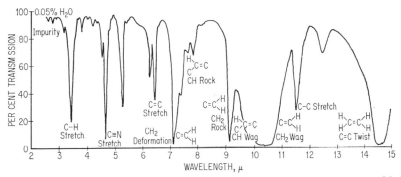

Fig. 10-4. IR absorption bands in spectrum of acrylonitrile. (*After run on Model 137 spectrophotometer; courtesy Perkin-Elmer Corporation, Norwalk, Conn.*)

made up, and their IR spectra are run to provide working curves of absorption versus concentration. From these curves, by comparison, the concentration of materials in the unknown sample can be rapidly determined.[110]

Prism and grating spectroscopy have also made it possible to carry out flame-emission measurements and combustion-problem studies. Investigation of the IR absorption spectra of thermally excited gases at high temperatures provides information on the higher energy levels in the molecules, and on transitions among them. Taylor[111] investigated the spectra of air, water vapor, and carbon dioxide in the 4- to 25-μ region using a Pfund-type multiple-reflection cell with an equivalent path length of 3 m, heated by strip heaters to 1000°C. The effects of absorption-band pressure broadening by gaseous impurities can also be investigated.

IR absorption studies on molecular groups like the OH, CN, and CS groups, which are chemically unstable but physically stable, are made in discharge tubes to obtain information on ground-state constants.

In organic chemistry, a large number of compounds have characteristic IR absorption spectra in the 2.5- to 15-μ region, known as the *fundamental* region. For this reason many of the less expensive commercial IR spectrophotometers operate in this spectral region. Techniques for the spectral analysis of chemicals in this region have been advanced by Colthup, Bellamy, Thompson, and many others.

A good example of the use of IR spectroscopy for the rapid identification and measurement of impurities in organic compounds occurs in the routine analysis required for a commercial product like carbon tetrachloride. The purity of this compound is of importance to both

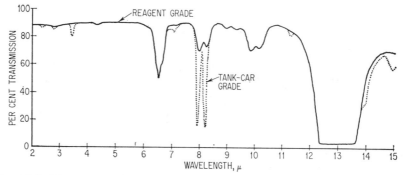

Fig. 10-5. IR spectra of carbon tetrachloride samples. Impurities in tank-car grade identified as chloroform and methylene chloride. (*Courtesy Beckman Instruments, Inc., Fullerton, Calif.*)

the manufacturer and the user. It can be rapidly checked on a commercial instrument such as the Beckman IR-5 double-beam spectrophotometer. The IR spectrum of a sample obtained from a tank car is shown in Fig. 10-5 compared with the IR spectrum of a commercial grade of purified carbon tetrachloride. In the IR spectrum of the sample, impurity absorption bands, at 7.9 and 8.2 μ, are found by comparison with reference spectra to be caused by methylene chloride and chloroform. The concentrations of these impurities in the sample are then obtained by comparing the intensities of the IR absorptions in the sample with those for known or synthetic blends.[112]

The preparation of potassium bromide sample disks is a relatively new technique developed independently by Stimson in the United States,[113] and by Schiedt at Tubingen, Germany.[114] The sample is finely ground and mixed with chemically pure potassium bromide powder. It is then pressed into a clear disk of known weight concentration

by means of a hydraulic molding press.   The sample disk is then placed
in the spectrophotometer.   This method avoids the problems of either
finding a suitable organic solvent, or of preparing the sample by the
Nujol mulling technique which results in scattering losses and is not
particularly suitable for quantitative analysis.

In the analysis of highly complex materials such as plastics, rubbers,
and other samples which are not suitable for liquid sampling or for
pressing into potassium bromide pellets, a technique developed by
Harms[115] is employed.   A small portion of the sample is rapidly
heated, in a test tube held horizontally over a bunsen burner flame,
until it is decomposed.   Pyrolysis products which condense in the
cooler portion of the test tube are spread on a salt plate which is then
mounted in the spectrophotometer.   Figure 10-6 illustrates the IR
spectra of two types of rubber gaskets obtained by this method.   Comparison with reference spectral curves prepared by Harms identifies
the upper sample as silicone rubber, and the lower sample as neoprene
rubber.[112]   This technique can also be used to identify the individual
components and estimate their concentrations in a mixture of rubbers.

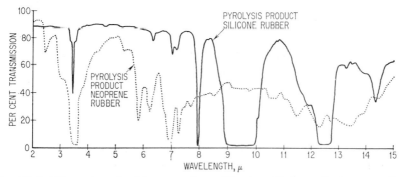

Fig. 10-6. IR spectra of rubber samples.   (*Courtesy Beckman Instruments, Inc.,
Fullerton, Calif.*)

10-3. IR APPLICATIONS IN THE BIOLOGICAL SCIENCES AND IN MEDICAL RESEARCH

In medical research, IR techniques are useful in the following main
groups of application.[116]

1. In analytical research and production of chemicals used in
medicine
2. In the study of naturally occurring biological samples, extracted
and handled as chemical mixtures
3. In the study of samples of tissues, bacteria, blood, serums, etc.

An example of the first category is the use of IR methods in the structural determination and synthesis of penicillin.[117] IR spectroscopic analysis was used to trace initial purification, establish structural groups, and identify synthetic and natural products. Similar use of IR analytical techniques was made in the development of cortisone, ACTH, and other modern drugs.

Examples of the second category of applications are studies of cholesterol in blood, barbiturate analysis,[118] and research on the role of steroids in metabolism. Steroids extracted from urine presented an analytical problem which only IR methods could solve. Using IR analytical techniques, steroid spectra were compared for normal and pathological cases; new natural steroids were isolated, identified, and classified; and isotopes were traced.

In the third category of applications, the IR microspectrometer (an example is discussed in Chap. 9), has proved extremely valuable. The development of the achromatic reflecting microscope by Barer, Burch, Grey, and others extended the spectral range of the microscope through the ultraviolet and visible regions to the IR region. When used in conjunction with a monochromator or spectrometer, microanalytic methods useful in biology and medicine as well as in chemistry and physics can be developed.

The reflection microscope is illuminated with an achromatic monochromator, and the image formed by the objective is focused on the entrance slit of a single-beam recording IR spectrometer. Microsamples are prepared by microtoming a 10- to 50-μ frozen section, mounting it on an IR transmitting plate, and drying it at a low temperature. In this way, IR spectra of tissues, muscle fibers, crystals, bacteria, and other microsamples are obtained in the 1- to 20-μ region. Ward[119] has obtained IR absorption spectra of various living muscle fibers in Ringer's solution. Stevenson and Bolduan[120] have sampled bacteria by spreading and drying colonies on a silver chloride plate. IR spectra of microscopic samples of antibiotics, vitamins, hormones, and serums have been obtained by these techniques. Various methods are used for image conversion from the invisible IR region to the visible spectral region.

It has been found that the IR absorption spectra of tissues are very similar between 2.5 and 7.5 μ, and are caused mainly by the protein content. Spectral differences can be observed at longer wavelengths. This type of IR analysis is being extensively used at the present time in hospitals and research clinics, and is a powerful tool in such work as cancer research.

IR flame photometry is used in the routine analysis of blood samples. Studies on premature and immature infants indicated a high mortality rate, due partly to adrenal immaturity. Daily blood analyses are carried out in the first weeks of life to maintain these infants in physiological balance. A method developed by Natelson[121] uses a Perkin-Elmer Model 52-A flame photometer for the rapid and accurate determination of sodium, potassium, chlorine, protein, sugar, and urea content in capillary blood samples.

IR absorption techniques are used in the study of hypersensitivity diseases such as asthma, rheumatic fever, rheumatoid arthritis, and tuberculosis. IR absorption spectra are run on dried film samples of normal and pathological blood serum, albumin, and gamma globulin. Reproducible differences in films of the latter were detected in the 7- to 11-μ region.[122]

Interesting examples of the application of IR techniques in medicine are the uses of mechanically chopped IR detectors employing sensitive photoconductive cells for studies of the brain by electroencephalography. These techniques are also used in diagnostic medicine for the study of local inflammations of the body.[123] Blood temperature corresponds to an IR source with its peak radiation occurring at just over 9 μ, this wavelength being increased by grease or hair. IR detectors used for these purposes consist of a transparent IR lens or filter to cut off radiation below a wavelength of 1 μ, a mechanical or electronic chopper to produce square-wave modulation of the signal, and a sensitive detector cell whose output is amplified by a narrow bandpass amplifier. In the electroencephalograph, six or eight detector units are mounted around the patient's head at a distance of a few inches from the scalp. Minute temperature changes in the scalp, considered to be caused by extremely high frequency emanations from the brain, make it possible to record strong emotions or concentrated thought.

A smaller hand-held detector using a mechanical chopping wheel to modulate the signal, is employed to detect slight temperature variations inside the body, which may be caused by inflamed joints or sources of local infection such as an inflamed appendix.

Examples such as these illustrate how IR principles and techniques can be applied to the development of invaluable medical equipment.

An excellent example of the advantages of IR spectroscopic techniques is afforded by the problem of identifying the various groups of tubercle bacilli.[124] Three groups of atypical bacilli may cause a disease often diagnosed as tuberculosis; these are the photochromogens, the nonphotochromogens, and the scotochromogens. True tubercle bacilli occur in three other groups; avian, bovine, and human, of which the last two cause the disease in human beings. Biological investigations have succeeded in isolating specific chemical compounds which occur exclusively in four out of these six groups. These specific compounds can be immediately identified by their IR spectra, thereby identifying the bacterial group involved.

10-4. IR APPLICATIONS IN ASTRONOMY, ASTROPHYSICS, GEOPHYSICS, AND METEOROLOGY

IR techniques have been employed for several years at the great observatories for the measurement of star temperatures and estimation of the heat emitted by celestial bodies. Sensitive thermopiles and bolometers can be employed for this work since long time exposures can be made.

However, with the advent of more sensitive detectors with faster time constants, and the development of prism-and-grating spectrometers using modern IR optical, filtering, and electronic techniques, the number and variety of IR applications in this field have greatly increased. In recent times the development of long-range missiles and artificial earth satellites has opened up new horizons where IR techniques are proving especially valuable (Chap. 12).

Table 10-3 lists some of the important applications of IR in astronomy and astrophysics, and illustrates the wide scope and adaptability of IR principles in these branches of science.

The atmospheres of the earth[125] and the sun[126–128] have been studied by Migeotte and Goldberg et al., using the techniques of IR grating spectroscopy. Observations made throughout the world at various observatories have identified a number of rare constituents in the earth's atmosphere, and information about their distribution and permanence has been obtained. Solar IR telescopes of the type described in Chap. 9 have been used to discover new atomic absorption lines in the sun, and obtain information on solar radiation exchanges in the atmosphere,[129,130] and on the photocombination of atoms in the upper atmosphere. Solar spectrum atlases[131,132] have been published from investigations made with high-resolution grating spectrographs. Solar measurements have also been made at high altitudes from manned balloons and from rockets.[133,134]

IR radiometers employing sensitive thermopiles or bolometers have long been used with IR telescopes to measure the heat generated by the stars,[135] and radiation temperatures of the surfaces of the moon and planets. These measurements are made from the ground through the

IR-transmitting windows of the earth's atmosphere. Figure 10-7 shows the temperature of the moon being measured with a Barnes radiometer, and the actual uncorrected recording made. Measurements of this type gave temperatures of 120°C fully illuminated, to

TABLE 10-3. SOME IR APPLICATIONS IN ASTRONOMY, ASTROPHYSICS, AND METEOROLOGY

Field of application	Remarks
1. Investigation of earth's atmosphere	Low- and high-altitude IR spectroscopy; investigation of transmission, scattering by atmospheric constituents
2. Atmosphere of sun, planets, stars...	IR telescopic-spectroscopic investigations of absorption spectra of the atmospheres of celestial bodies provide information about their composition
3. Temperature measurements of celestial bodies	IR radiometers used with IR telescopes enable temperatures of celestial bodies to be determined
4. Tracking and observation of artificial satellites	IR tracking techniques, using natural and artificial sources on satellite, provide information on orbit perturbations, on earth's gravitational field
5. Measurement of terrestrial and celestial phenomena from artificial satellites	Information on earth's cloud cover; astronomical information obtained outside earth's atmosphere
6. Star tracking....................	IR-sensitive star trackers used for automatic celestial-navigation purposes to correct drift of inertial stable platforms
7. Terrestrial and celestial photography	IR photography of celestial bodies; IR photography of earth and the heavens from high-altitude rockets and from artificial satellites
8. Heat transfer measurements in the upper atmosphere	Studies of atmospheric heat balance
9. Auroral research................	Spectral and luminescent studies of auroral phenomena provide information about earth's magnetic field

−150°C when not illuminated by the sun. Measurements of the temperatures of planets varied from 400°C for Mercury to −150°C for Saturn.[136]

IR photographic techniques have been used with IR telescopes to obtain information about the stars and planets,[137] and IR photographic plates have been exposed from balloons and high-altitude rockets to photograph the earth's surface.

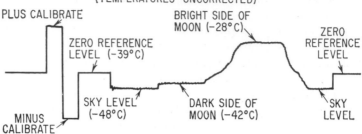

CHART OF MOON TEMPERATURE RECORDINGS
(TEMPERATURES UNCORRECTED)

PLUS CALIBRATE

ZERO REFERENCE
LEVEL (−39°C)

BRIGHT SIDE OF
MOON (−28°C)

ZERO
REFERENCE
LEVEL

SKY LEVEL
(−48°C)

DARK SIDE OF
MOON (−42°C)

SKY
LEVEL

MINUS
CALIBRATE

1/6/56, 5:55AM, TEMPERATURE −5°C, LOW HUMIDITY, CLEAR NIGHT
MOONRISE 1:40AM, LAST QUARTER OF MOON, ICE HAZE PRESENT

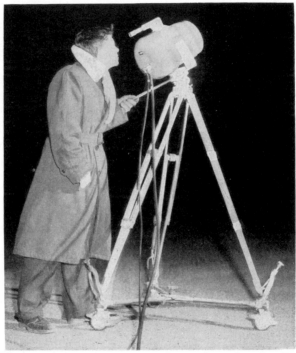

FIG. 10-7. Measurement of temperature of moon's surface by IR radiometer. (*Courtesy Barnes Engineering Company, Stamford, Conn.*)

IR spectral studies of auroral phenomena[138-140] provide valuable information about the earth's magnetic field. As part of the International Geophysical Year program, IR optical systems were developed for instrumented satellites launched by the United States Navy Vanguard project, to measure the distribution and movement of clouds covering the earth's surface.   An IR detector for this purpose has also been developed by the Perkin-Elmer Instrument Company, and is described in Chap. 12.

In the field of long-range missiles, IR detectors have been used in star trackers for the diurnal and nocturnal detection of stars to correct errors in inertial navigation systems.   Star observations are made by telescopes of long focal length and extremely narrow field of view (a few minutes of arc), mounted on a stable platform and controlled by punched tape.   By this means inertial guidance systems are monitored and corrected for errors caused by cumulative drift in the gyroscopes.

Both natural and artificial sources have been used to track artificial satellites by means of emitted IR radiation.   Observations of this type made by Zwicky at Mt. Palomar Observatory, California, with a Schmidt camera, were used to deduce information about the earth's gravitational field from measured perturbations of the satellite's orbit. Artificial meteors launched by the United States Air Force from an Aerobee rocket over the New Mexico desert[141] have been used to investigate the temperature, density, and winds of the earth's upper atmosphere.   Aluminum pellets attached to shaped charges were placed in the nose of the rocket.   At an altitude of 35 miles the nose section separated from the rocket and coasted to an altitude of approximately 54 miles, when the shaped charges were detonated.   In this way the aluminum pellets were blasted to a speed of about 33,000 mph, great enough to place them in an orbit around the earth.   Pellet tracks were photographed by Schmidt meteor cameras located at observatories in New Mexico and in California.

After the Russian satellite "Sputnik I" had successfully been placed in orbit it was discovered that a relatively strong IR signal was being radiated from it.[142]   The satellite was detected on numerous occasions as it passed over Boston, Massachusetts, by simple IR radiometer equipment.   These sightings were confirmed by simultaneous visual sightings.   The radiometer used employed an uncooled lead sulfide detector.   The field of view of the instrument was 26 by 2° with the smaller angle oriented along the predicted flight path of the satellite. IR radiation received from the satellite was recorded on an oscillograph, calibrated simultaneously by time signals from radio station WWV. Detection was achieved by night and by day.

With increased emphasis being placed on studies in space by means of instrumented artificial earth satellites, IR techniques are destined to play an important role in this new field.   An outline of some of the interesting and important applications of IR radiation techniques in the science of space technology is given in Chap. 12.

REFERENCES

2. Nielsen, A. H.: Recent Advances in Infrared Spectroscopy, *Office of Ordnance Research Tech. Memo* 53-2, December, 1953.
88. *Perkin-Elmer Instr. News Sci. Ind.*, vol. 4, no. 2, p. 8, Winter, 1953.
89. Rubens, H., and Nichols, E. F.: *Ann. Physik*, vol. 3, no. 60, p. 418, 1897.
90. Rubens, H., and Nichols, E. F.: *Ann. Phys. Chem.*, no. 60, 1897.
91. Nichols, E. F.: *Phys. Rev.*, vol. 4, p. 314, 1897.
92. Porter, P.: *Astrophys. J.*, vol. 22, p. 229, 1905.
93. Rubens, H., and Woods, R. W.: *Phil. Mag.*, vol. 21, p. 249, 1911.
94. Jentzch, F., and Laski, G.: "Geiger-schiels Handbuch der Physik," vol. 19, p. 802, Julius Springer, Berlin, 1926–28.
95. Strong, V.: *Phys. Rev.*, vol. 37, p. 1661, 1931.
96. Schaefer, C., and Matossi, F.: "Das Ultrarote Spektrum," p. 60, J. Springer, Berlin, 1930.
97. O'Loane, J. K.: *J. Chem. Phys.*, vol. 21, p. 669, 1953.
98. Plyler, E. K., and Acquista, N.: *J. Chem. Phys.*, vol. 23, p. 752, 1955.
99. Randall, H. M.: *J. Opt. Soc. Am.*, vol. 44, p. 97, 1954.
100. Randall, H. M., and Firestone, F. A.: *Rev. Sci. Instr.*, vol. 9, p. 404, 1938.
101. Strong, J.: *Phys. Today*, vol. 4, p. 4, 1951.
102. Oetjen, R. A., et al.: *J. Opt. Soc. Am.*, vol. 42, p. 559, 1952.
103. Carnegie Institute of Technology, "Catalog of Infrared Spectral Data, American Petroleum Institute Research Project 44," Carnegie Press, Pittsburgh, Pa.
104. Bellamy, L. J.: "The Infrared Spectra of Complex Molecules," John Wiley & Sons, Inc., New York, 1954.
105. Colthup, N. B.: *J. Opt. Soc. Am.*, vol. 40, p. 397, 1950.
106. "Infrared Spectral and Bibliographic Punch Cards," National Research Council, Committee on Spectral Absorption Data, National Bureau of Standards, Washington, D.C.
107. "Sadtler Catalog of Infrared Spectrograms," Samuel P. Sadtler and Sons, Inc., Philadelphia, Pa.
108. "Documentations of Molecular Spectroscopy," Butterworth Publications, Ltd., London.
109. Infrared Quantitative Analysis Data, published in *Anal. Chem.*
110. "Model 137 Infrared Spectrophotometer Bulletin," Perkin-Elmer Corporation, Norwalk, Conn., June, 1958.
111. Taylor, J. H.: *J. Opt. Soc. Amer.*, vol. 42, p. 286, 1952.
112. Double-Beam IR-5 Spectrophotometer, *Bull.* 724, Beckman Instruments, Inc., Fullerton, Calif., December, 1957.
113. Stimson, Miriam M., and O'Donnell, Marie J.: *J. Am. Chem. Soc.*, vol. 74, no. 7, p. 1805, 1952.
114. Schiedt, U., and Reinwein, H.: *Z. Naturforsch.*, vol. 76, no. 5, p. 270, 1952.
115. Harms, D. L.: *Anal. Chem.*, vol. 25, p. 1140, 1953.
116. *Perkin-Elmer Instr. News Sci. Ind.*, vol. 7, 1956.

117. Randall, H. M., Fuson, N., Fowler, R. G., and Dangl, J. R.: "Infrared Determinations of Organic Structures," D. Van Nostrand Co., Inc., Princeton, N.J., 1949.
118. Umberger, C. J., and Adams, G.: *Anal. Chem.*, vol. 24, p. 1309, 1952.
119. Ward, D. L.: *Nature*, vol. 114, p. 36, 1951.
120. Stevenson, H. J. R., and Bolduan, D. A. E.: *Nature*, vol. 116, p. 111, 1952.
121. Natelson, S.: *Am. J. Clin. Pathol.*, vol. 21, no. 12, p. 1153, 1951.
122. Agnew, J. T.: *J. Opt. Soc. Am.*, vol. 42, p. 285, 1952.
123. Osborne, W. E.: Infrared Detector Aids Medical Diagnosis, *Electronics*, Oct. 1, 1957, p. 155.
124. Randall, H. M., MacLennan, A. P., and Smith, D. W.: "Infrared Spectroscopy in the Field of Tuberculosis," paper given at 43d annual meeting of Optical Society of America, Detroit, Oct. 9-11, 1958.
125. Migeotte, M.: *Astrophys. J.*, vol. 107, p. 400, 1948.
126. McMath, R. R., and Goldberg, L.: Recent Exploration of the Infrared Solar Spectrum at the McMath-Hulbert Observatory, *Proc. Am. Phil. Soc.*, vol. 93, p. 362, 1949.
127. Goldberg, L., et al.: New Solar Lines in the Spectral Region 1.97 to 2.49 Microns, *Astrophys. J.*, vol. 111, p. 565, 1950.
128. Pierce, A. K., et al.: Observations of Solar Limb Darkening between 0.5 and 10.2 Microns, *Astrophys. J.*, vol. 112, p. 289, 1950.
129. Strong, J., and Plass, G. N.: "Heat Transfer in a Gravitational Atmosphere," Johns Hopkins Press, Baltimore, July, 1950.
130. London, J.: "Study of the Atmospheric Heat Balance," New York University College of Engineering, New York, August, 1951.
131. Goldberg, L., et al.: "Atlas of the Solar Spectrum from 0.84 to 2.52 Microns," University of Michigan Press, Ann Arbor, 1950.
132. Mohler, O. C.: "Table of Solar Spectrum Wavelengths from 1.20 to 2.55 Microns," University of Michigan Press, Ann Arbor, 1955.
133. Adel, A.: "Infrared Solar Spectra from Manned Balloon Altitudes," Michigan University Engineering Research Institute, Ann Arbor, April, 1947.
134. Goldberg, L.: "High Altitude Solar Spectroscopy," Michigan University Engineering Research Institute, Ann Arbor, February, 1948.
135. Mouzon, J. C., and Dyer, C. A.: *J. Opt. Soc. Am.*, vol. 39, p. 203, 1949.
136. *Barnes Engineering Co. Tech.*, Barnes Engineering Co., Stamford, Conn., Spring, 1956.
137. Hynek, J. A., and Harding, G. H.: "Daylight Photography of Stars," Ohio State University Research Foundation, Columbus, February, 1949.
138. Meinel, A. B.: "The Night Sky and Auroral Research," Lick Observatory, Mt. Hamilton, Calif., 1951.
139. Currie, B. W., and Petrie, W.: "Auroral Research," Saskatchewan University, Canada, August, 1951.
140. Hunter, D. M.: "A Rapid Scanning Auroral Spectrometer," *Rept.* AR-10, Saskatchewan University, Canada, 1951.

141. USAF Launches Artificial Meteors, *Aviation Week*, Dec. 2, 1957, p. 34.
142. Sputnik is Radiating Strong Infrared Signal, *Aviation Week*, Nov. 4, 1957, p. 31.

ADDITIONAL BIBLIOGRAPHY

Barnes, E. S., and Motzel, W.: Infrared and Ultraviolet Absorption Spectra of Proteins in the Solid State, *Nature*, vol. 174, p. 1144, 1954.

Barnes, R. B., Gore, R. L., Liddel, U., and Williams, V. Z.: "Infrared Spectroscopy—Industrial Applications and Bibliography," Reinhold Publishing Corporation, New York, 1944.

Dobringer, K., Katzenellenbogen, E. K., and Jones, R. N.: "Infrared Absorption Spectra of Steroids," Interscience Publishers, Inc., New York, 1953.

Farmer, C. C.: The Pressed-disc Technique in Infrared Spectroscopy, *Chem. and Ind.*, p. 586, 1955.

Harrison, G. R., Lord, R. C., and Loofbourow, J. R.: "Practical Spectroscopy," Prentice-Hall, Inc., Englewood Cliffs, N.J., 1949.

Herzberg, G.: "Infrared and Raman Spectra of Polyatomic-Molecules," vol. 2 of "Molecular Spectra and Molecular Structure," D. Van Nostrand Company, Inc., Princeton, N.J., 1945.

Miller, Foil: "Applications of Infrared and Ultraviolet Spectra to Organic Chemistry," vol. 3 of H. Gilman (ed.), "Organic Chemistry: An Advanced Treatise," John Wiley & Sons, Inc., New York, 1953.

11

IR Applications in Industry

Specific examples of IR applications in industrial fields are discussed. The adaptability of the principles of IR technique discussed in earlier chapters, and the IR instruments described in Chap. 9, to versatile and important industrial uses is emphasized. The rapidly growing use of IR techniques in automatic-control processes is illustrated.

In recent years, commercial models of IR radiometers, pyrometers, spectrometers, microscopes, cameras, and process analyzers have become available. These and other instruments incorporate the latest IR materials and techniques to achieve accuracy, high sensitivity, wider waveband coverage, and in many instances, rapid automatic recording of data. This has resulted in increasing application of IR techniques and instruments to industry. Applications to the rapid analysis of raw materials and finished products, and automatic monitoring of production-line processes for quality-control purposes save considerable time and money.

Some of the earliest commercial applications of IR techniques were employed in the chemical and petroleum industries. Today dozens of important industries make use of IR methods, and the field of applications is constantly growing. Of the many hundreds of examples available, a few are selected from diverse industries and described in this chapter to illustrate the uniqueness and versatility of modern IR technology.

11-1. IR APPLICATIONS IN AGRICULTURE

Methods developed by Toth (Department of Soils, Rutgers University, New Jersey) and others are employed in the mass analysis of soils and plant tissues, to detect deficiencies in the minerals essential to plant nutrition. The content of sodium, calcium, potassium, etc., can

247

be rapidly determined with great accuracy by means of an IR flame photometer.[143]   The causes of food deficiency in soils, and food hunger in plants, can be investigated and corrective agricultural measures applied.

In the citrus-fruit industry it had been noticed that frostbite damage occurred in orange groves at temperatures above the freezing point. IR radiometer measurements made on a clear night showed that crop freezing could occur at temperatures as high as 30 to 40°F, because heat was radiated by the fruit to the clear sky faster than it was picked up from the surrounding air.[143]   This discovery led to the use of *smudge pots* burning crude fuel oil to cloud the atmosphere surrounding the orange trees, and prevent premature freezing by reducing the heat radiation loss.

A summary of some of the more important applications of IR techniques to this field is given in Table 11-1.

TABLE 11-1. SOME IR APPLICATIONS IN AGRICULTURE

IR instrument	Application
IR recording spectrometers..	Qualitative and quantitative analysis of liquid and solid fertilizers, organic phosphorus, organic sulfur and fluorine compounds, urea-formaldehyde, limestone, insecticides, and insecticide residues[110]
	Identification of chlorides, ammonium salts, and nitrates in soil
	Investigation and control of silica and alumina in soil; their effects on fertilizers[110]
IR flame photometers.......	Detection of deficiencies in plant nutrition; food deficiencies in soils
IR radiometers.............	Investigation and prevention of premature freezing in citrus fruit groves

11-2. IR APPLICATIONS IN THE RUBBER INDUSTRY

IR techniques played a major role in the development of *cold* rubber,[143] a superior-quality synthetic rubber manufactured at temperatures near −20°C, and used today in many passenger-car tires.   Cold rubber is a copolymer of butadiene and styrene with a high degree of uniformity in the spatial configuration of its molecules.   One of the atomic groups common to both natural and many synthetic rubbers is the substituted ethylenic group $> C = C <$ which is not destroyed by polymerization.   This *building block* exhibits characteristic IR absorption bands.   By employing an IR spectrometer to evaluate various reaction conditions, the United States Rubber Company was able to measure the differences and the degree of uniformity produced in the molecular spatial arrangements of the molecular constituents. No chemical tests capable of differentiating between the various compounds under these conditions have ever been devised.

The proportion of each type of molecule present was determined by spectroscopic determinations of the absorption strengths of the characteristic IR bands. It was found that a superior quality of synthetic rubber resulted when the polymerization temperature was lowered from 100 to about $-20°C$.

Low-temperature IR radiation pyrometers are used for temperature-control purposes in the manufacturing process and in test work.

Important applications of IR techniques in the rubber industry are summarized in Table 11-2.

TABLE 11-2. IMPORTANT IR APPLICATIONS IN THE RUBBER INDUSTRY

IR instrument	Application
IR recording spectrometers..	Analysis and development of synthetic rubbers Investigations of the structure and reactions of monomers, polymers, and synthetic polydienes Studies of rubber oxidation and rubber derivatives
IR recording spectrometers..	Studies of crystallinity and chain configurations Identification of polyisoprene from different plants
IR flame photometers.......	Control of sulfur vulcanization, chlorination, and hydrochlorination of rubber[110]
IR radiation pyrometers....	Temperature control of manufacturing processes

11-3. IR APPLICATIONS IN THE PETROLEUM INDUSTRY

The rapidity and accuracy of IR analytical techniques compared to the more conventional chemical methods led to their early employment in the petroleum industry. Pioneer work in spectroscopic analysis was carried out in this industry before the war. During World War II, major problems such as the development of a rapid and accurate method for the analysis of the C_4 hydrocarbon fractions in petroleum resulted in the commercial production of automatic recording spectrometers.

Today, the use of these spectrometers is widespread in the industry for the qualitative (identification) and quantitative (assay) analysis of complex organic compounds. Other applications are the detection and identification of impurities, the study of reaction mechanisms, the determination of molecular association and geometrical structure in complex molecules, the discovery of intermediate products in chemical reactions, and the study of such phenomena as polymerization and isomerization.

IR methods are also used in the industry for the rapid analysis of river and stream water for the detection of hydrocarbon oil and phenol contamination.   These are detected in water samples by bromination followed by extraction with carbon tetrachloride and IR spectroscopic analysis.   Sensitivities of less than 1 part in 1 billion are achieved. Optical-density measurements at 2.84 μ for phenol and at 3.4 μ in the case of hydrocarbon oils are made on an IR spectrophotometer.[144]

IR process stream analyzers such as the Perkin-Elmer Model 14 automatic multicomponent IR analyzer, which can continuously monitor up to six components simultaneously, are used for the control of experimental and commercial processing plants.   In this instrument, in which the IR transmittance at each of six selected wavelengths is automatically recorded, the effects of varying temperature, pressure, composition, and flow rate can be studied.[145]

Applications of IR techniques in this industry are summarized in Table 11-3.

TABLE 11-3. SOME IR APPLICATIONS IN THE PETROLEUM INDUSTRY

IR instrument	Application
IR recording spectrometers..	Quantitative analysis of oils; quantitative determination of trace components, anti-icing additives in motor gasoline, and bicyclic sulfur compounds in kerosene-extract tar oil[110]
	Identification and structural determinations of hydrocarbons in oils.
	Determination of octane numbers of gasoline
	Checking composition of lubricating oil additive blends
	Identification of synthetic oils, antiwear additives, viscosity improvers, pour-point depressants, extreme-pressure additives, corrosion preventatives[110]
	Study of polymerization and isomerization
	Analysis of river-water pollution
IR process-stream analyzers.	Control of experimental and commercial processing plants

11-4. IR APPLICATIONS IN THE PRINTING INDUSTRY

IR techniques are used in the industry for selection and quality control of raw materials and for speeding up printing processes.   Paper is run through the presses at a temperature as close as possible to the scorching point, in order to dry the printing ink as rapidly as possible. For improved control, and to save time and money, this process is monitored by an IR radiometer.[143]   The use of a Barnes IR radiometer for this purpose on a high-speed printing press is illustrated in Fig. 11-1.

In the graphic arts industries, IR spectroscopic analysis is used for the rapid and accurate selection and control of raw materials. IR analyses of supernatant extracts are employed for the quality control of manufactured inks. The origin and nature of flocculations separating from ink vehicles and of nonsaponifiable residues are identified by their IR absorption spectra. Types of oils, natural waxes, and wax mixtures used in papers are rapidly identified and classified by comparing their IR absorption curves with standard reference curves of

FIG. 11-1. Measurement of paper temperature on experimental high-speed printing press by Barnes radiometer at research laboratories of Time, Inc. (*Courtesy Barnes Engineering Company, Stamford, Conn.*)

known materials.[145] Additional IR applications are listed in Table 11-4.

Aldehyde impurities in alcohol drums are checked in a fraction of the time required by conventional titration tests. The amount of free alcohol in commercial 99 per cent grades of ethyl acetate is rapidly assayed by measuring the intensity of the IR absorption bands. Polarized IR radiation is employed to determine the relative amount of molecular orientation in plastic sheets, and IR techniques are used to detect chemical-component migrations between sections of stencil assemblies.[145]

TABLE 11-4. IR APPLICATIONS IN PRINTING AND GRAPHIC ARTS INDUSTRIES

IR instrument	Application
IR spectrometers....	Qualitative identification of carnauba and candelilla waxes, long-chain acid groups, long-chain ester groups, hydroxy acids and alcohols found in waxes[110]
	Quality control of alcohol, manufactured inks, and raw materials
	Quantitative measurements of aromatic content, carbonyl content, petroleum-derived wax, oxidized microcrystalline wax in solid waxes; determination of formulation of complex waxes[110]
	Quality control of wax formulation during mixing and plant processing
IR radiometers......	Automatic speed control of high-speed printing presses

11-5. IR APPLICATIONS IN THE CEMENT INDUSTRY

In low-alkali cements, the total alkali (soda and potash) content is limited to 0.6 per cent. Analysis by conventional chemical methods is complicated and requires up to two days to complete. IR flame photometers are used to accurately determine the alkali content in a few minutes' time, and to exercise close control over the manufacturing process.[146]

11-6. IR APPLICATIONS IN THE RAILROAD INDUSTRY

Overheating of the journal boxes on railroad rolling stock may lead to structural failure and cause costly accidents. Rapid detection of hot journal boxes is ensured by hand-held or trackside IR detection systems. A typical trackside detector consists of suitable optics, a bolometer, and an amplifier. Thermistor radiometers are also used for these applications.

11-7. IR APPLICATIONS IN THE AIRCRAFT AND MISSILE INDUSTRIES

In addition to the important military applications of a classified nature such as IR search and tracking devices for aircraft, and IR seeker and homing devices for guided missiles of various types, widespread use of other IR techniques is made in these industries.

An important safety device being manufactured for use in commercial aircraft is an air-borne IR seeker head with wide angular coverage. This is designed to warn the pilot of the proximity of other aircraft so that appropriate maneuvers may be made in time to avoid a collision. The application of IR techniques in the construction of beacons and landing aids has been described in earlier chapters.

IR cameras are widely used for aerial reconnaissance and mapping. IR photography is also extensively employed (Chap. 9) in the determination of surface temperatures of aircraft and missiles. IR radiometers, pyrometers, and flame photometers are used to investigate combustion in jet exhaust and rocket flames.

In very high speed aircraft and missiles it is important to investigate the effect of aerodynamic heating on the skin, and heat flow to the interior. Unbalanced thermal expansion may cause dangerous buckling of load-carrying members, warping of flight surfaces, failure of electronic components, or failure of propulsion units. To investigate these effects, thermal test systems operating under controlled conditions are simulated by groups of General Electric T-3 quartz-crystal IR heat lamps.[147] These are arranged over the part to be tested to duplicate aerodynamic heating effects previously calculated or predicted from flight-test results. By this means a radiant-heat oven is produced, in which each group of lamps is programmed by computing and curve-following consoles and ignition power controllers to duplicate the heat variations predicted for a given flight mission. With the heat lamps run at over 1,000 watts input, skin temperatures up to 2500°F and temperature increases as rapid as 150°F/sec can be produced.[147] This new type of research tool is now being used by the major aircraft companies. Figure 11 2 shows such a thermal test being run at North American Aviation, Inc.

With the increased use of titanium in the construction of supersonic aircraft and missiles, a method has been developed by the aircraft and missile industry to control the hot-forming process used in the manufacture of titanium parts. In this process the titanium part is raised to the forming temperature in a few seconds by resistance heating. An IR radiation pyrometer is used to control the heating process rapidly and accurately from a distance. Automatic close temperature control which is practically independent of ambient temperature changes is achieved.[148] IR radiometers are used to measure the temperature gradients of aircraft tires under landing-shock conditions.

IR spectrometers are used for the analysis of aircraft fuels, including the high-energy fuels; for the analysis of the complex propellant mixtures used in missiles, and that of aircraft lubricating greases. IR techniques are also extensively used to study the reactions and breakdown of fuels when burned, and for the identification of exhaust gases.[110]

Fig. 11-2. Photograph of thermal test using quartz lamps. (*Courtesy North American Aviation, Inc., Los Angeles, Calif.*)

11-8. IR APPLICATIONS IN THE DRUG AND PHARMACEUTICAL INDUSTRIES

IR techniques have proved to be invaluable in these industries, where accurate analysis and positive identification of minute samples are essential.

The majority of pharmaceutical and biochemical products are refined from expensive concentrates, or manufactured by difficult synthetic processes. Their discovery and production development are frequently a long and costly process. It may also be a gamble, since there is always the possibility that a new and expensive product may be supplanted soon afterwards by a newer and more efficient drug. It is, therefore, important in this industry to employ the best research and production techniques.

Examples of modern drugs of this type are ACTH and Cortisone, used in the treatment of rheumatoid arthritis. These drugs are manufactured from steroid nuclei in plant concentrates or in bile acids, by extremely difficult synthetic processes and are, therefore, expensive.

Reflecting microscope-objective attachments to an IR spectrometer, as described in Chap. 9, are employed to obtain the IR absorption spectra of minute samples such as single cells, nerve fibers, and single crystals of vitamins. Since steroids have characteristic IR absorption spectra, these IR techniques save considerable time and money as compared to chemical analytical methods. Structural analysis of reaction products and isolated compounds, analytical techniques for differentiating optical isomers, for the study of amino acids, and for the specification of production materials have been developed.

The assaying of two similar drugs by chemical methods is extremely difficult and can be a very lengthy process. IR techniques give improved accuracy, more positive identification, and save time. For example, the relatively new drugs Visnagrin and Khellin, present in plant fractions and in pharmaceutical mixtures, are very similar in their chemical structures (Fig. 11-3) and, therefore, are extremely difficult to assay by chemical methods. Accurate assaying is rapidly carried out by examining a solution of the crude extract in chloroform, contained in a standard liquid absorption cell, in an IR spectrophotometer. Using silver chloride optics, differences in the IR absorption spectra of the two drugs in the 8- to 9-μ region permit an assay to be made in about 20 min.[149]

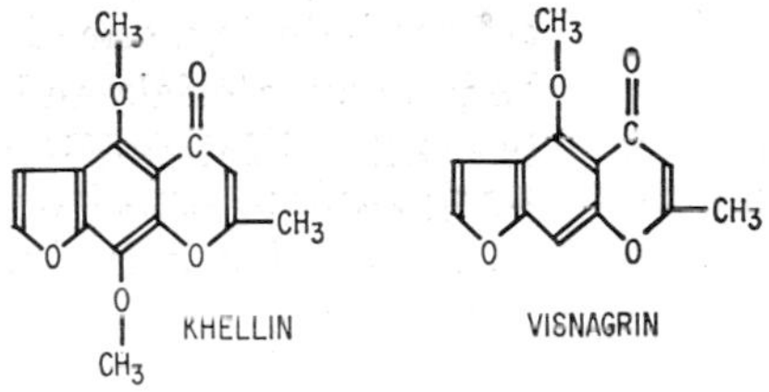

FIG. 11-3. Chemical structures of similar drugs.

IR techniques are extensively employed in modern pharmaceutical laboratories. The foregoing and other applications are summarized in Table 11-5.

TABLE 11-5. SOME IR APPLICATIONS IN THE DRUG AND PHARMACEUTICAL INDUSTRIES

IR instrument	Application
IR Spectrometers....	Qualitative functional-group analysis; identification of compounds; molecular-structure determinations; determination of structure of new synthetic compounds, antibiotics, alkaloids, steroids, and growth substances; identification of ingredients; quantitative analytical control of products and intermediaries; identity control of compounds entering or in process in pharmaceutical plants;[110] assaying of similar drugs

11-9. IR APPLICATIONS IN THE COSMETIC AND PERFUME INDUSTRIES

The unique properties of IR spectroscopic analytical methods, namely, rapid and positive identification of minute samples and the recoverability of expensive samples which are unaltered by IR techniques, have in recent years led to the increasing employment by modern cosmetic and perfume laboratories of IR methods for analysis and quality control.

IR spectrophotometers with microscope attachments are widely used, as in the drug industry, for the identification of unknown and expensive samples, and for the study of compound structures. The presence of impurities in expensive oils can be quickly detected, and the distillation and purification of essential oils can be controlled by IR instruments. IR analysis is used to grade raw materials. Errors in compounding a mixture are revealed by comparison of its IR spectrum with a standard spectrum. Routine checks are made on the concentration of important minor ingredients such as preservatives and bactericides in the final product, and for impurities as well.

In the perfume industry, one of the most important problems is the analysis of odorous materials and the study of the structure of their constituents. Ultraviolet and Raman spectrometry provide valuable information but only describe part of the molecule. Many of the constituents are oxygenated derivatives such as ketones, alcohols, aldehydes, etc., belonging to the terpene family, and have numerous isomers differing only in the number and position of their linkages. This makes conventional analytical methods extremely lengthy or even impossible. IR spectral-analysis methods are well suited to the study of these difficult problems. The commercial IR recording spectrometers available are used for the rapid and systematic analysis of mixtures of odorous substances, for checking the quality of raw materials without damaging costly samples, and for the quality control of manufactured products.[150]

11-10. IR APPLICATIONS IN THE PLASTICS INDUSTRY

Modern plastics are composed of highly complex organic molecules, which makes their identification and analysis by conventional chemical methods a difficult and time-consuming process. Qualitative analysis by IR spectroscopic methods is more reliable and considerably faster. Periods of 1 hour or less are required as compared to one to two days for conventional techniques. Using a spectrophotometer such as the

Beckman Model IR-2 with a fast-response thermocouple, the direct percentage IR transmission spectrum of a plastic such as polystyrene can be recorded over the 1- to 15-μ region in about 40 min (Fig. 10-1).

More time is often required to prepare the plastic sample than to record its IR absorption spectrum.   There are three basic methods of preparing a sample.   In the first method a *mull* or suspension of solid plastic powders in a high-boiling paraffin oil is prepared, spread between rock salt plates, and examined in the spectrophotometer.   This method is time consuming and the spectrum of the paraffin oil interferes with that of the plastic sample.[151]

The second method requires special equipment to roll the plastic sample into a thin film which is then cut to fit the rock salt holder. The third and most convenient method is to compound the plastic sample in a suitable low-boiling solvent such as distilled *o*-dichlorobenzene, cyclohexane, or freshly distilled cresylic acid.   The solution of the purified resin sample is spread on a rock salt window and the solvent is evaporated at 160 to 200°C, leaving a film 0.02–1 mm thick. By this method the IR spectra of the basic resin, the copolymer, plasticizers, and any other organic additives are recorded.[151]

11-11. IR TELEVISION APPLICATIONS

Recent developments have made it possible to televise in complete darkness scenes that are illuminated by IR radiation.   Standard lighting equipment using IR filters to mask out visible light is employed. This *Noctovision* system was developed by Nippon Electric and the Broadcasting Corporation of Japan.   It uses an IR attachment consisting of an image converter sensitive to IR radiation with its output feeding a photomultiplier, to replace one of the objective lenses in a standard TV camera.[152]

A useful application of Noctovision in the medical field has been tested by Nippon Electric and the Kero University Hospital, Japan.[152] In ophthalmic diagnosis, the eye pupil which usually closes according to the amount of incident visible light is often required to remain wide open.   This can be achieved by illuminating the eye pupil in complete darkness with IR radiation.

In tests run by the Japanese Maritime Safety Board, Noctovision equipment was used together with IR searchlights and a telephoto lens to evaluate its usefulness as a navigational safety device.   A small object at a distance of $\frac{3}{4}$ mile offshore that could not be seen by the naked eye was clearly viewed by this device.[152]

11-12. IR PHOTOGRAPHIC APPLICATIONS

Photographic plates for use in the near-IR spectral region at about 1.4 μ are sensitized with special dyes. Since near-IR radiation penetrates the skin surface, near-IR photography is an important diagnostic aid in the subcutaneous study of varicose veins.[153]

It is also a valuable aid in ophthalmoscopy for the study of the eye. The use of IR radiation to illuminate the eye pupil in darkness has been mentioned (Sec. 11-11). The iris and inner eye can be studied either with the aid of an image-converter tube or by means of photographs. Photographs of the iris through an opaque turbid cornea can

FIG. 11-4. Thermal photograph of Viscount turboprop airliner on loading ramp, made by Barnes far-IR camera. (*Courtesy Barnes Engineering Company, Stamford, Conn.*)

be obtained by this method.[154] IR radiation has been employed in therapeutic medicine for several years, and IR exposure meters are useful for the exact measurement of therapeutic and photographic exposure.[155]

In the photographic darkroom, an IR image-converter tube used in conjunction with an IR illuminating source in the near- or intermediate-IR spectral regions is a useful darkroom aid in the processing of photographs.

In research and industry, the use of a Barnes far-IR camera and a Polaroid Land camera to obtain rapid, calibrated photographs for temperature distribution studies (Figs. 11-4 and 11-5), location of hot spots, location of electrical overloads, etc., has been discussed in Chap. 9.

Because of the superior haze-penetration ability of IR radiation over visible light, IR terrestrial and air-borne photography is extensively used for reconnaissance and mapping, and is widely employed for military purposes.

FIG. 11-5. Thermal photograph of electronic chassis, made by Barnes far-IR camera, showing hot spots. (*Courtesy Barnes Engineering Company, Stamford, Conn.*)

11-13. IR MILITARY APPLICATIONS

The majority of IR military applications are classified and cannot be discussed here. This section is therefore confined to a description of some of the applications (mostly World War II developments), which are no longer classified, and about which information is published in available sources. The original impetus accelerating the development of IR devices for military purposes occurred during World War II and has been outlined in Chap. 1. Many of the devices such as image-converter tubes, phosphors, and optical systems have been discussed in previous chapters.

Several of the IR devices that were extensively used in the later stages of World War II employed image-converter tubes operating in the near- and intermediate-IR spectral regions. Image-tube development had reached quite an advanced stage of development in the United States, Great Britain, Germany, and Japan before the end of the war, and some of the ingenious IR devices in which they were employed will be described.

The German *Spanner IIA* near-IR viewer[45] employed an image tube similar in construction to the unipotential image tube (Chap. 5), but with two electrodes, and operated with a 15-kv power supply and a 12-volt d-c to 220-volt a-c converter. An $f/0.85$ objective lens consisting of eight glass elements and a six-element ocular large enough to accommodate both eyes was used. A collimated reticle sight enabled the viewer to be used for gun-laying purposes.[45]

This type of near-IR viewer and its modifications were produced in limited quantity toward the end of the war and mounted on tanks, self-propelled 88-mm field guns, and half-track vehicles, together with powerful IR searchlights for active use. They were also employed in active and passive antiaircraft viewing systems. Viewers ranged from small hand-held types for use by infantry and tank commanders to large, $f/1.4$ aperture 63-cm focal length types used for antiaircraft gun-directing purposes.[45]

The German *Uhu* equipment consisted of a 24-in. filtered-arc IR searchlight and an $f/1.0$ aperture, 11-in. focal length *Adlergerate* near-IR viewer mounted on a half-track vehicle. The limited number of tank engagements fought on the Eastern front with this equipment resulted in very heavy Russian tank losses. Enemy tanks illuminated with the IR searchlights could rapidly be brought under fire by 88-mm guns and tanks. German tanks and *Uhus* were equipped with IR night-driving equipment enabling them to pursue the enemy at speeds equivalent to those possible in night driving with low-beam headlights.[45] A typical use of this equipment in a tank engagement is illustrated in Fig. 11-6.

Extensive use was made of IR photography for both day and night, long- and short-range applications. The *Lichtsprecher* and similar communication systems, also used widely by the German armed forces during the war, employed a collimated pencil-beam of IR radiation, which was modulated by voice frequency signals or by a blinker system. Active IR systems of this type were used for short- and long-range IR telephone and telegraph purposes. In the intermediate-IR spectral region most wartime devices were of German origin, using the new photoconductive detectors developed during that period. They were employed for the detection and tracking of aircraft and ships at ranges up to about 30 miles, and for missile-homing devices.

The United States developed sniperscopes and snooperscopes,[45] which were used extensively in the later years of the war in the Pacific Theater. The snooperscope used an 1P25A IR image tube with an objective lens in front of the photocathode, and an eyepiece to allow the operator to view the phosphor screen. Since the cesium silver oxide cathode was sensitive only in the 1.2-μ wavelength region, it required a tungsten light source with an IR filter to illuminate the target with IR radiation.   The IR image formed by reflected radiation from the target on the photocathode was then converted by the image tube into a visible image viewed through the eyepiece.   When mounted

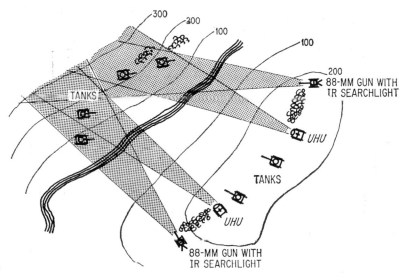

FIG. 11-6. Use of IR-equipped Uhus and guns in typical nighttime tank engagement. (*After Reference 45.*)

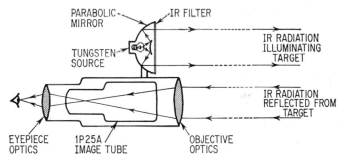

FIG. 11-7. Optical schematic of IR sniperscope.   (*After Reference 45.*)

on a carbine and boresighted, the *snooperscope* became a *sniperscope* (Fig. 11-7).   This device proved invaluable in checking night infiltration by enemy patrols.

The helmet-mounted IR binocular[45] (Fig. 11-8) employed two IR image tubes, with focusing and centering optics and a 4,000-volt power supply mounted on the back of the helmet as a counterbalancing weight.   This equipment, used for the night driving of vehicles equipped with IR filters over their headlights, provided a level of IR illumination approximating that of normal low-beam visible headlights.   It was also used for reconnaissance purposes when operated in conjunction with an IR-filtered searchlight.

The metascope (Chap. 5), developed in the United States, is a readily portable IR imaging device, requiring no power supply, used for target detection and signalling purposes.

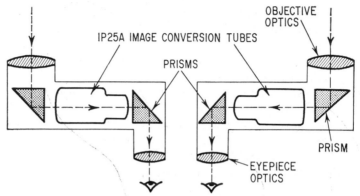

FIG. 11-8. Optical schematic of IR binoculars.   (*After Reference 45.*)

11-14. IR APPLICATIONS IN FOOD INDUSTRIES

With the increasing use of preservatives and additives in a multitude of canned, bottled, and packaged foods, IR techniques are extensively used for production control and inspection.   IR recording spectrometers are employed for the identification and analysis of carbohydrates, vitamins, acids, oils, fats, enzymes, and proteins in food products. They are used for the identification of yeasts and sugars; to detect residual pesticides in citrus fruits, vegetables, and other foods; for the analysis of starch in meat products.[110]

In dairy products, IR techniques are used for the control of fat, protein, and carbohydrate contents; of the water content in butter; in the process control of dried milk manufacture; and for the quantitative determination of concentrations of triglycerides in milk and butterfat.[110]

11-15. IR APPLICATIONS IN THE TOBACCO INDUSTRY

Modern IR techniques are extensively used in this industry for product improvement, quality control, and research.   The complex pyrolysis and combustion products of tobacco can be rapidly identified

and analyzed. Quantitative analysis of the concentration of aldehydes, ketones, ammonia, cyanogen, hydrogen sulfide, in the condensa-
ble and noncondensable fractions of tobacco smoke, and the rapid
identification and measurement of various components can be speedily
and efficiently accomplished with IR techniques.[110]

11-16. IR APPLICATIONS IN CRIMINOLOGY AND TOXICOLOGY

IR techniques are employed in police laboratories for the identification and source tracing of drugs, narcotics, poisons, as well as of
clothing samples, soils, and other forms of evidence. The rapid, positive characteristics of IR spectrometry are invaluable for both qualitative and quantitative analyses.

Narcotics contain many alkaloids; opium, for example, contains 24
different alkaloids. Spectral analysis of these, and of their hydro-
chlorides and derivatives, reveals valuable information regarding the
purity and concentration of narcotics and can be used to determine
whether a narcotic is natural, illicit, or synthetic. Even the origin of a
narcotic can often be determined from an IR spectral analysis, since
the relative proportion of alkaloids present often varies with the location in which a plant is grown, making it possible to determine the
source of the plant.[110]

Rapid classification and positive identification of various organic
poisons can be made from an IR spectroscopic analysis. Quantitative
analysis can be made of barbiturates found in body fluids and organs.
IR microspectroscopy is usually the only effective method for the toxi-
cological analysis of tissue extracts containing organic compounds.[110]

11-17. IR APPLICATIONS IN THE PAINT AND COATING INDUSTRIES

Wide use is made of IR techniques for the routine analysis and
improvement of paints and coatings, the development of new products,
the quality control and process control of paints, lacquers, varnishes,
pigments, shellacs, and other coatings.

Investigation of the curing rates, blending conditions, and the ionic
forces which are important to the holding properties of coatings to
various materials are greatly facilitated by IR examination of epoxy
resins, monomers, and polymers. IR quantitative analysis of the
pyrolysates determines the composition of polymer blends and copoly-
mers. IR spectroscopic analysis greatly speeds up the identification of
fatty acids, oils, silicone elastomers, urea-formaldehyde resins, and
phenolic resins present in these products.[110]

11-18. IR APPLICATIONS IN AIR-POLLUTION STUDIES AND CONTROL

The increasing importance of air-pollution research studies and control in industrial areas has led to the widespread adoption of IR techniques for the economical, rapid, and positive identification and quantitative analysis of pollutants. Used in conjunction with gas chromatography and other collection or preseparation systems, IR facilitates the rapid identification of organic acids, ketones, and aldehydes present in smog. The concentration of carbon monoxide, atmospheric fluorides, hydrogen sulfide, and oxides of sulfur produced by factories in the atmosphere is measured and controlled. Rapid qualitative and quantitative analysis is made of ozone, exhaust gases, organic combustion products, oxides of nitrogen, petroleum hydrocarbons, and mercaptans present in the atmosphere. Studies of incinerator combustion products and gaseous organic halides emitted into the atmosphere are facilitated. Long-path cells are employed to study very dilute reactions and to simulate reactions at high altitudes.[110]

11-19. IR APPLICATIONS IN ATOMIC ENERGY

In the production of heavy water, IR techniques are used for the strict analytical control of the deuterium content. Rapid identification can be made of the products resulting from the radiation decomposition of organic compounds. In experimental process studies, the impurities of solvents are identified and analyzed. IR methods are used for the analysis of impurities in gases such as boron trifluoride used in neutron counters, and for the structural investigation of complex ruthenium compounds and other solid materials.[110]

Radiation effects on foods; organic compounds such as greases, paints, and protective coatings; and on metals and alloys used in the aircraft and missile industries are studied by IR methods.

Radiation rates and surface temperatures of cyclotrons and atomic piles are accurately determined and monitored by IR radiation pyrometers.

11-20. IR APPLICATIONS IN THE COAL INDUSTRY

In this industry with its numerous byproducts, often with highly complex organic structures, IR techniques are employed for a wide variety of investigations. The composition and structural features of the various types of coal are studied economically and rapidly on IR recording spectrophotometers. Minerals, carbohydrate chars, bituminous anthraxylons, and coal extracts are identified. Residues from vacuum distillation are studied. The presence of chemical groups in coals and coallike products is rapidly detected.[110]

11-21. IR APPLICATIONS IN THE TEXTILE INDUSTRY

The characteristic advantages of IR techniques are extensively applied in this industry to basic research in new synthetic fibers and materials, the study and improvement of existing materials, and to applied problems such as the monitoring and control of manufacturing processes.

In fibrous materials, the structure, orientation, and degree of crystallinity are studied, and quantitative measurements are made of crystallinity and amorphism. Intermolecular forces within the fiber structure and interactions with other molecules of functional groups of fiber molecules are investigated. The effects of heat, dyestuffs, and exposure to light on the chemical breakdown of fibers are studied.[110]

11-22. IR APPLICATIONS IN INDUSTRIAL AUTOMATION

In the past, process control of many manufacturing operations was obtained by the following procedure: Operating variables such as pressure, temperature, flow rate, etc., were set to predetermined values. A batch of products was then run off and analyzed by conventional methods. The information obtained enabled the variables to be reset to produce more uniform and desirable end products. This method of process control is like putting the cart before the horse. The modern technique is to carry out product analysis and operate the variable corrections simultaneously, thereby achieving continuous process control.

With the availability today of accurate, versatile, commercial IR process analyzers, radiometers and pyrometers with rapid-response times, continuous process control is possible in many plant operations. Manufacturing processes are speeded up and uniformity of the product is achieved with greater efficiency. In many cases, standard commercial IR instruments can be directly employed or easily adapted to a specific manufacturing problem. In others, a sensitized and adjusted IR instrument is specially designed to solve the production problems encountered in a specific manufacturing operation.

Several examples of the application of various IR instruments to automatically controlled operations have been discussed in the preceding chapters. Table 11-1 lists some typical applications in modern

TABLE 11-6. SOME TYPICAL IR APPLICATIONS IN INDUSTRIAL AUTOMATION

IR instrument	Industrial application
IR radiometers..............	Paper-temperature control in printing presses
IR pyrometers..............	Induction, dielectric, panel heating, IR drying and heat curing of assembly-line products
	Hot-forming of titanium
	Temperature control of high-speed rotating machinery
	Detection of hot spots, electrical overloading
	Temperature measurement and control of drying, curing, glueing, dyeing, sizing, and coating of cotton, synthetics, paper, etc.[157]
	Temperature measurement and control of rolling, molding, pressing, extruding, and curing of plastic in sheet-roll or tubing form. Control of critical change-of-state temperatures of plastics and synthetic fibers[157]
	Temperature measurement and control of synthetic rubber processes and product testing, refinery processes, manufacture of asphalt shingles, coating procedures, precision drying of photographic black and white and color film[157]
	Temperature measurement and control of metals, both ferrous and nonferrous, in sheet, bar, roll, or tubing form, undergoing machining, induction hardening, extrusion, molding, casting, drawing, rolling, melting, oven heating, annealing, forging, cutting, boring, stamping, finishing, enamel baking, and other metal-fabrication processes; control of dies, jigs, rollers, and other shaping tools[157]
	Temperature measurement and control of crystal-growing, mineral-processing, glass-rolling, polishing, and annealing processes[157]
IR flame photometers.......	Control of cement-manufacturing processes
	Water analysis
	Control of calcium in lubricating oils
	Determination of tetraethyl lead in gasoline
IR process-stream analyzers..	Control of furnace atmospheres
	Monitoring of CO_2 in hydrocarbon streams
	Monitoring of CO and CO_2 in combustion processes
	Control of trace water in liquid Freon and liquid benzene
	Detection of trace water in hydrocarbons
	Control of methyl vinyl ketone in butadiene
	Monitoring purity of ethylene in ranges 90–100 per cent
	Monitoring purity of butadiene in ranges 95–100 per cent
	Detection of remaining methane in reforming of natural gas to hydrogen
	Measuring alcohol vapor in air-hydrocarbon mixture
	Monitoring methane and ethane in ethylene[86]

industry. With the increasing trend toward automation, new applications of IR techniques in this field are constantly being devised.

A typical example is a recent application in a large wire mill in the United States which manufactures wire in all sizes up to $\frac{3}{4}$ in. in diameter.[156] The annealing furnace consists of a heating zone and a cooling zone in which uniform forced-air circulation is maintained by multiple fans. To prevent oxidation and decarbonizing of the wire, an endothermic generator produces a reducing atmosphere, low in water-vapor and carbon dioxide content, for both zones. Due to variations in wire size and in metallurgy, the composition of this protective atmosphere is quite critical. It is, therefore, automatically controlled by IR analyzers. These accurately control the atmospheric composition and thereby improve the quality and consistency of the finished product.

Leeds and Northrup IR analyzer-cell assemblies, with a range of 0 to 3 per cent carbon dioxide, and the necessary calibrating equipment are mounted adjacent to the furnace. IR radiation from a constant source passes through the sampling cell, and simultaneously through a known reference gas. A thermopile, consisting of differentially connected Chromel-constantan thermocouples, shielded from vibration and from stray electrical pickup, detects the radiation difference between the sample and reference cells. Variations in the thermopile output are recorded on a Speedomax recorder located in a control room and calibrated directly in per cent of the gas compound in the sample cell.[156]

IR pyrometers can be used for process-control applications in any manufacturing process in which heat is employed. Numerous examples in various industries are listed in Table 11-6.

REFERENCES

45. Canada, A. H.: Infrared Military and Peacetime Uses, *General Electric Company Data Folder* 87516, December, 1947.
86. Troy, Daniel H.: Infrared Process-stream Analyzers, *Control Engineering*, November, 1957, p. 116.
110. "Model 137 Infrared Spectrophotometer Bulletin," Perkin-Elmer Corporation, Norwalk, Conn., June, 1958.
143. *Perkin-Elmer Instr. News Sci. Ind.*, vol. 1, no. 2, Winter, 1950.
144. Simard, R. G., et al.: *Anal. Chem.*, vol. 23, p. 10, 1951.
145. *Perkin-Elmer Instr. News Sci. Ind.*, Summer, 1953.
146. Bogue, R. H.: "Chemistry of Portland Cement," Reinhold Publishing Corporation, New York, 1947.
147. Cushman, Robert H.: Infrared Simulates Aerodynamic Heating, *Aviation Week*, Sept. 30, 1957, p. 81.

148. *Aviation Age*, p. 156, January, 1958.
149. *J. Am. Pharm. Assoc. Sci. Ed.*, vol. 40, No. 6, p. 280, 1951.
150. Naves, Y. R.: Infrared and the Perfume Industry, *Perkin-Elmer Instr. News Sci. Ind.*, vol. 3, no. 3, Spring, 1952.
151. Hausdorff, H. H.: Short Cuts to the Analysis of Plastics by Infrared Spectroscopy, *Soc. Appl. Spectroscopy Bull.*, August, 1951.
152. *Electronics*, September, 1957.
153. Barker, N. W., and Julin, L. A.: Demonstration of Superficial Veins by Infrared Photography, *Proc. Staff Meetings, Mayo Clin.*, vol. 9, p. 68, 1939.
154. Mann, W. A.: Infrared Photography of the Eye, *A.M.A. Arch. Ophthalmol.*, vol. 13, p. 985, 1935.
155. Evans, D. S., and Mendelssohn, K.: The Measurement of Infrared Radiation for Medical Purposes, *J. Sci. Instr.*, vol. 23, p. 94, 1946.
156. Infrared Analyzers Monitor Furnace Atmospheres, *Production*, vol. 40, no. 3, p. 73, September, 1957.
157. "Infrared Process Control," Servo Corporation of America, Hicksville, N.Y., 1958.

12

Applications of IR in Space Technology

Space and earth's atmospheric boundaries, the solar system planets, and the units of measurement employed in interplanetary space are discussed.   Important IR applications and measurements are described.

12-1. SPACE AND IR RADIATION

With the launching of Sputnik I a new age began.   Old technologies are being adapted and new ones developed by man in the conquest of space.   New concepts of navigation, guidance, and communication are required.   Precise, reliable instrumentation, capable of operating for long periods under severe environmental conditions, is required for a variety of measurements.   Space and weight are at a premium.

Because IR instruments employ optical techniques, transistorized electronics, and small components, and are capable of high resolution and great precision over a wide wavelength band, they are most suitable for a large variety of measurements and applications in space.

These may be broadly classified into three categories; surface-to-space, many examples of which have already been described in previous chapters; space-to-surface; and space-to-space.   Before proceeding to a description of IR applications in these fields, however, a brief outline of the areas in which we shall be operating is necessary.

Atmospheric and Space Regions.   In comparison to the vast reaches of space the extent of the atmosphere surrounding the earth is infinitesimal.   In its effects on rockets and satellites launched from the earth's surface or returning to earth, however, it is of paramount importance.

Figure 12-1 summarizes in pictorial form the different boundary regions of the earth's atmosphere and of space.   The approximate altitudes of the boundaries separating these arbitrary regions are given.

269

Commencing at the earth's surface and increasing in altitude, the *troposphere* extends to the *tropopause*, or boundary, separating it from the stratosphere.   Because the earth is elliptical in shape the height of the tropopause varies from approximately 54,000 ft or 10 miles at the equator, to approximately 28,000 ft at the poles.   Approximately 50

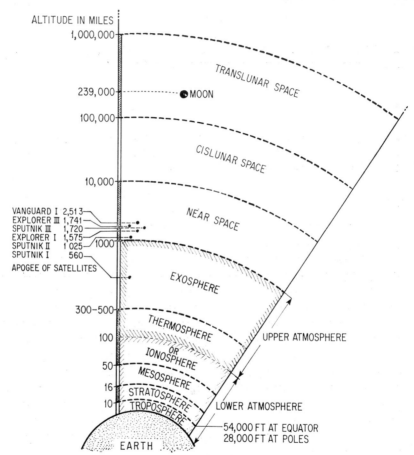

Fig. 12-1. Earth's atmosphere and space regions.   (*After Reference 158.*)

per cent of the earth's atmosphere is contained in the troposphere at altitudes below 4 miles, and about 85 per cent below 10 miles.   As we have seen in Chap. 4 this region of the atmosphere is of primary importance in its absorption, emission, and scattering of IR radiation.   Density and temperature of the air decrease with altitude in this region; the latter reaches a constant value of $-69.7°F$ at about a 36,000-ft altitude on a standard summer day.

The *stratosphere* extends from the tropopause to approximately 16 miles in altitude.   Pressure continues to decrease with altitude, but the temperature remains constant at about $-69.7°F$ throughout this region.

The next atmospheric region, the *mesosphere*, between 16 miles and approximately 50 miles in altitude, contains a relatively dense ozone layer between about 80,000 and 130,000 ft.   This ozone layer protects the earth from a great deal of cosmic-ray and ultraviolet radiation from the sun.   The latter causes a rise in temperature between approximately 100,000 and 170,000 ft on a standard day, to a maximum of about 160°F.   Above the 200,000-ft altitude a temperature decrease to about $-50°F$ at 50 miles occurs.

The *ionosphere* or *thermosphere* extends from 50 miles to a loosely defined upper boundary between 300 and 500 miles altitude.   In this region four ionization layers occur, the D, E, F_1, and F_2, caused by the ionization of the atoms and molecules of the atmosphere under intense electromagnetic-wave bombardment from the sun.   These ionized layers, by reflecting radio waves back to the earth, make long-distance radio communication possible at lower altitudes.   Temperature in the ionosphere increases steadily to above 2000°F.

Above the ionosphere and extending into near space is the upper layer of the earth's atmosphere, known as the *exosphere*.   The upper limit of the exosphere represents the outer limit of the earth's atmosphere and is loosely defined at very roughly 1,000 miles altitude.

The region beyond the upper limits of the earth's atmosphere to an arbitrary 10,000-mile altitude is sometimes referred to as *near space*.   Beyond this to approximately 100,000 miles altitude is the region of space known as *cislunar space*, and extending past the moon, approximately 239,000 miles from the earth, out beyond the 1-million-mile range is *translunar space*.   The outermost limit from the earth or apogee of the first six artificial satellites that have successfully been placed in orbit is shown in Fig. 12-1.   The more recent attempts to orbit the moon have passed through translunar space on their journey toward an ultimate orbit around the sun.

Above the mesosphere no atmospheric shielding from cosmic rays is experienced.   Above an altitude of about 75 miles, in the ionosphere, the atmosphere ceases to afford any measure of protection from meteors.   The effect of prolonged cosmic radiation on some IR detector and optical materials requires further investigation.

The Solar System.   The first space probes will investigate the planets within our solar system.   IR techniques, which have already contributed by photographic, radiometric, and spectroscopic measurements from observatories and balloons, to our knowledge of planetary atmospheres and temperatures, will play an important role in space-probe investigations.

Figure 12-2 illustrates the relative diameters and average distances from the sun of our solar system planets. The first space probes will be launched to investigate those planets which are nearest to the earth, namely Venus, Mars, and the moon.

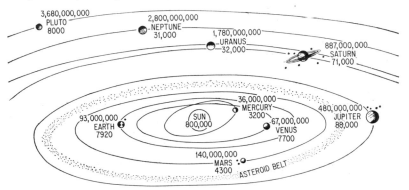

FIG. 12-2. Distances from sun and diameters of solar-system planets. Approximate average distance given above, diameter given below planet's name, in miles.

Space Units of Distance. The vast distances encountered in space require realistic units for their measurement. Within the earth's solar system the *astronautical unit*, based upon the average distance between the sun and the earth, is commonly used.

$$1 \text{ astronautical unit} = 93{,}000{,}000 \text{ miles} \qquad (12\text{-}1)$$

Alternatively, the *light-second*, or the distance traversed at the speed of light in one second, is employed.

$$1 \text{ light-second} = 186{,}284 \text{ miles} \qquad (12\text{-}2)$$

Where distances of the order of those to the nearest stars are involved, the *parsec*, or *parallax-second*, the distance at which the mean radius of the earth's orbit around the sun subtends an angle of one second of arc, is employed as a unit of measurement.

$$1 \text{ parsec} = 19.15 \times 10^{\,2} \text{ miles} \qquad (12\text{-}3)$$

Alternatively, the *light-year*, or the distance that light would travel in one year at a speed of 186,284 mps, is used.

$$1 \text{ light-year} = 5.88 \times 10^{12} \text{ miles} \qquad (12\text{-}4)$$

In the categories of IR measurements and experiments which are described in the following pages, the term *space* is used to include measurements from balloons, rockets, or satellites at altitudes below the upper limits of the earth's atmosphere; thus astronomical measurements from a skyhook balloon at a 100,000-ft altitude would be classified in the space-to-space category.

In the following sections several important surface-to-space applications of IR are described.

12-2. ASTROPHYSICAL AND METEOROLOGICAL APPLICATIONS

The large amount of data available from IR radiometric and spectroscopic measurements at the world's observatories provides a great deal of information about planet and star temperatures, their composition, and that of their atmospheres. Earthbound measurements, however, require correction for the absorption of radiation by the earth's atmosphere and are frequently degraded by poor seeing conditions.

More accurate data are obtained from high-altitude balloon-borne instrumentation, and will be forthcoming from IR measurements from orbiting satellites, planetary probes, and in the future, from moon-based observatories.

Provisional estimates of the composition of planetary atmospheres, after Kuiper,[159] are given in Table 12-1.

IR spectroscopic investigations of the sun to determine the composition of its atmosphere, and investigations of the moon's surface temperature, have been discussed in Chaps. 3 and 10.

Establishment in the future of moon-based astronomical and meteorological observatories will have the advantage of perfect seeing conditions in the absence of any atmosphere. In addition to other astronomical observations employing IR techniques, continuous observation of the earth's weather on a global basis will be possible since the moon always presents one face toward the earth as it encircles us.

12-3. DETECTION OF MISSILES, ROCKETS, AND SATELLITES

IR signals radiated from rockets and artificial satellites enable these objects to be detected from the earth by means of sensitive IR radiometers and trackers. Mention has been made in Sec. 10-4 of the detection of Sputnik I by this means.

In July, 1958, a team of engineers and physicists from the Avionics Division of the Aerojet-General Corporation successfully tracked and recorded Sputnik III as it passed overhead.* Using an AGC Model S8

---

* Data for this section and Fig. 12-3 by courtesy of the Avionics Division, Aerojet-General Corporation, Azusa, California.

Planet	Gas	Estimated amount, cm. N.P.T.
Venus...........	CO_2	100,000
	CO	<100
	N_2O	<100
	CH_4	<20
	NH_3	<4
	C_2H_4	<3
	C_2H_6	<1
Mars...........	N_2	96 per cent
	CO_2	440
	N_2O	200
	CH_4	<10
	C_2H_4	<2
	NH_3	<2
	C_2H_6	<1
	O_3	<0.05
	SO_2	<0.003
Jupiter..........	$H_2 + He$	$>10^5$
	CH_4	15,000
	NH_3	700
Saturn..........	$H_2 + He$	$>10^5$
	CH_4	35,000
	NH_3	250
	O_3	<0.1
	SO_2	<0.01
Uranus..........	$He + H_2$	$>10^5$
	CH_4	220,000
	O_3	<0.1
	SO_2	<0.01
Neptune..........	$He + H_2$	$>10^5$
	CH_4	370,000
Titan...........	CH_4	20,000
	NH_3	300
Moon...........	O_3	<0.005
	SO_2	<0.0003
Earth...........	N_2	625,000
	O_2	168,000
	CO_2	220
	CH_4	1.2
	N_2O	0.4
	O_3	0.3

IR tracker mounted on a naval gun mount in a mobile laboratory situated in the San Gabriel Mountains north of Glendora, California, recordings were obtained of IR signals radiated from the large rocket casing of Sputnik III.   As the rocket tumbled in orbit, an IR signal approximately three times greater than the background noise was received.   This is clearly indicated on the trace made on a Brush recorder, shown in Fig. 12-3.

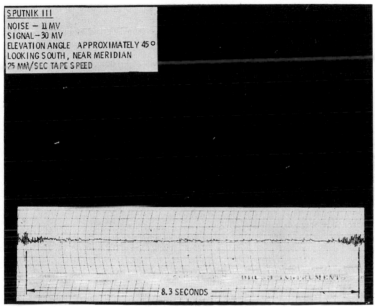

FIG. 12-3. Photograph (*upper part*) and recorded IR signal reflected from Sputnik III cylinder in orbit.   (*Courtesy Avionics Division, Aerojet-General Corporation, Azusa, Calif.*)

Studies of this nature on the radiation characteristics of artificial satellites are helpful in establishing the sensitivity and optical requirements of specialized IR trackers.   The data obtained are useful in research and in the development of various types of IR instruments for space applications.

Rockets used to launch satellites, and piloted rocket-research craft develop extremely high temperatures at their leading edges when passing through the earth's atmosphere at high speeds, due to aerodynamic heating of their surfaces.   Thermal studies of nose-cone and structural materials are required for design purposes.   Radiometers and pyrometers are used to measure temperatures attained in high-speed wind-tunnel tests.   Emissivity studies of various coating materials are required to achieve a high rate of heat dissipation in order to reduce the heat absorption of the structure.

An example of this is the X-15 manned research rocket built by North American Aviation Inc., Los Angeles, California, for high altitude, and reentry studies (Fig. 12-4). This aircraft will probe the fringes of space at a maximum altitude of over 100 miles. Nose and wing leading-edge temperatures exceeding 1000°F will be experienced

Fig. 12-4. The X-15 manned research rocket aircraft. (*Courtesy North American Aviation, Inc., Los Angeles, Calif.*)

upon reentering the earth's atmosphere. For rapid dissipation of the heat generated on these surfaces, the air vehicle is painted black for maximum surface emissivity.

The following sections describe some important applications of IR techniques in space-to-surface measurements.

12-4. WEATHER OBSERVATIONS FROM A SATELLITE

As part of the International Geophysical Year program, an IR weather-reconnaissance satellite was placed in orbit. This 20-in.-diameter spherical satellite contains an IR reconnaissance system called the *weather eye*, developed by the Perkin-Elmer Corporation, Norwalk, Connecticut,[160] for the U.S. Navy Signal Research and Development Laboratory to record the IR radiation reflected from the earth's cloud layer. By this means, cloud cover and movement over a large portion of the earth's surface can be mapped.   The data thus accumulated will be used by meteorologists for the study of weather systems, particularly in the large areas of the earth's surface not at present covered by meteorological observation stations, and to improve weather forecasting.

The weather eye consists of two simple optical systems mounted back to back in a fixed position on the central core of the satellite and looking outwards through holes in the satellite shell.   The direction of view of each eye makes a fixed angle of 45° with the spin axis of the satellite.   Each eye covers a solid angle of approximately 1°.   Scanning along a path approximately 600 miles wide on the earth's surface,

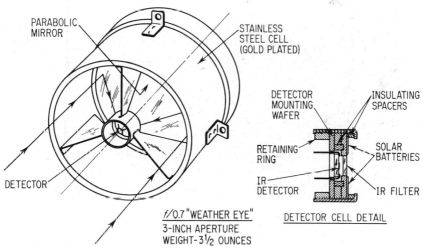

FIG. 12-5. Schematic of satellite IR weather eye.   (*Courtesy Perkin-Elmer Corporation, Norwalk, Conn.*)

with each eye resolving an area of about 10 square miles on the outer edges when the satellite is at an altitude of 300 miles, is achieved by spinning the satellite at 1 rps about an axis which lies along the line of orbit.   Orientation of the spin axis relative to the earth is determined by a comparison of the measured pulse lengths from each detector as they sweep the earth from horizon to horizon.[161]

Signals from each detector are recorded on magnetic tape, where they are stored until read out and transmitted to the earth by command from ground telemetering stations.   Successive orbits of the satellite build up a comprehensive picture of cloud cover and movement over a wide belt of latitude.

Each weather eye weighs $3\frac{1}{2}$ oz.   An optical schematic and details of construction are shown in Fig. 12-5. The received IR energy is focused by a very fast, $f/0.7$ optical system consisting of a 3-in.-aperture parabolic mirror on a lead sulphide detector with a sensitive surface area of 1 mm^2. Figure 12-6 shows the detector being mounted at the focal point of the parabolic mirror.

Silicon solar batteries mounted adjacent to the detector are used to provide a bias signal which switches off the tape-recorder motor when no reflected sunlight signal is present. In this way tape time and batteries are conserved when the satellite is on the dark side of the earth.[161]

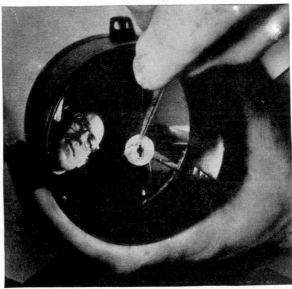

Fig. 12-6. Construction of satellite IR weather eye. (*Courtesy Perkin-Elmer Corporation, Norwalk, Conn.*)

The implications of this first weather-reconnaissance system are tremendous. Land-based meteorological observation stations cover a very small portion, about 5 per cent, of the total surface area of the earth. More sophisticated versions of IR reconnaissance systems in satellites orbiting from pole to pole will achieve complete global coverage of the earth's weather.

Weather is global in nature. Climatic changes in one area produce far-reaching effects. The altitude and orbital paths of meteorological satellites will be chosen to provide coverage of areas comparable to those presently included in forecasters' working charts. Geographic features as well as cloud areas will be monitored at frequent intervals so that rapid changes in the weather situation can be spotted.

Higher-resolution optics will facilitate the study of tropical storms, and provide more accurate forecasting and warning services. Because of the paucity of upper-atmosphere meteorological data, much has yet to be learned about the part played by solar radiation in affecting weather in the troposphere, the relationship between the earth's heat balance and climate, and the long-term effects of these factors on the earth's weather. Weather-reconnaissance satellites will provide a tremendous amount of heretofore unobtainable knowledge in these fields.

Once the factors exercising control on weather have been determined, tremendous benefits will be derived from the reliable long-range weather-forecasting techniques that will result. Agriculture, transportation, and communications are but three of the many fields that will profit therefrom. Some measure of control over the earth's weather by man is indeed possible. With the forces at man's disposal today, vast areas in the polar regions could be made habitable and fertile. Control of the weather would revolutionize military strategy.

12-5. RECONNAISSANCE FROM SATELLITES

Because of its passive nature, the satellite-borne IR scanner will play an important part in military reconnaissance. This type of equipment, however, involves problems of a more difficult nature than those encountered in a weather-reconnaissance scanner.

Much higher resolution is needed to distinguish small areas on the surface of the earth. If the satellite orbits at a relatively low altitude, its life is reduced by friction in the earth's atmosphere, serious thermal conditions are introduced by aerodynamic surface heating, and the shock waves generated at the high orbiting speed greatly reduce the efficiency of the IR system.

The effective surface temperature of the earth is about 287°K. Factories, cities, rockets, and other man-made sources radiate IR energy over a wide range of temperatures, up to several thousand degrees centigrade in the case of the latter. The radiation contrast between such objects and the ground is limited by several factors. By day, direct solar reflection, which varies with the nature of the earth's surface and the cloud cover, peaks in the visual region of the spectrum. The average reflectance, or *albedo*, also varies with the zenith angle of the sun. The albedo of cloud cover is practically constant at a wavelength of 3 μ. The average albedo of the earth varies from approximately 0.32 to 0.52. Indirect radiation caused by absorption and reradiation in the earth's atmosphere peaks at about 12 μ.[162]

The longer-wavelength radiation from the earth is more highly attenuated by the atmosphere than shorter-wavelength solar radiation, consequently a large amount of the energy radiated from the earth is trapped by the atmosphere, the so-called *greenhouse effect*. To a satellite in orbit in the upper atmosphere or outside of the atmosphere, the effective radiating temperature of the earth is reduced by these factors to that of a black body at 250°K.

The radiation contrast between objects and artificial sources on the earth's surface and their environment is attenuated by absorption, scattering, distortion, and turbulence in the intervening atmosphere.

A further limitation on resolution is imposed by diffraction. The diffraction pattern of a point-source image is known as the Airy disk, and appears as a bright circular disk surrounded by concentric rings of decreasing intensity which are alternately light and dark. The minimum resolvable distance of two close point sources is equal to the radius of the first dark ring of the Airy disk. Expressed in terms of design parameters

$$\Delta\theta = \frac{\lambda}{D_o} \tag{12-5}$$

where $\Delta\theta$ = minimum resolvable angle, radians

λ = wavelength of radiation, cm

D_o = diameter of aperture of objective lens, cm

Because of these limitations, IR reconnaissance systems will require more sophisticated optics, and some form of image enhancement by video processing at the detector-output stage to improve image contrast before telemetering picture information back to the earth.[162] Initially, IR reconnaissance will probably take place at night, using long-wavelength detector systems operating in the 8- to 14-μ atmospheric "window." Future developments in high-resolution and high-detectivity image-converter tubes and mosaic detectors will undoubtedly have important applications in this field, not only for military reconnaissance, but also for the scientific exploration of the atmospheres and surface features of the planets.

12-6. IR HORIZON-EDGE SCANNERS

A different type of IR scanner is that designed to distinguish the edge of a planet's apparent horizon from a satellite or rocket at high altitude. Such devices will be used to control the orientation and angular alignment of the velocity vector of a satellite-carrying rocket during its final velocity-boost phase, in order to place the satellite in its correct orbit.

Horizon-edge scanners will also be employed for the attitude stabilization of a satellite in orbit by determination of the local vertical with reference to the earth; to control the angular motion of a manned satellite within acceptable limits; and for the terminal guidance of a satellite or space vehicle approaching a distant planet.

The earth, as viewed through its atmospheric belt by a satellite in space, has an effective black-body temperature of 250°K compared to a temperature of about 4°K for deep space.   Although the atmosphere extends to an altitude of hundreds of miles above the earth's surface, its density decreases rapidly with increase in altitude, so that approximately 85 per cent of the atmospheric mass occurs below an altitude of 10 miles.   The bulk of the water-vapor content and about 50 per cent of the atmospheric mass lie within the first 4 miles of altitude.

The apparent earth horizon edge lies between 4 and 10 miles above the earth's surface when viewed tangentially from a distant satellite. This is the same order of distance as perturbations in the earth's radius caused by high mountains and the difference in the earth's radius at the equator and the poles (13 miles).   To a satellite in orbit at 500 miles altitude, for example, viewing the earth's horizon edge along a tangent line of sight, a 10-mile altitude subtends an angle of about 0.3°. Within less than this 0.3° subtended angle the apparent earth horizon edge appears to an IR-detection system as a very steep IR-radiation gradient, varying from a 250°K source to a 4°K source within a fraction of an angular degree.

This means that a simple reflective optical system with a narrow field of view, and therefore small size and light weight, can be employed. For operation in a satellite at a 500-mile altitude, a fixed optical system with a 1° field of view and a $\frac{3}{4}$-in. aperture would be adequate. Scanning motion is imparted by the spin of the satellite.   Two or more fixed optical systems of this type scanning across diametrically opposed earth horizons would be capable of determining the local vertical to a fraction of a degree.

Choice of the optimum spectral region is of primary importance. Background radiation due to scattered solar radiation from the atmosphere, reflected solar radiation from clouds, direct solar radiation, and specular reflection from water areas and false gradients observed at water-land boundaries that could possibly be mistaken for the earth's horizon edge, are largely eliminated by filtering out all received IR radiation below 7 μ.   Approximately 99 per cent of all radiation from a 250°K black body, and less than 1 per cent of direct solar-radiated energy, occurs at wavelengths greater than 7 μ.   Furthermore, the use of long-wavelength detectors, with peak detectivity at 7 μ or beyond, gives an operating capability that is independent of the time of day.

The horizon scanner should be insensitive to amplitude variations in the received signal caused by radiation differences in equatorial and polar areas, and on either side of the twilight zone on the earth. This requirement, together with that for detecting a sharp radiation gradient, indicates that pulse-width discrimination techniques should be employed in signal processing.

12-7. INVESTIGATION OF PLANETS FROM PROBES AND SATELLITES

Investigation of the planets of the solar system has commenced with the successful launching of two lunar probes by the United States and the U.S.S.R. Soviet scientists have circumnavigated the moon by a rocket probe which photographed its far side for the first time. Succeeding probes carrying more sophisticated instrumentation will be launched to orbit the moon as satellites. IR scanners will be used for reconnaissance and surface mapping. IR spectroscopic analysis of the atmospheric constituents and radiometric measurements of the surface temperature distribution will provide valuable information.

These techniques will then be applied to investigations of the more distant planets. Investigation of Mercury, about one and one-half times the size of the earth's moon, will utilize experience gained in orbiting and landing on the moon. Just as the moon always presents one face to the earth, so Mercury keeps one face to the sun. Extremely high surface temperatures occur on this face in contrast to temperatures approaching absolute zero on the opposite side. Like the moon, Mercury has a rocky surface, devoid of any known atmosphere. IR investigations will probably consist of radiometric measurements, and reconnaissance of the surface.

Venus, similar in size to the earth, is permanently shrouded by a dense atmosphere which is opaque to visible light. Spectroscopic analysis of its upper atmospheric layer shows that carbon dioxide is predominant, with traces of other gases (Table 12-1). IR measurements from satellites and probes should yield valuable information concerning atmospheric content and heat balance in the upper layers of the atmosphere. Since the surface of Venus is probably hot, with perpetual dust storms, severe attenuation of IR radiation in the shorter wavelengths of interest may inhibit the application of IR scanning techniques for surface-reconnaissance purposes.

The flat, desertlike surface of Mars, the high nitrogen content of its atmosphere, its winter polar caps of apparently thin layers of ice, and the possibility that some form of vegetable life exists on its surface, make this planet a fascinating subject for investigation. Much information has already been accumulated from IR measurements from the earth's surface and from high-altitude balloons, when Mars is about 34 million miles distant from the earth at its closest proximity.

Seasonal changes in color have prompted spectroscopic and IR reflectivity measurements. These suggest that the dark areas on the Martian surface may be due to organic matter.[164] Tikhov[165] and his coworkers in the Soviet Union have measured differences in the infrared reflection from arctic, temperate, and tropical plants under terrestrial conditions. Extrapolating to conditions on Mars indicates that the dark areas there are some form of vegetable life.

IR measurements from instrumented probes and satellites orbiting Mars will yield conclusive evidence on this question. Spectroscopic measurements will determine whether traces of free oxygen and water vapor are present in the Martian atmosphere. IR reconnaissance will require the use of long-wavelength detectors, since the surface temperature of Mars varies between approximately -100 to 80 or 90°F.[166] IR terminal-guidance methods will undoubtedly be employed for surveillance and landing attempts on this planet.

The large-diameter, low-density outer planets with similar atmospheres consisting primarily of helium and hydrogen gases have several other similar characteristics. Because of their great distance from the sun, temperatures range from about -200 to -300°F at the upper surface of their atmospheres.[166] They all rotate rapidly about their axes. Spectral investigations suggest that these planets consist of a relatively small core of rock surrounded by ice and compressed hydrogen and helium.[166] The satellites of Jupiter, Saturn, and Neptune vary in size up to diameters which may be as large as that of Mercury. Several of these satellites are larger than the earth's moon and may well be more suitable for IR investigation than their parent planets. Here again, for IR measurements, long-wavelength detectors would be required because of the low surface temperatures encountered.

In the space-to-space category, we shall consider some important IR measurements of vehicle environments, applications of IR techniques to communication between space vehicles, and IR aids to space navigation. Included in this category also are IR measurements from balloons cruising at very high altitudes within the earth's atmosphere.

12-8. IR MEASUREMENTS FROM PLASTIC BALLOONS

The advantages of obtaining astrophysical observations at a very high altitude, and if possible above the earth's atmosphere, have long been recognized, and naturally the first attempts were made from instrument-carrying balloons. As early as 1863 solar spectroscopic measurements were made in a series of ten balloon flights by Glaisher in England.[167]

The first plastic balloons, made of cellophane, were used by Piccard in 1935 at Swarthmore, Pennsylvania.[168] The development of large hydrogen- or helium-filled balloons made of polyethylene extruded film at the University of Bristol, England, and in the United States for cosmic-ray measurements led to their use for other experiments including IR spectroscopic, radiometric, and photographic measurements of the planets, stars, galaxies, and nebulas. Such balloons are capable of cruising for hours at altitudes as high as 145,000 ft and can carry payloads weighing up to 1 ton.[168]

In the United States, an extensive program of manned (strato-lab) and unmanned (stratoscope) flights with instrumented skyhook balloons has been planned by various individuals, universities, and research organizations, sponsored by the Office of Naval Research.[169] Manned flights in a sealed cabin with an artificial atmosphere have been made to an altitude of 103,000 ft. IR instruments carried aloft in this research program include IR spectroscopes, cameras, telescopes, and radiometers. Observations include solar spectrum studies, studies of the IR spectra of the planets in the solar system, of the stars, nebulas, and galaxies.

These types of observations are a prelude to further measurements from instrumented probes and satellites as described in the previous sections of this chapter. The cost of balloon observations is, of course, very low by comparison, and already valuable information about the Martian atmosphere, the solar spectrum, and variations of the gaseous content of the earth's upper atmosphere has been obtained.

12-9. IR DATA LINK AND COMMUNICATION SYSTEMS

As interplanetary and space travel is developed, rapid means of communication over vast distances will be required for the transmission of scientific observations and control of probes, and for the navigation of space ships and voice communication between them. Various forms of electromagnetic radiation will be used for this purpose.[170] Traveling at a speed of 6.696×10^8 mph, radio, infrared, or optical beams will take approximately 3 min to reach Mars at its closest point to the earth, and approximately $4\frac{1}{2}$ years to reach the nearest star, from the earth.

With the development of more sensitive IR detectors and improved techniques, there is no doubt that modulated beams of IR radiation will be used for many applications in this field.   Employing techniques similar to those developed for IR signalling, voice communications, and beacons on the earth, modulated beams of IR radiation could be employed for the remote control of planetary probes, and communication between space vehicles and with space stations.   Compared with radio and radar, the light weight, small size, and greatly reduced power requirements of IR instrumentation would be most advantageous.

12-10. IR APPLICATIONS IN SPACE NAVIGATION

The applications of IR horizon scanners for attitude control during the power-boost stages on takeoff and for terminal guidance during the final approach to a planet have been discussed in the preceding sections. For midcourse guidance during interplanetary flight, IR planetary and solar measurements will be of value in supplementing visual and radio navigation methods.

For celestial navigation on the earth's surface and within its atmosphere by measurements of the angular positions of the sun and stars, the familiar concept of the celestial sphere is used to establish a reference system of spherical coordinates with the earth at its center, Fig. 12-7.   The celestial equator is a projection of the earth's equator on an imaginary sphere of infinite radius, its center coinciding with the earth's center.   The earth's polar or spin axis is tilted approximately $23\frac{1}{2}°$ off the perpendicular to the plane of its orbit around the sun.   Because of this, to an observer on the earth, the sun appears as a star which travels in a great circle inclined at $23\frac{1}{2}°$ to the celestial equator, known as the ecliptic.   The ecliptic intersects the celestial equator at two points known as the vernal or spring equinox and the autumnal equinox.   The spring equinox, also called the first point of Aries (Υ), is taken as the zero point of celestial longitude.   The hour circle of a star is that great circle on the celestial sphere passing through the poles and the star.   Hour circles correspond to meridians on the earth.   The hour circle of Υ on the celestial sphere corresponds, for reference purposes, to the meridian of Greenwich on the earth.   The *right ascension*, or *celestial longitude* of a star, is the angle at the pole between the hour circle of the star and that of Υ measured in degrees from 0 to 360 east from Υ.   The *declination*, or *celestial latitude* of a star, is the angular distance measured along its hour circle from the celestial equator to the star, in degrees from 0 to 90 North or South of the equator.   Declination and right ascension are therefore analogous to latitude and longitude on the earth (Fig. 12-7).

For interplanetary navigation a different coordinate system, with the

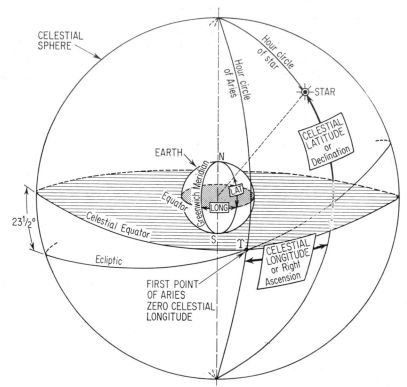

FIG. 12-7. Coordinate system used for terrestrial navigation.

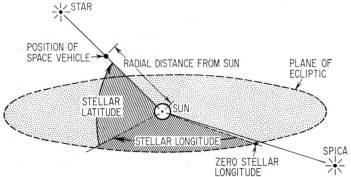

FIG. 12-8. A coordinate system proposed for interplanetary navigation. (*After Reference 171.*)

sun at its center, is required. Of the several schemes considered, one of the most attractive is a spherical coordinate system with the plane of the ecliptic as reference, proposed by Larmore. A bright star such as Spica near the plane of the ecliptic is chosen as zero longitude reference. The three coordinates of position are then stellar longitude, an angular

TABLE 12-2. SOME IR APPLICATIONS IN SPACE TECHNOLOGY

IR instrument	Applications
Surface-to-space: IR telescopes, spectroscopes, radiometers	Astronomical and astrophysical measurements from surface of Earth, Moon, other planets, or their moons. Temperatures of stars and planets Observation of planetary atmospheres Meteorological observations Satellite tracking Detection of rockets, satellites on reentering Earth's atmosphere
Space-to-surface: IR telescopes, cameras, spectroscopes, radiometers, IR communication systems, IR horizon scanners	Investigation of planetary atmospheres Measurement of surface temperatures of planets IR photography and reconnaissance of planetary surfaces Studies of solar atmosphere, solar energy measurements Studies of Earth's heat balance Weather observations and correlation with upper-atmosphere measurements ICBM launch detection Terminal guidance and navigation Data links and communications
Space-to-space: IR telescopes, spectroscopes, and radiometers	Astronomical and astronautical observations from high-altitude balloons, satellites, and space vehicles IR star tracking for navigational purposes Upper-atmosphere research Measurements of vehicle environment Determination of vehicle velocity Determination of distance from sun
IR horizon scanners	Attitude control of space vehicle after launching Terminal guidance and attitude control on approaching space station or planet
IR communication systems, beacons	Voice communication and data links between passing space ships; between space ships and space stations; between reconnaissance probes and controlling vehicle; homing beacons for terminal guidance on space stations and planets

distance measured along the ecliptic from the zero longitude reference; stellar latitude, an angular distance measured above or below the plane of the ecliptic; and a radial distance measured from the center of the sun, Fig. 12-8. The distance of the space vehicle from the sun could be determined by an IR measurement of the apparent solar diameter by means of an IR horizon-edge scanner device, or by a radiometric measurement of the IR solar flux density.[171]   Another use of an IR edge-scanning device would be to measure the angular distance between the horizon of a fully illuminated planetary surface and a star.   Several stars give a sufficiently high signal-to-noise ratio in the near-IR spectral region with existing detectors to be used for inertial star-tracking purposes.

Table 12-2 summarizing important IR applications in the field of space technology is by no means exhaustive.   As new developments occur, IR techniques will play an increasingly important role in this new science.

REFERENCES

158. Leavitt, W., Loosbrock, J. F., Skinner, R. M., and Witze, C.: The Space Frontier, *Air Force Mag.*, March, 1958, p. 43.
159. Kuiper, G. P.: "The Atmospheres of the Earth and Planets," University of Chicago Press, Chicago, 1952.
160. Data for this section by private communication courtesy of the Perkin-Elmer Corporation, Norwalk, Conn., 1958.
161. Fusca, James A.: *Aviation Week*, Aug. 18, 1958, p. 82.
162. Fusca, James A.: Satellite Reconnaissance Optics, *Aviation Week*, Jan. 19, Jan. 26, Feb. 2, 1959.
163. Klass, Philip J.: Space Navigation Challenges Designers, *Aviation Week*, June 16, 1958, p. 217.
164. Sinton, W. M.: "Further Evidence of Vegetation on Mars," paper presented at meeting of American Astronomical Society, at Gainesville, Fla., Dec. 27–30, 1958.
165. Tikhov, G. A.: Is Life Possible on Other Planets? *J. Brit. Astron. Assoc.*, vol. 15, no. 3, p. 193, April, 1955.
166. "Space Handbook: Astronautics and its Applications," Government Printing Office, Washington, D.C., 1959.
167. Glaisher, J.: Scientific Balloon Ascent, The Lines of the Spectrum, *Proc. Brit. Met. Soc.*, vol. 1, no. 7, March, 1863.
168. Ross, Malcolm D.: *Proc. Am. Astron. Assoc.*, paper presented at 4th annual meeting, New York, January 29–31, 1958.
169. Ross, M. D., and Lewis, M. L.: To 76,000 feet by Strato-Lab Balloon, *Natl. Geog. Mag.*, February, 1957.
170. Prew, Henry E.: *Proc. Am. Astron. Assoc.*, 4th annual meeting, New York, January 29–31, 1958.
171. Larmore, Lewis E.: Some Applications of Infrared to Interplanetary Navigation, Office of Naval Research, *Proc. Infrared Inform. Symposia*, vol. 4, no. 1, p. 168, March, 1959.

Appendix

Books on Infrared Radiation and Related Subjects

INFRARED RADIATION AND ITS APPLICATIONS

Barnes, R. B., R. C. Gore, U. Liddell, and Van Zandt Williams: "Infrared Spectroscopy—Industrial Applications and Bibliography," Reinhold Publishing Corporation, New York, 1944.

Bellamy, L. J.: "Infrared Spectra of Complex Molecules," John Wiley & Sons, Inc., New York, 1954.

Brügel, W.: "Einfuhrung in die Ultrarotspektroscopie," Dietrich Steinkopf, Darmstadt, Germany, 1954.

Clark, W.: "Photography by Infrared," 2d ed., John Wiley & Sons, Inc., New York, 1946.

Forsythe, W. E.: "Measurement of Radiant Energy," McGraw-Hill Book Company, Inc., New York, 1937.

Herzberg, G.: "Infrared and Raman Spectra of Polyatomic Molecules," 2d ed., D. Van Nostrand Company, Inc., Princeton, N.J., 1954.

Lecomte, J.: Le Spectre infrarouge, Les Presses Universitaires de France, Paris, 1928.

Margolin, A.: "Fundamentals of Infrared Technology," Military Publishing House, Moscow, 1955.

Rawlins, F. I. G., and A. M. Taylor: "Infrared Analysis of Molecular Structure," Cambridge University Press, London, 1929.

Schaeffer, C., and F. Matossi: "Das ultrarote Spektrum," Springer-Verlag, Berlin, 1930 (reprinted by Edwards Bros., Ann Arbor, Mich., 1943).

Smith, R. A, F. E. Jones, and R. P. Chasmar: "The Detection and Measurement of Infrared Radiation," Oxford University Press, London, 1957.

RELATED SUBJECTS

Dekker, A. J: "Solid State Physics," Prentice-Hall, Inc., Englewood Cliffs, N.J., 1958.

290 Appendix

Ditchburn, R. W.: "Light," Interscience Publishers, Inc., New York, 1955.
Dunlap, W. C.: "An Introduction to Semiconductors," John Wiley & Sons, Inc., New York, 1957.
Gibb, Thomas R. P., Jr.: "Optical Methods of Chemical Analysis," McGraw-Hill Book Company, Inc., New York, 1942.
Goody, R. M.: "Physics of the Stratosphere," Cambridge University Press, London, 1954.
Jenkins, F. A. and H. E. White: "Fundamentals of Optics," 3d ed., McGraw-Hill Book Company, Inc., New York, 1957.
Jones, R., Performance of Detectors in Visible and Infrared Radiation, vol. 5, chap. 1, in "Advances in Electronics," Academic Press, Inc., New York, 1953.
Kittel, C.: "Introduction to Solid State Physics," 2d ed., John Wiley & Sons, Inc., New York, 1956.
Kuiper, G. P.: "The Atmospheres of the Earth and Planets," University of Chicago Press, Chicago, 1949.
Lecomte, J.: Spectroscopie dans l'infrarouge, vol. 26, pp. 244–936, in "Encyclopedia of Physics," Springer-Verlag, Berlin, 1958.
Martin, L. C.: "Applied Optics," Pitman Publishing Corporation, New York, 1950.
Mees, C. E. K., ed.: "The Theory of the Photographic Process," The Macmillan Company, New York, 1954.
Moss, T. S.: "Optical Properties of Semiconductors," Academic Press, Inc., New York, 1959.
Moss, T. S.: "Photoconductivity in the Elements," Butterworth and Co., Ltd., London, 1952.
Mott, N. F., and R. W. Gurney: "Electronic Processes in Ionic Crystals," Oxford University Press, London, 1950.
Richtmeyer, F. K., and E. H. Kennard: "Introduction to Modern Physics," 4th ed., McGraw-Hill Book Company, Inc., New York, 1955.
Sanderson, J. A.: Emission, Transmission, and Detection in the Infrared, chap. 5, pp. 126–175, in Arthur S. Locke (ed.), "Guidance," D. Van Nostrand Company, Inc., Princeton, N.J., 1955.
Sawyer, R. A.: "Experimental Spectroscopy," 2d ed., Prentice-Hall, Inc., Englewood Cliffs, N.J., 1951.
Shive, J, N.: "The Properties, Physics, and Design of Semiconductor Devices," D. Van Nostrand Company, Inc., Princeton, N.J., 1959.
Sommer, A. H.: "Photoelectric Tubes," Methuen & Co., Ltd., London, 1951.
Strong, J.: "Concepts of Classical Optics," W. H. Freeman and Co., San Francisco, 1958.
Strong, J.: "Procedures in Experimental Physics," Prentice-Hall, Inc., Englewood Cliffs, N.J., 1938.
Van de Hulst, H. C.: "Light Scattering by Small Particles," John Wiley & Sons, Inc., New York, 1957.
Von Hippel, Arthur R.: "Dielectric Materials and Applications," John Wiley & Sons, Inc., New York, 1954.

Weber, R. L.: "Heat and Temperature Measurement," Prentice-Hall, Inc.,
Englewood Cliffs, N.J., 1950.

White, H. E.: "Introduction to Atomic Spectra," McGraw-Hill Book Company, Inc., New York, 1934.

Wolfe, H. C., ed: "Temperature—Its Measurement and Control in Science,"
Reinhold Publishing Corporation, New York, vol. 1, 1941, vol. 2, 1955.

Wood, W. P., and J. M. Cork: "Pyrometry," 2d ed., McGraw-Hill Book Company, Inc., New York, 1941.

Wooster, W. A.: "A Textbook on Crystal Physics," Cambridge University
Press, London, 1938.

Zdenek, Kopal, ed.: "Astronomical Optics and Related Subjects," Interscience
Publishers, Inc., New York, 1956.

Zworykin, V. K., and E. G. Ramberg: "Photoelectricity and Its Applications,"
John Wiley & Sons, Inc., New York, 1949.

INDEX

293